STUDIES IN MODERN TOPOLOGY

Studies in Mathematics

The Mathematical Association of America

Volume 1: STUDIES IN MODERN ANALYSIS
edited by R. C. Buck

Volume 2: STUDIES IN MODERN ALGEBRA
edited by A. A. Albert

Volume 3: STUDIES IN REAL AND COMPLEX ANALYSIS
edited by I. I. Hirschman, Jr.

Volume 4: STUDIES IN GLOBAL GEOMETRY AND ANALYSIS
edited by S. S. Chern

Volume 5: STUDIES IN MODERN TOPOLOGY
edited by P. J. Hilton

P. J. Hilton
Cornell University

Gordon T. Whyburn
University of Virginia

Wolfgang Haken
University of Illinois, Urbana

V. K. A. M. Gugenheim
University of Illinois at Chicago Circle

Eldon Dyer
City University of New York

Valentin Poénaru
Northeastern University

Studies in Mathematics

Volume 5

STUDIES IN MODERN TOPOLOGY

P. J. Hilton, editor
Cornell University

Published by
The Mathematical Association of America

Distributed by
Prentice-Hall, Inc.

Library of Congress Catalog Card Number 68-11402

Printed in the United States of America
Prentice-Hall, Inc., Englewood Cliffs, N. J.

Current printing (last digit):

10 9 8 7 6 5 4 3 2 1

PREFACE

This volume is the fifth in the MAA Studies in Mathematics series. It contains a comprehensive and illuminating introduction to the current research in topology by the editor of the volume, P. J. Hilton, and expository articles on some of the most active areas of work at the present time by G. T. Whyburn, W. Haken, V. K. A. M. Gugenheim, E. Dyer and V. Poénaru. The volume is aimed at advanced undergraduates, graduate students, and college and university teachers. S. Eilenberg, in a lecture† on algebraic topology, observed that "the whole field changes radically over every ten-year period, and someone who has been away from it for any length of time might not understand a single word if he tries to read a paper." This rapid growth in topology suggests that another volume on this subject will be needed before long. Nevertheless it is hoped that all interested persons can get their bearings in this fast-moving field from a study of this book, and that the book will help its readers to appreciate the new developments as they occur.

These volumes can also be viewed from the standpoint of the MAA's concern with the teaching of mathematics. Some of the activities of the MAA involve the analysis and revision of the contents of mathematics courses. The volumes in this series deal with the mathematical ideas themselves, and should serve to narrow the gap between teaching and research.

CHARLES W. CURTIS

† p. 98, Lectures on Modern Mathematics, T. L. Saaty, Editor, vol. I, John Wiley and Sons, New York, 1963.

CONTENTS

STUDIES IN MODERN TOPOLOGY

INTRODUCTION: MODERN TOPOLOGY

P. J. Hilton

The branch of mathematics known as *topology* has grown enormously in the years since the second world war, not only in depth but also in breadth. It has strong interactions† with the various other branches of mathematics, particularly with aspects of modern algebra, algebraic geometry, functional analysis, and the theory of partial differential equations, receiving strength from them and imparting insights in return. Thus we might properly speak today of pure and applied topology, and it is surely a sign of the health of mathematics as a whole that the comparative isolation of to-

† An interesting example of this interaction is afforded by the solution of the problem of the existence of division algebras over the reals, referred to in this article and in Curtis' article in the companion *Studies in Modern Algebra.* The solution was by means of the methods of algebraic topology based on a result of Bott, originally proved by the methods of the calculus of variations. This result of Bott may now be proved using the methods of algebraic topology, and it has been generalized using the theory of Banach algebras.

pology in the immediate postwar world has now been replaced by an almost embarrassing involvement of topology, and topologists, in the general development of mathematics.

Moreover, algebraic topology has itself given rise to (at least) two branches of mathematics which now enjoy independent status, namely homological algebra and category theory. Topology continues to feed into these two theories, but not even the most parochial topologist could claim them to be part of topology. Thus no attempt is made to cover these extremely active areas of mathematics in the present volume. The second article by MacLane in the Mathematical Association of America publication *Studies in Modern Algebra* has brief sections devoted to each homological algebra and category theory, and it is to be expected that each will soon warrant a publication devoted exclusively to itself.

Similarly, this volume contains no reports on the applications of the methods of algebraic and differential topology to algebraic geometry and analysis. The far-reaching generalizations of the Riemann-Roch theorem, initiated by Hirzebruch and carried on by him and many others, have had to be omitted. The comprehensive work of Atiyah and Singer, giving a profound and insightful characterization of the index of an elliptic differential operator, and the later work of Atiyah and Bott generalizing the Lefschetz fixpoint formula to elliptic operators, together with numerous other elegant and far-reaching applications of topology—all these matters must be regarded as beyond the scope of the present volume. For it is clear that to do such applications justice would require us to increase the size of this volume at least fourfold.

Thus we are concerned here with *pure* topology. This already enormous subject divides into four natural and well-defined—though overlapping—areas, namely algebraic topology, differential topology, geometric topology, and general, or set-theoretic, topology.

General topology perhaps has least contact with other areas of topology and its advance, at any rate in the United States and Western Europe, has been much less sensational. This latter is, perhaps, due in part to the fact that it does not have so clearly defined a methodology as the rest of topology, so that progress is not achieved by the systematic development and applications of powerful techniques. It is also true that most of the applications of general topology to other branches of mathematics are classical so that the stimulus given to algebraic and differential topology by their contact with problems outside topology has been somewhat lacking in general topology. Nevertheless there certainly has been considerable progress, notably in the Soviet Union and other countries of Eastern Europe, but also elsewhere; a summary of the present situation and main developments are to be found in the survey article by P. S. Aleksandrov, "On some basic directions in general topology," which appears in English translation in *Russian Mathematical Surveys*, **19** (1965), 1–39; **20** (1965), 177–78. G. T. Whyburn contributes an article to this volume entitled "What is a curve?" which exhibits the need for a precise definition of a curve and shows how such a definition is furnished by set-theoretic topology. Different types of curves are classified topologically and the article closes with a recent application, due to the author, of the topological theory to a proof (not proceeding via Cauchy's theorem and the Cauchy integral formula) that if a function of a complex variable is differentiable, then it is infinitely differentiable.

Geometric, algebraic, and differential topology are very closely linked one with another. One may regard geometric topology as historically the precursor of algebraic topology since it was in the attempt to solve geometric problems that the algebraic methods characteristic of algebraic topology arose. It is true that in the early days of geometric topology the pioneers developed highly articulated combinatorial techniques to tackle the basic classification problem, but the failure to prove the *Hauptvermutung*, asserting the equivalence of topological and combinatorial classifications, led the topologists of the early 1930's to seek more algebraic methods and turn their main attention to the homology groups of polyhedra (following Poincaré) and developments of these constructs.

Nowadays, as a matter of terminology, one includes combinatorial methods under the general head of geometric topology, but one certainly also includes other methods and ideas, for example, the study of topological manifolds. It is an undoubted fact that geometric topology is once again today an extremely active area of research. Stimulus has been provided by many exciting results and interesting ideas. To instance but a few: in 1960 Stallings and Zeeman, following work of Smale to which we refer later, proved the *generalized Poincaré conjecture*, in dimensions $n \geq 5$, asserting that a closed orientable $(n - 1)$-connected *combinatorial* n-manifold is topologically an n-sphere; in 1956 Thom defined rational Pontryagin classes for combinatorial manifolds, and S. P. Novikov has very recently announced a proof that these classes are topological invariants; in 1960 Kervaire gave the first example of a combinatorial manifold admitting no (topologically compatible) differential structure; in 1960 Milnor exhibited two polyhedra which are homeomorphic but not combinatorially equivalent (this example disproves the Hauptvermutung for general compact polyhedra but leaves open the question whether topologically equivalent manifolds are necessarily combinatorially equivalent); in 1951 Moise embarked on a series of papers in which he proved that every 3-manifold could be endowed with a combinatorial structure and that this structure was unique—Bing later published a simplification of the argument; in 1957 Papakyriekopoulos proved the celebrated *Dehn lemma*, which had remained unproved for many decades and thus reawakened interest in the *Poincaré conjecture* that every closed orientable simply connected 3-manifold is a sphere; in 1960 Zeeman showed that an n-sphere knots combinatorially in $(n + k)$-space only if $k = 2$. This is, of course, a very brief list which surely does not do justice to the many who have made key contributions to the field of geometric topology.† Some idea of the scope and directions of the field may be obtained from a perusal of the contributions to the 1961 Topology Institute held in Athens, Georgia and published under the title *Topology of 3-Manifolds and Related Topics* (Englewood Cliffs, N.J.: Prentice-Hall, Inc., 1962).

† One should, in particular, mention the name of J. H. C. Whitehead, who died in 1960 at the age of 55. His key contributions to combinatorial topology in the 1930's and early 1940's, for example, the theory of regular neighborhoods and simple homotopy theory, have come to fruition in the present renascence of the subject.

It is a striking fact that the celebrated Poincaré conjecture (not the *generalized* conjecture; we refer here to dimension 3), which has occupied the attention of mathematicians for 60 years, remains unproved. Nevertheless, attempts to prove it have led to very deep insights into 3-dimensional manifolds. We publish in this volume an article by W. Haken entitled "Some results on surfaces in 3-manifolds," reporting on results achieved by the author and others in this direction. The reader will note that in this field great importance attaches to the capacity for visualization; as the author remarks, this carries with it the danger of serious error, so that extreme caution is called for.

As we have already mentioned, algebraic topology has been studied not simply for its own sake, as an independent discipline, but also as a tool in other branches of mathematics. Indeed, its applicability to geometric topology constituted its origin. Milnor's disproof of the Hauptvermutung used very special algebraic-topological ideas, going back to the Reidemeister-Franz notion of torsion and J. H. C. Whitehead's variant of torsion which lies at the heart of his theory of simple homotopy types; needless to say, Milnor's work and other exciting developments in topology have led to enormous activity and interest in torsion and simple homotopy theory, and fascinating algebraic problems have emerged—one might instance the work of Bass in this connection. However, one of the most exciting new domains of mathematics in which algebraic topology finds application is that of differential topology. This domain first came to recognition as a field of study in its own right with Milnor's announcement in 1956 that the 7-dimensional sphere can carry several different differentiable structures. This famous theorem, proved using the part of algebraic topology known as fiber bundle theory, is so important a landmark in the history of topology that it is worthwhile explaining its meaning at this stage with some care.†

An open set in Euclidean space has a natural smooth or differ-

† We are not attempting any precise definitions in the next paragraph; these will be found in the appropriate articles. The notions of topological, combinatorial, and differentiable manifolds have, of course, already occurred in this article.

entiable structure—the structure we are all familiar with through the usual differential calculus of several variables. A *topological manifold* is a Hausdorff space which, locally, has the topological structure of an open set of some Euclidean space $\mathbb{R}^n$; the *dimension* of the manifold is then n. It may be that the manifold has locally even the smooth structure of an open set in $\mathbb{R}^n$; we then say we have a *differential* manifold. Intermediate between these notions is that of a *combinatorial* manifold; this is a topological manifold endowed with a combinatorial structure, that is, an equivalence class of triangulations in which the star of a vertex is combinatorially equivalent to the star of a vertex in the standard triangulation of the n-sphere. This notion is intermediate between that of a differential manifold and that of a topological manifold because, on the one hand, one may "throw away" the combinatorial structure of a combinatorial manifold and one is then left with a topological manifold; while, on the other, a theorem of J. H. C. Whitehead asserts that every differential manifold carries an essentially unique smooth combinatorial structure.† With each class of manifold there is associated an appropriate sort of function from one manifold to another; differentiable maps of differential manifolds, preserving the differential structure; *piecewise-linear* maps of combinatorial manifolds, preserving the combinatorial structure; and continuous maps of topological manifolds, preserving the topological structure. Moreover a differentiable map can be approximated by a piecewise-linear map with respect to the associated combinatorial structures of the smooth manifolds, and a piecewise-linear map is continuous with respect to the underlying topological structure of the combinatorial manifolds. We may represent the situation schematically as

$$\text{Diff} \longrightarrow \text{PL} \longrightarrow \text{Top}, \tag{1}$$

---

† Cairns had shown earlier that every differential manifold could be triangulated, but Whitehead demonstrated the existence (and uniqueness) of a compatible smooth triangulation. Of course, in this brief survey we skate over many real difficulties associated with the passage from differential manifolds to combinatorial manifolds. These problems have been studied deeply, in particular by Lashof and Rothenberg.

where Diff refers to the class of differential manifolds (with their appropriate maps), PL to the class of combinatorial manifolds (with their appropriate maps), and Top to the class of topological manifolds (with their appropriate maps); and the arrows refer to the passage from one class to another as described above. For convenience of reference let us label the arrows in (1):

(2)
$$\text{Diff} \xrightarrow{W} \text{PL} \qquad \text{(W for Whitehead)}$$
$$\text{PL} \xrightarrow{F} \text{Top} \qquad \text{(F for “forgetful,” since we forget the combinatorial structure).}$$

The reader should think of W and F as generalized functions, and our notation will reflect this point of view. Thus we have the composite $\text{Diff} \xrightarrow{FW} \text{Top}$.

We remark that in each *category* Diff, PL, and Top there is the appropriate notion of *equivalence* between objects and of an *isomorphism* (or equivalence) from one object to another. In any category this latter would mean a map, of the appropriate sort,

$$f\colon M \longrightarrow N$$

such that there exists

$$g\colon N \longrightarrow M$$

with the composite gf being the identity map of M and the composite fg being the identity map of N; we then call g the *inverse* of f, and we say that M and N are equivalent if there is a map $f\colon M \longrightarrow N$ possessing an inverse (i.e., f is an isomorphism). We then write $M \sim N$ or $f\colon M \sim N$ if we wish to stress the isomorphism. An isomorphism $f\colon M \sim N$ in Diff is called a *diffeomorphism*† and M and N are then said to be *diffeomorphic;* an isomorphism $f\colon M \sim N$ in PL is called a *PL-isomorphism* (or combinatorial equivalence); and an isomorphism $f\colon M \sim N$ in Top is called a *homeomorphism.* Now we may express Milnor's result (or, at least,

† This is merely an amalgamation of "differentiable" and "homeomorphism"; but not every differentiable homeomorphism is a diffeomorphism since, for the latter, we also require that the inverse be differentiable.

a very exciting part of it): let S^7 be the 7-dimensional sphere with its usual smooth structure as a closed subspace of $\mathbb{R}^8$; then there exists a smooth manifold M such that $FW(M) \sim FW(S^7)$ but $M \nsim S^7$. That is, M and S^7 are equivalent as topological spaces but not as smooth manifolds. In fact it turns out that there are 28 smooth manifolds, all of which are homeomorphic to S^7 but no two of which are diffeomorphic.

It is not too gross an oversimplification to say that differential and piecewise-linear topology are very largely concerned with the diagram (1). Indeed we may formulate the results of Thom, Novikov, and Kervaire already referred to in terms of this diagram. Thus Thom defined certain cohomology invariants of *combinatorial* manifolds; their interest was derived from the fact that Pontryagin had defined† certain cohomology classes of a differential manifold M, which we shall write $p(M)$, and the classes $\bar{p}$ defined by Thom have the property

$$\bar{p}(WM) = p(M). \tag{3}$$

Then Novikov's result is that if $FN_1 \sim FN_2$, then $\bar{p}(N_1) = \bar{p}(N_2)$; that is, combinatorial manifolds which are homeomorphic have the same rational Pontryagin classes. Kervaire's result is that there is a 10-dimensional combinatorial manifold N such that there is no differential manifold M with $FW(M) \sim FN$; subsequently others have found examples of this phenomenon in other dimensions, starting with the minimum dimension 8. Notice that Kervaire's statement is stronger than the assertion that there is no differential manifold M with $W(M) \sim N$; for it says that no combinatorial structure on M (not only the one with which it was originally endowed) is compatible with a differentiable structure. Further, Eells and Kuiper have demonstrated the existence of combinatorial 8-manifolds whose homotopy type, in fact, contains no differential manifold. The Hauptvermutung for manifolds asserts that if M and N are two combinatorial manifolds with $FM \sim FN$, then $M \sim N$. Moise's theorem asserts that to every topological

† Actually Pontryagin defined integer cohomology classes, whereas Thom defines rational classes; the equality (3) is to be understood to hold when the Pontryagin classes are taken with rational coefficients.

3-manifold M there exists a unique equivalence class of combinatorial manifolds N such that $FN \sim M$. These examples should serve to illustrate the ubiquity of the diagram (1) in present-day topology;† but, of course, it does not suggest ways to solve the problems it raises. However, it is highly pertinent to remark that the work of Thom, Novikov, Kervaire, Eells and Kuiper—and, of course, Milnor—about which we have been speaking, all used the methods of algebraic topology. Thus we come to distinguish really three areas of topology, closely clustered together, rather than just algebraic and differential topology: namely, (i) algebraic methods in differential topology, (ii) analytic methods in differential topology, and (iii) algebraic topology as the algebraic study of topological spaces and continuous maps. In this volume we devote one article to each of these areas. In all of them the work done in recent years has been so exciting and progress has been so rapid that it is quite impossible to do them justice in this relatively brief introduction. Some picture of the nature of the developments, and their extraordinary rate, may be gathered by a study of three articles, published over a 16-year period, each enumerating the major problems of algebraic or differential topology. First, Eilenberg gave a list of such problems in 1949 under the title, "On the problems of topology," *Ann. Math.*, **50** (1949), 247–60. It is noticeable that this list was compiled just before the revolution in algebraic topology brought about by Serre's application of the Leray theory of spectral sequences to the study of the homology of (generalized) fiber spaces ("Homologie singulière des espaces fibrés. Applications," *Ann. Math.*, **54** (1951), 425–505). This paper might be said to have ushered in the golden age of algebraic topology, an age of rapid advance in which many of the problems listed by Eilenberg were solved and in which algebraic topology won many adherents among the younger mathematicians and was largely studied for its own sake. This period was still current when Massey published "Some problems in algebraic topology and the

† We should really complete the diagram by adding $\longrightarrow \Pi$ at the right-hand end, where Π is the category of topological manifolds, but the equivalence relation is that of homotopy equivalence instead of homeomorphism. We may then even formulate the Poincaré conjecture within the enlarged diagram.

theory of fiber bundles," *Ann. Math.*, **62** (1955), 327–59. Algebraic topology as a self-contained discipline was still very much in vogue (recall that Milnor published his paper on differentiable structures on the 7-sphere in 1956) but the theory of fiber bundles (which includes the study of Lie groups and global differential geometry) was recognized as being of particular significance at that time.† Just as Massey's list grew out of a conference on fiber bundles and differential geometry held at Cornell University (Hirzebruch published a corresponding list of problems in differential geometry and complex structures), so Lashof, the author of the third compilation, made a selection from problems proposed by the participants at a Summer Institute in Differential and Algebraic Topology held in Seattle in 1963 ["Problems in differential and algebraic topology," Seattle Conference, 1963, *Ann Math.*, **81** (1965), 565–91]. The problems themselves, as well as the very title of the conference, testify to the dominant role within topological research occupied at that time (and since!) by differential topology and the largely ancillary role being played by algebraic topology. This is not meant to downgrade algebraic topology and the achievements of algebraic topologists over the past 5 years—nor indeed to suggest that the boundary between algebraic and differential topology is rigidly defined. But the problems to which algebraic topologists are increasingly devoting their expertise are concerned with structures lying outside the domain of topology—differentiable structures, analytic structures, complex manifolds, Lie groups operating on manifolds, and so forth.‡

---

† Already, in 1953, Thom had initiated cobordism theory in his paper, "Quelques propriétés globales des variétés différentiables," *Comm. Math. Helv.*, **27** (1953), 198–232. The ideas in this paper (which won for its author a Fields Medal at the Edinburgh International Congress in 1958) have proved enormously influential and pervasive, and Massey recognized their importance. Thom used standard methods of algebraic topology (computation of homotopy groups) to obtain information on the cobordism rings of oriented and nonoriented differential manifolds, so his work might be regarded as a prototype for the sort of "applied algebraic topology" we describe below.

‡ There was also another movement of algebraic topologists—in the direction of algebra, particularly homological algebra and categorical algebra. These latter two branches of algebra, attracting both topologists and algebraists, continue to feed back into algebraic topology.

Thus the three papers, by Eilenberg, Massey, and Lashof, both reflected and (to some extent) influenced the direction of progress of topological research over the past 2 decades. Indeed, the Russian topologist S. P. Novikov analyzed the problems listed by Lashof and enumerated, by author and title, the papers presented at the Seattle conference in his paper, "The Topology Summer Institute, Seattle, 1963," *Russian Mathematical Surveys*, **20** (1965), 145–68; it is a remarkable tribute to Novikov's insight that he was able to announce solutions of some of these problems and offer highly illuminating commentaries on virtually all of them.

Without claiming in any way to attempt a comprehensive coverage of the exciting results of even the last decade, it may be worthwhile to list at least some of the most striking achievements; in doing so it is necessary to apologize in advance to those whose work is omitted simply because of lack of space—and to explain again that the items mentioned are to be regarded as *examples* of outstanding work.

Serre's great paper, to which we have already referred, gave a tremendous impetus to homotopy theory and in particular to the problem of calculating homotopy groups. Much very significant work was done on this problem in the subsequent years, by Serre himself, Cartan, Toda, Moore, and many others; moreover a key idea due to Eilenberg and MacLane, that of a complex with a single nonvanishing homotopy group, played an important role in many of the arguments. These complexes are, in a sense, the bricks of homotopy theory; besides, it was observed that the cohomology groups could be regarded as groups of homotopy classes of maps into such Eilenberg-MacLane complexes, thus presaging the emergence of one of the most important algebraico-topological concepts of recent times, that of a representable cohomology theory. Serre also observed that primary cohomology operations which had been intensively studied by Steenrod, Adem, and others were in fact elements of the cohomology groups of Eilenberg-MacLane complexes, thus giving a further stimulus and a definite direction to their study. A particular contribution of Moore, influenced by Eilenberg, was to draw attention to the singular simplicial complex of a space, pointing out that all significant algebraic homotopy invariants of a space were contained in the singular complex. This idea was taken further by many, and Kan described a free simplicial group which in a sense represented the space and thus reduced homotopy theory, in principle, to group theory.† In his contribution to this volume, "Semisimplicial homotopy theory," V. K. A. M. Guggenheim describes the developments due to Moore and Kan and introduces some very recent advances in the theory. He presents this theory as something logically quite self-contained but motivated either through the singular functor or through a standard construction ("triple," in the modern terminology) from the study of topological spaces.

Great advances in algebraic topology are associated with the names of Adams and Bott. In 1958, Adams announced the solution of a long-standing problem in a paper entitled "The nonexistence of elements of Hopf invariant one," [*Bull. Am. Math. Soc.*, **64** (1958), 279–82; see also *Ann. Math.*, **72** (1960), 20–104]. Hopf showed, back in 1935, that if n is even, then there are infinitely many distinct homotopy classes of maps of S^{2n-1} into S^n. This he did by exhibiting a numerical invariant, now universally known as the *Hopf invariant*, of the homotopy class, which could take all even values. The question naturally arose, and was indeed posed by Hopf, as to whether it could take odd values; this is equivalent to the question of whether it can take the value 1. The answer is affirmative if $n = 2, 4$, or 8, as shown by Hopf. G. W. Whitehead showed that the existence of elements of Hopf invariant 1 for $n \geq 4$ required that n be divisible by 4; Adem, using primary cohomology operations, showed that their existence requires that n be a power of 2; and Toda showed that no such element exists if $n = 16$. Adams, using a very deep spectral sequence of his own invention which relates cohomology to homotopy, and secondary cohomology operations, gave the complete answer to the problem—such elements exist only for $n = 2, 4, 8$.

---

† Among many other important contributions, Kan also established a precise relation between free simplicial groups and the CW-complexes of J. H. C. Whitehead, thus linking his approach with Whitehead's combinatorial homotopy theory, one of the most successful tools of algebraic topology.

This does not end the story,† but we turn now to Bott's famous *periodicity theorem*. Much attention had been given (for example by G. W. Whitehead and Toda) to the computation of the homotopy groups of the classical groups; this problem had intrinsic interest but also arose in fiber bundle theory and other applications (see, e.g., Steenrod, *Topology of Fibre Bundles*. Princeton, N.J.: Princeton University Press, 1951). Consider for example the *unitary* group of unitary transformations of $\mathbb{C}^n$; we write it as $U(n)$. There is a natural embedding of $\mathbb{C}^n$ in $\mathbb{C}^{n+1}$ as the set of $(n+1)$-vectors whose last component is zero; this leads to a natural embedding of $U(n)$ in $U(n+1)$. Let U be the union $\bigcup_n U(n)$; we call this the *big* or *stable* unitary group and its homotopy groups are called the *stable* homotopy groups of the unitary group. In fact $\pi_r(U(n)) = \pi_r(U)$ if $n \geq \frac{1}{2}(r+1)$, so that we see that $\pi_r(U(n))$ *stabilizes* [at $\pi_r(U)$] for large n. Bott proved the remarkable theorem that there is a canonical isomorphism

$$\pi_r(U) = \pi_{r+2}(U); \tag{3}$$

in fact, these groups are zero for r even and $\mathbb{Z}$ for r odd. Thus the homotopy groups of U have period 2. If we take $\mathbb{R}$ instead of $\mathbb{C}$ and consider the *big orthogonal group* O, we have a similar remarkable phenomenon; here the period is 8 and Bott gave a group-theoretical interpretation of each intermediate term in the period. These results were published in 1957 ["Stable homotopy of the classical groups," *Proc. Nat. Acad. Sci.*, U.S.A., **43** (1957), 933–35] and had many consequences. Refinements of the calculations of $\pi_r(O(n))$ and $\pi_r(U(n))$ were made; Kervaire and Milnor obtained independent proofs, based on Bott's work, of the nonparallelizability of S^n for $n > 7$; and Atiyah and Hirzebruch, basing their investigations on ideas due to Grothendieck, developed real and

† We mean that Adams' proof was superseded, largely due to his own work on K-theory (see below); but the Adams spectral sequence, on which his original proof was based, retains its importance. Moreover there is a mod p version of Adams' theorem; and, perhaps most important, Adams' result implies the nonexistence of division algebras over the reals of dimensions $\neq$ 1, 2, 4, 8.

complex *K-theory*. This theory is an *extraordinary* cohomology theory, extraordinary in the sense that it satisfies all the Eilenberg-Steenrod axioms but violates the *dimension axiom* which affirms that the (reduced) cohomology groups of the 0-sphere (pair of points) vanish in dimensions different from zero. It turns out that equivalence classes of real (complex) vector bundles over the complex X yield an extraordinary cohomology theory and that this theory is representable, just as ordinary cohomology theory is representable by Eilenberg-MacLane complexes. The representing object is usually regarded as a spectrum, generalizing the notion of a complex; and the appropriate spectra for real (complex) K-theory are the orthogonal (unitary) spectra. K-theory is in many ways more "natural" than ordinary cohomology theory, since we are so familiar with operations on vector spaces and hence on vector bundles. In particular, Adams studied the primary operations in K-theory and then proved in 1961 his celebrated theorem on the number of independent vector fields on a sphere. Given a positive integer n, there is a well-known Hurwitz-Radon-Eckmann number $\rho(n)$, defined as follows. Factorize n as $n = 2^b k$, where k is odd, and let $b = c + 4d$ with $0 \leq c \leq 3$; then $\rho(n) = 2^c + 8d$. The significance of $\rho(n)$ is that there exist $\rho(n) - 1$ linear fields on S^{n-1} but there do not exist $\rho(n)$ fields. Adams proved that the number $\rho(n)$ not only solves the linear problem but also solves the continuous problem; there do not exist $\rho(n)$ independent (real) fields on S^{n-1} ["Vector fields on spheres," *Ann. Math.*, **75** (1962), 603–32]. Another triumph for (complex) K-theory is that it leads to a solution of the Hopf invariant 1 problem which, in Atiyah's phrase, "can be written on a postcard." † There are two very important connections between K-theory and ordinary cohomology (apart from their formal resemblance through the Eilenberg-Steenrod axioms). One is the Atiyah-Hirzebruch spectral sequence which relates ordinary cohomology H with any given cohomology theory h; in this spectral sequence for a finite dimensional complex X, E_2 is $H(X; h(S^0))$ and E_∞ is the graded group associated with the filtration of $h(X)$ induced by the skeleton decomposition of X.

† Note that Adams' original proof occupied 85 pages!

An excellent account of this is to be found in Atiyah-Hirzebruch, "Vector bundles and homogeneous spaces," *Proc. Sym. Diff. Geom., AMS* (1961), pp. 7–38. A second connection is the *Chern character* which is a multiplicative homomorphism from (complex) $K(X)$ to $H(X; Q)$, the ordinary cohomology of X with rational coefficients. This is described in Hirzebruch's report to the International Congress in Edinburgh (1958). A very elegant version is to be found in Dold, "Relations between ordinary and extraordinary cohomology," *Coll. Alg. Top. Aarhus* (1962), 2–9.

We have already referred briefly to Thom's cobordism theory, initiated in 1953. This has been studied, developed, extended, and applied widely. The fundamental idea is to classify (closed) manifolds according to whether they form together the boundary of an open manifold of the same kind—indeed, the Russian term for cobordism theory was, at least until recently, "intrinsic homology." More precisely, if closed oriented differential manifolds are under consideration, then two such n-dimensional manifolds M_1 and M_2 are cobordant if there exists an open $(n + 1)$-dimensional oriented differential manifold whose boundary consists of the disjoint union of M_1 and $-M_2$ (that is, M_2 with the opposite orientation). This is an equivalence relation and we write Ω^n for the collection of equivalence classes. The disjoint sum gives Ω^n the structure of an abelian group and the topological product induces a product $\Omega^m \times \Omega^n \longrightarrow \Omega^{m+n}$ which turns $\Omega = \bigoplus_n \Omega^r$ into a graded commutative ring, called the (*oriented*) *cobordism ring*. Thom showed that Ω^n could be calculated as a certain stable homotopy group (of what is now called the Thom complex of the special orthogonal group). Atiyah observed that this led to a cobordism theory for a space X (by mapping X into the Thom complex) and the Thom theory was then cobordism theory for the sphere. Atiyah further observed that there was a bordism theory which stood in relation to cobordism theory very much as homology is related to cohomology; this point of view led to many simplifications and to new results ("Bordism and cobordism," *Proc. Cam. Phil. Soc.*, **57** (1961), 200–208). The calculation of Ω, initiated by Thom, was completed by Wall. Important contributions to the theory have also been made by Milnor, Dold, E. H. Brown, Peterson, and others. Milnor published in 1962 "A survey of cobordism theory" [*L'Enseignement Mathématique*, **8** (1962), 16–23] in which he discussed known results and unsolved problems of the theory; this survey serves to emphasize the tremendous advances the theory has made since 1962, quite apart from the role it played in the first proof of the Atiyah-Singer index theorem.† We shall have something to say below of a further development, the so-called h-cobordism theorem of Smale. E. Dyer contributes an article to this volume entitled "The functors of algebraic topology" in which he sketches a comprehensive treatment of algebraic topology based on the fundamental notions of combinatorial homotopy theory. Having set up the theory, he considers as special applications (or aspects) cobordism theory and the theory of stable vector bundles (K-theory).

We have now devoted some space to "pure" and "applied" algebraic topology. We must now discuss, however inadequately, what we have referred to as the use of analytical methods in differential topology. Fortunately, the literature of differential topology is relatively rich in survey articles. In particular we note the article by Smale, "A survey of some recent developments in differential topology," *Bull. Am. Math. Soc.*, **69** (1963), 131–45; that by Wall, "Topology of smooth manifolds," *Jour. L. M. S.*, **40** (1965), 1–20; lecture notes by Wall, "Differential topology," issued by Cambridge University; the book by Milnor, "Morse theory," *Ann. Math. Studies No.* 51, Princeton, N.J. (1963); and that by Munkres, of a more introductory nature, "Elementary differential topology," *Ann. Math. Studies No.* 54, Princeton, N.J. (1963).

Probably the most significant new tools of differential topology are the use of Morse theory, as refined by Smale, to produce a structure theory for differential manifolds and the associated concept of spherical modification or, as it is now usually called, "surgery." The final article in this volume, "On the geometry of differentiable manifolds," by V. Poenaru, discusses these new tools

---

† Another of its remarkable applications is to be found in Hirzebruch's original proof of the Riemann-Roch-Hirzebruch theorem. See Hirzebruch, *Topological Methods in Algebraic Geometry*. (Berlin: Springer-Verlag, 1966.)

of differential topology and the results obtained by them in some detail. Here we merely sketch some of the principal ideas in outline.

Let M^n be a manifold with boundary ∂M and let $f: S^{k-1} \times D^{n-k} \longrightarrow \partial M$ be a smooth embedding, where D^s is the s-dimensional disk bounded by S^{s-1}. We may then take the disjoint union of M and $D^k \times D^{n-k}$ and glue these two manifolds together by means of f. In other words, we use f to attach $D^k \times D^{n-k}$ to M; by smoothing out corners, we obtain a new manifold $\tilde{M}$. Then $D^k \times D^{n-k} \subset \tilde{M}$ is called a *k-handle* and M is said to be obtained from M by *attaching a k-handle.* If we look at ∂M, we see that in the passage from ∂M to $\partial \tilde{M}$ we have removed $S^{k-1} \times D^{n-k}$ from ∂M and replaced it by $D^k \times S^{n-k-1}$ to obtain $\partial \tilde{M}$. This process is called *surgery in dimension k;* it may be applied to closed manifolds which do not necessarily appear as boundaries of other manifolds. Smale and Wallace proved independently that every manifold has a handle decomposition. Smale based his arguments on a theory of *nice functions* which constitutes a development of Morse theory. Morse had shown that any smooth function on a manifold can be approximated by a function having only isolated nondegenerate critical points; Smale goes further and shows the following. Suppose M_1 and M_2 are two cobordant closed manifolds, so that there is a manifold W whose boundary consists of M_1 and $-M_2$. Then there is a function f on W such that f has only isolated nondegenerate critical points, none of which are on $M_1 \cup M_2$, and if α is a critical point of f of index k, then $f(\alpha) = k$ ($f = \frac{1}{2}$ on $M_2, f = n - \frac{1}{2}$ on M_1). Following Morse, Smale analyzes the way W is built up starting from M_2 and shows that it may be regarded as obtained by attaching handles of index k as we pass from the set $f(\alpha) \leq k - \epsilon$ to the set $f(\alpha) \geq k + \epsilon$. Using this handle decomposition of W, Smale proved the celebrated *h-cobordism theorem* ["On the structure of manifolds," *Am. Jour. Math.*, 84 (1962), 397–99].

Given the situation described above, we say that W is a cobordism between M_2 and M_1. If W may be retracted by deformation onto M_1 as well as onto M_2, then we call W an *h-cobordism* and say that W_1 and W_2 are *h-cobordant* (the concept is due to Thom). It is not too difficult to see that diffeomorphic manifolds are h-cobordant. Smale, by using the structure of W and arguments about canceling handles, proved the converse: if W is simply connected and of dimension ≥ 6, then it is itself diffeomorphic to† $M_2 \times I$ and M_1 is diffeomorphic to M_2. From this he deduced the *generalized Poincaré conjecture* for differential manifolds of dimension ≥ 6 (a special argument enabled him to include also the case of dimension 5): a differential manifold of the homotopy type of an n-sphere is homeomorphic to the n-sphere.‡ It should be noted that the conclusion of this theorem, as for the combinatorial version due to Stallings and Zeeman, is purely topological (i.e., it is a statement in the category Top); Connell and Newman have recently announced a version of the generalized Poincaré conjecture (in dimensions ≥ 5) in which the hypothesis, like the conclusion, is purely topological. There is also a version of the h-cobordism theorem in which one dispenses with the condition of simple connectivity. The price one pays is to replace the notion of "deformation retraction" by that of "combinatorial deformation retraction" due to J. H. C. Whitehead [see Mazur, "Differential topology from the viewpoint of simple homotopy theory," *Publ. Math.*, I.H.E.S., **15** (1963); "Errata," *ibid.*, **22** (1964), 81–91]. Proofs have also been given by Barden and Stallings. A very readable account of this s-cobordism theory is to be found in Kervaire, "Le théorème de Barden-Mazur-Stallings," *Comm. Math. Helv.*, **40** (1965), 31–42. Surgery has been used very extensively in differential topology.§ One may note as an example the work of Browder, Novikov, and others on problems of applied homotopy theory of the following kind: Given a complex K with certain properties, does there exist a smooth manifold of the homotopy type of K? Given a homotopy class of smooth manifolds, how many distinct diffeomorphism classes does it contain? Very roughly speaking, Browder tackles

† I stands for the unit interval $0 \leq t \leq 1$.

‡ This was also proved by Wallace.

§ The first account of it in the context we are considering is probably in Milnor, "A procedure for killing the homotopy groups of differentiable manifolds," *AMS Sym. Pure Math.*, III (1961), 39–55, but it had, of course, been used earlier (e.g., by Wallace).

the former problem by setting up a first approximation, that is, a smooth manifold M and a map f between M and K and then doing (delicate!) surgery on M in order to render f, ultimately, a homotopy equivalence. This kind of argument is becoming increasingly standard among differential topologists; it has led one always to expect, in this type of problem, to distinguish three cases, according to whether the dimension of the manifold is (i) odd, (ii) $\equiv 2 \bmod 4$, (iii) $\equiv 0 \bmod 4$. The difficulty is connected with surgery "in the middle dimension." Thus case (i) is the easiest since there is no middle dimension. In case (iii) there is an obstruction to surgery in the middle dimension which is very closely related to the Hirzebruch index (see footnote on p. 16); in case (ii) the obstruction is the so-called Arf invariant which has been extensively studied but still remains a little mysterious. It is an invariant of a quadratic form mod 2 (obtained by considering cup products of cohomology classes in the middle dimension); the reader may find information about this and many other important topics in the paper by Kervaire and Milnor, "Groups of homotopy spheres (I)," *Ann. Math.*, 77 (1963), 504–37.

A further class of problems deserving special mention, and certainly related to what has gone before, is that of trying to embed or immerse one smooth manifold in another (an immersion is a smooth map which is locally an embedding, but self-intersections are permitted). Very commonly the containing manifold is Euclidean space, $\mathbb{R}^m$, and typically one would ask, for a given manifold M, what is the minimum value of m for which M embeds† (immerses) in $\mathbb{R}^m$. M. W. Hirsch, one of the leading workers in this area, contributed an extraordinarily comprehensive statement of known results and important problems to the 1963 Seattle Conference. Though there have been many recent advances, this remains a very useful document as it not only enumerates the known results at the time, but also sufficiently indicates the type of problem

† The starting point is Whitney's classical theorem that M^n embeds smoothly in $\mathbb{R}^{2n+1}$. We only discuss here the existence of embeddings; the classification of embeddings may be regarded as the (generalized, smooth) *knot* problem.

being considered (thus for example, particular interest attaches to the case $M = P^n$, real projective n-space). There are also extremely interesting negative results in this direction, asserting that M does *not* embed (immerse) in $\mathbb{R}^m$; these results tend to be obtained by more algebraic methods. Such problems often lead to the development of an appropriate *obstruction theory*. Another such problem, for which Munkres, following Thom, has developed an obstruction theory is that of trying to smooth out a combinatorial structure—that is, in the notation of (2), of trying to construct, for a given combinatorial manifold M, a differential manifold $\tilde{M}$ such that $W(\tilde{M}) = M$; the coefficients for this latter obstruction theory are certain very interesting groups, the so-called Γ-groups, whose elements are equivalence classes of "exotic" differentiable structures on spheres. Thus our discussion returns to the virtual starting point of differential topology—Milnor's 1956 paper on differentiable structures on the 7-sphere. An excellent account of the obstruction theory is to be found in Hirsch, "Obstruction theories for smoothing manifolds and maps," *Bull. A.M.S.*, **69** (1963). 352–56.

As we have said, the diagram

$$\text{Diff} \xrightarrow{W} \text{PL} \xrightarrow{F} \text{Top}$$

contains, symbolically, a statement of the main problems in the theory of manifolds. In each of the categories one seeks some complete set of invariants to characterize the equivalence classes of manifolds. Progress, while partial, has been truly sensational. Special classes have indeed been classified (see, for example, Wall's paper, "On the classification of $(n-1)$-connected $2n$-manifolds," *Ann. Math.*, **75** (1962), 163–89, and "Manifolds which are like projective planes," *Publ. Math.*, **14** (1962), 181–221, by Eells and Kuiper. The Hauptvermutung for manifolds seems within our grasp; and we have known for some years that a cell carries a unique differentiable structure. What is striking is that topologists are taking up again, along with the new problems, the fundamental problems which were being considered in the 1920's and 1930's by the pioneers of topology, problems whose intractability led to their temporary abandonment in favor of algebraic homotopy theory.

An interesting feature of present-day work in the theory of manifolds is that many statements (but certainly not all)† remain true, with only slight modification, if one passes from differential to combinatorial manifolds (there is, for example, a piecewise-linear Smale theory). In many cases the essential difficulty in the passage from one category to the other resides in the problem of finding useful translations of concepts proper to the one category into language meaningful in the other. One example has already been given (but not really described)—Thom's translation of the rational Pontryagin classes. A second example must now suffice—Milnor's translation of the tangent bundle to a differential manifold. Milnor invented the concept of a microbundle [*Microbundles and differentiable structures*, Princeton University (1961)]. Such microbundles may be defined in any of our three categories (indeed they may be defined more generally because the base of a microbundle, like that of a vector bundle, need not be a manifold). Every vector bundle determines a microbundle; associated with any combinatorial or topological manifold, there is a particular microbundle which, if the manifold admits a compatible smooth structure, is the microbundle induced by the tangent bundle with respect to the smooth structure. Thus it is proper to think of the tangent structure to a combinatorial manifold even if no differentiable structure is present. A recent and comprehensive account of microbundles is to be found in Kuiper and Lashof, "Microbundles and bundles I. Elementary theory," *Inv. Math.*, **1** (1966), 1–12.

This introduction—and indeed the whole volume—will have served its main purpose if it gives the reader some impression of the enormous vitality of topology today and some of the principal uses to which that vitality is being directed. It only remains for the editor to thank the contributors for their estimable articles, to thank his friends Paul Olum and Nicolaas Kuiper for some very

† A striking difference appears in combinatorial knot theory and differentiable knot theory. As we have said, Zeeman has shown that S^k knots combinatorially only in $\mathbb{R}^{k+2}$; but Haefliger has shown that S^{4k-1} knots differentiably in $\mathbb{R}^{6k}$ [*Ann. Math.*, **75** (1962), 452–66]. Thus, for example, given any smooth embedding of S^3 in $\mathbb{R}^6$, we can bring it into standard position by combinatorial moves, but we may not be able to do so by smooth moves.

helpful comments; and to apologize, first to his colleagues, both those mentioned and those unmentioned in this introduction, for the injustices he has done them and second, to his readers who have tried to follow his tortuous and badly charted path through the maze of modern topology.

WHAT IS A CURVE?

Gordon T. Whyburn

1. INTRODUCTION

When the searching light of modern mathematical thinking is focused on the classical notion of a curve, this idea is found to involve elements of vagueness which must be clarified by accurate and exact definition. Fortunately this has been made possible and relatively simple by development in the field of set-theoretic topology. We shall endeavor to set forth below, first, the need for explicit definition of a curve, then the definition itself, and finally several illustrations of types of simple curves which can be completely characterized by their topological properties and which more nearly approach the classical notion of a curve. We conclude by discussing a recent application of the classical curve notion and other topological methods in classical analysis.

2. THE CLASSICAL NOTION

The concept of a curve as the "path (or locus) of a continuously moving point" usually is accompanied by intuitive notions of *thinness* and *two-sidedness*. When the curve is in a plane, these were thought to be consequences of the rather vaguely formulated definition of a curve as just given.

That the path of a continuously moving point is not necessarily a thin or curve-like set was shown by Peano and somewhat later by E. H. Moore, who demonstrated the remarkable fact that a square plus its interior can be exhibited as the continuous image of the interval. In other words, if S denotes a square plus its interior, we can define continuous functions $x(t)$ and $y(t)$ on the interval $0 \leqq t \leqq 1$ so that as t varies from 0 to 1, the point $P[x(t), y(t)]$ moves continuously through all the points of S.

A still more striking result in this direction is the remarkable theorem proved independently by Hahn and Mazurkiewicz about 1913. This theorem asserts that in order for a point set M (in Euclidean space of any number of dimensions) to be representable as the continuous image of the interval $0 \leqq t \leqq 1$, it is necessary and sufficient that M be a locally connected continuum. (A *continuum* in Euclidean space is a closed, bounded, and connected set; and a continuum M is *locally connected* provided that for any $\epsilon > 0$, a $\delta > 0$ exists such that any two points x and y of M at a distance apart $<\delta$ can be joined by a subcontinuum of M of diameter $<\epsilon$.) Thus since obviously not only a square but also a cube, an n-dimensional interval, an n-dimensional sphere, and a multitude of other sets are locally connected continua, any such set M can be represented as the path of a continuously moving point in the sense that we can define continuous functions

$$x_i = x_i(t) \qquad 0 \leqq t \leqq 1, i = 1, 2, \ldots, n,$$

such that as t varies from 0 to 1, the point P with coordinates $(x_1, x_2, \ldots, x_n)$ moves continuously through all the points of M.

Even when a set is sufficiently "thin" or "1-dimensional" so that we would probably call it a curve, it may be in a plane and still not be two-sided. To illustrate, we note that in Fig. 1 any point

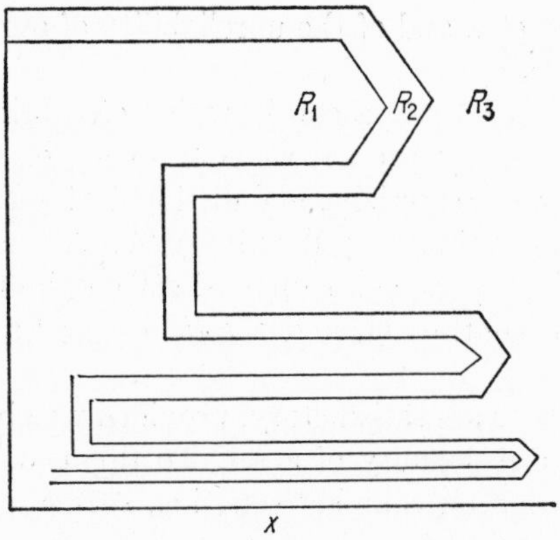

FIG. 1

on the base of the continuum, such as x, is a boundary point of each of the three regions R_1, R_2, R_3 into which the continuum divides the plane. Hence there are *three sides* of the base of this continuum. (Clearly we could add extra oscillating curves to the figure so as to make an arbitrarily large number or even an infinite number of regions each having all base points x on their boundaries.) Nevertheless our continuum is a thin 1-dimensional set made up of an infinite number of line segments. Now, it is possible to construct in a plane a continuum which is thin in the sense that it will not contain the interior of any circle and yet is so unusual that it will divide the plane into any finite number or an infinite number of regions and, further, it will be the boundary of each one of these regions. Also a plane continuum can be constructed which not only itself cuts the plane into infinitely many regions but has the remarkable property that every subcontinuum of it (any "piece" of it) also cuts the plane into infinitely many regions.

3. DIMENSIONALITY. GENERAL DEFINITIONS OF CURVE, SURFACE, SOLID

Undoubtedly sufficient evidence has been given about the necessity of being precise in our definitions and statements concerning curves, surfaces, etc., and of the unreliability of our intuition concerning these concepts.

We shall return later to a consideration of continuous traversibility of a set. For the present we concentrate on dimensionality as a criterion for characterizing and distinguishing between curves, surfaces, solids, etc., in a very definite sense. It seems natural and adequate to define a *curve* as a 1-dimensional continuum, a *surface* as a 2-dimensional continuum, and a *solid body* as a 3-dimensional continuum.

These definitions are satisfactory, provided we give an adequate definition of dimensionality of a set. To this end, let us concentrate our attention on compact sets, i.e., sets K which have the property that any infinite subset has a limit point belonging to K, sets which are closed and bounded if they lie in a Euclidean space.

We then define the dimensionality of the empty set to be -1 and agree the dimensionality of any other set is to be $\geqq 0$. Assuming, then, that we have defined the dimensionality concept for dimensions $\leqq n - 1$, by induction we define a set K to be of dimensionality n provided (1) every pair of distinct points p and q of K can be separated in K by some set X of dimensionality $\leqq n - 1$; i.e., $K - X$ falls into two separated sets K_p and K_q containing p and q, respectively; and (2) some pair of points of K cannot be separated in K by a subset of K of dimensionality $< n - 1$. Thus for $n \geqq 0$, a set K is of dimension n provided n is the least integer such that every pair of distinct points of K can be separated in K by the removal of a subset of dimension not greater than $n - 1$.

According to this definition, then, a compact set K is of dimension 0 provided every two points of K can be separated in K by omitting the empty set, i.e., provided they are already separated in K. Hence a 0-dimensional set is one which is nonempty but is totally disconnected in the sense that its only connected subsets are single points. A compact set K is 1-dimensional provided any two points can be separated in K by omitting from K a 0-dimensional or totally disconnected set but some two points cannot be separated without omitting some points from K. A compact set K is 2-dimensional provided each pair of points of K can be separarated in K by omitting a 1-dimensional set but not every pair can be separated by omitting a 0-dimensional set, and so on.

Stated in other terms, if we accept our definition that a curve is a 1-dimensional continuum, a surface is a 2-dimensional continuum, and a solid body is a 3-dimensional continuum, we see that a non-empty compact set K is 0-dimensional if every pair of its points are separated in K. The set is 1-dimensional at most provided we can (with shears if you like) separate any two of its points by cutting the set along a 0-dimensional set, i.e., by cutting out only single points as connected pieces. The set is 2-dimensional at most provided we can separate any two points by cutting the set along a 1-dimensional set, i.e., by cutting out only curves as connected sets. The set is 3-dimensional at most if we can separate any two points by cutting (with a saw perhaps) the set along a 2-dimensional set, i.e., by cutting out only surfaces as connected sets.

4. SOME SIMPLE TYPES OF CURVES

Having defined exactly the notions of curve, surface, and solid in terms of their topological properties in such a way that they correspond roughly to the geometrical notions of line, plane, and space, we consider now some interesting particular kinds of curves which may be similarly characterized.

Take first a straight line interval ab joining two points a and b and ask the question "What properties of a set make it essentially like an interval?" or "When are the points in a set associated together like those in the interval ab?" For example, if ab is a taut string and we release the tension and let it go slack but do not allow it to loop over onto itself, it is no longer straight but it retains its same essential structure. It can still be severed by cutting out any one of its points other than a or b; and it is this property in particular which characterizes the interval completely from the topological point of view. In other words, if we understand by a *simple arc* any set of points which is topologically equivalent to an interval in the sense that its points can be put into one-to-one and continuous correspondence with the points of an interval, then *in order that a continuum T be a simple arc, it is necessary and sufficient that T contain two points a and b such that the removal of any point of T other than a or b will disconnect T.* Thus in Fig. 2, (a) is a simple arc, but (b) is not a simple arc because the removal of neither a, b, nor x will separate the set (i.e., will make it fall apart).

Consider next a circle C and let us ask similar questions. If C is

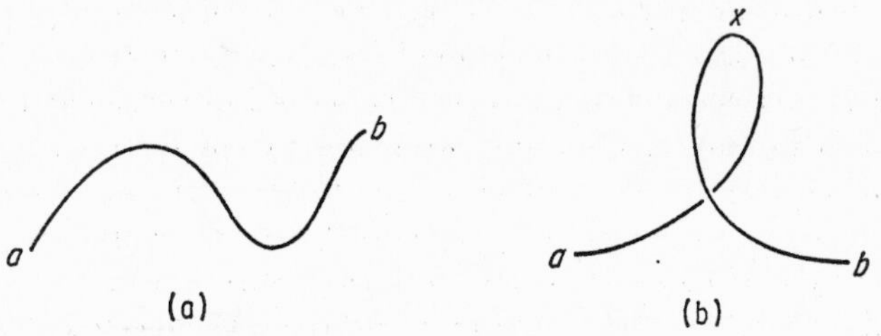

FIG. 2

distorted, as our interval was, by letting it slacken and bend but not fold onto itself or be broken violently, it is seen to retain its essential set structure. It retains the property, for example, of being severed by the removal of any two of its points whatever. Here again the property mentioned is characteristic for the type of curves which are topologically equivalent to the circle. In other words, if we define a *simple closed curve* as a set which can be put in one-to-one and continuous correspondence with a circle, then *in order that a continuum C be a simple closed curve, it is necessary and sufficient that C be disconnected by the omission of any two of its points.* Thus in Fig. 2, (a) is not a simple closed curve since the removal of both a and b leaves the set connected. In Fig. 3, (a) and (b) are simple closed curves but (c) is not a simple closed curve because the removal of x and y leaves the set connected.

A curve which is made up of a finite number of simple arcs which overlap with each other only at end points of themselves is called a *graph* or a *linear graph.* A graph, then, could be regarded as being constructed by putting together in any one of numerous ways a finite number of simple arcs so that no two of the arcs will overlap anywhere except possibly at an end point of both. All the curves illustrated in Figs. 2 and 3 are graphs; and of course many more complicated structures could be made which would still be graphs. However, if a graph is in a plane, it, like the simpler curves previously discussed, will have the classical property of two-sidedness which does not belong to all curves.

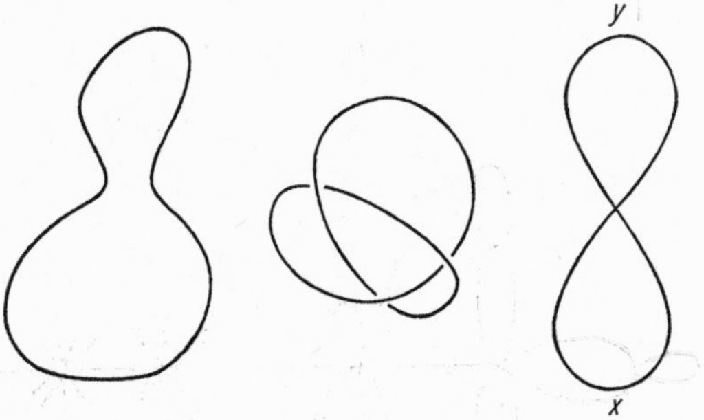

(a) (b) (c)

FIG. 3

Finally, we mention two further types of curves which in general are not graphs and yet whose structure is interesting and simple, namely the *dendrite* or *acyclic curve* and the *boundary curve*. A *dendrite* is a locally connected continuum which contains no simple closed curve. It may contain infinitely many simple arcs [see Fig. 4(a)]. In fact it may be impossible to express it as the sum even of countably many arcs, and yet it has the property that any two of its points are end points of one and only one arc in the curve. A *boundary curve* is a locally connected continuum which can be so imbedded in a plane that it will be the boundary of a connected region of the plane. Although it is true that every dendrite is a boundary curve, in general a boundary curve will contain one and may contain infinitely many simple closed curves [see Fig. 4(b)]. However, it is interesting to note that no such curve could contain a crossbar on a simple closed curve. In other words, the most that any two simple closed curves can overlap is in a single point (point of "tangency"). Thus any boundary curve breaks up into so-called

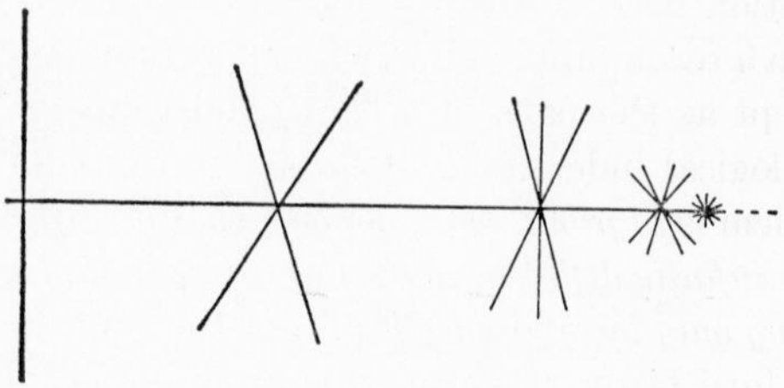

(a)

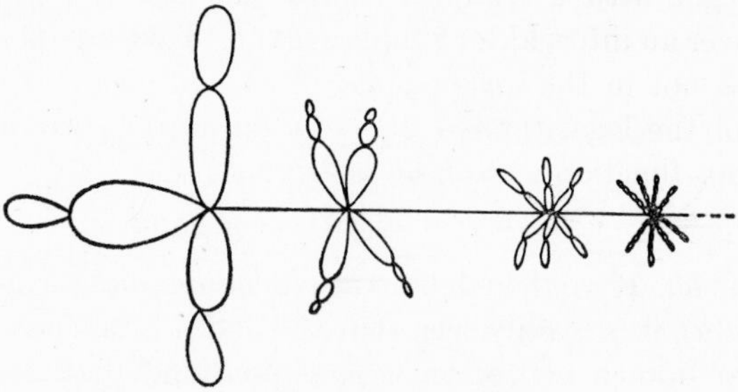

(b)

FIG. 4

cyclic elements which are either single points or simple closed curves; no two of these have more than one common point, and these fit together to make up the curve and give it a structure relative to these elements which is very similar to that of a dendrite. [Compare Fig. 4(a) with Fig. 4(b).]

5. ANALYTIC CURVES IN TOPOLOGICAL ANALYSIS

We return now to a brief discussion of the classical path-type curve mentioned earlier. This notion is most important in modern mathematics and pervades nearly all phases of current mathematical research, particularly where topology plays a rôle. It serves as a unifying force in mathematics and even an enumeration of the many connections and uses it serves to effect would be out of the question here. Instead we shall be content to outline the procedure in a recent application which has been made of the plane curve concept as the path of a continuously moving point along with a topological index easily definable in this connection.

The problem is *to prove, using topological and differential calculus methods, the infinite differentiability of a function of a complex variable assuming only the existence* (and not the continuity) *of the first derivative.* Until fairly recently, this proof could be effected only by using the complex integral and Cauchy's integral theorem, more or less following the lines set out in the original proof by Goursat.

We begin with a complex-valued function $z = \phi(t)$, where t ranges over an interval (or simple arc) ab. Take any point p in the z-plane Z not in the image $\phi(ab)$ of ab and choose a continuous branch of the logarithm of $\phi(t) - p$ on ab; i.e., we determine a continuous function $u(t)$ on ab satisfying

$$e^{u(t)} = \phi(t) - p$$

for all t on ab. If we then define the *circulation index* $\mu_{ab}(\phi, p)$ to be $u(b) - u(a)$, it is readily seen that this index is independent of the particular branch $u(t)$ of $\log \phi(p)$ chosen and that it is additive over any subdivision of the arc ab. In general this index μ can take on any complex number as its value; but in case our "curve" $\phi(t)$ is closed; i.e., $\phi(a) = \phi(b)$, the index is the difference in two values of the logarithm of the same number and thus has a value of the form $2k\pi i$ where k is an integer.

Now let $w = f(z)$ be a continuous complex-valued function defined on a part of the z-plane including all points of a simple closed curve C. Let $z = \zeta(t)$ be a positive traversal mapping of ab onto C; i.e., as t moves on ab from a to b, $\zeta(t)$ moves around C exactly once in the positive sense beginning and ending at the common point $\zeta(a) = \zeta(b)$. Under these conditions the "curve" given by the composite function $w = \phi(t) = f\zeta(t)$ is automatically closed in the sense above so that its index is an integral multiple of $2\pi i$. Thus if we define the *winding number* $w_c(f, p)$ of f on C about any point p in the w-plane not on $f(C)$ by the relation

$$w_c(f, p) = \frac{1}{2\pi i}\, \mu_{ab}(f\zeta, p),$$

this number is always an integer and represents $1/2\pi$ times the net change in amplitude of $f(z)$ when C is traversed once in the positive sense. Thus it is the net number of times $f(z)$ winds around p as z winds once around C in the positive sense. We remark that the applications to be made of these notions here are confined to the simple case in which C is a rectangle. In this case if we take the origin at the center of C, the traversal ζ may be taken as that given by

$$\zeta(t) = r(t)e^{it}, \qquad 0 \leqq t \leqq 2\pi,$$

where $r(t)$ is the length of the segment of the ray $\theta = t$ lying in C plus its interior.

The winding number $w_c(f, p)$ is thus defined and integer-valued for all $p \in W - K$ where $K = f(C)$. As a function of p, it is readily seen to be continuous and thus it is constant in each component of $W - K$. Also, since it necessarily vanishes whenever the set K subtends an angle less than 2π at p, it must always vanish for p in the unbounded component of $W - K$ because p can then be taken as remote as we like from K.

We are now in position to prove with minimal difficulties the propositions listed next which lead up to and establish the Maximum Principle.

(1) *If f is defined and continuous on the interior R of the rectangle C as well as on C, then for any $p \in W - f(C + R)$, $w_c(f, p) = 0$.*

This is proved by dividing R into a finite number of rectangles by lines parallel to the sides of C small enough so that the winding number of f about p on the boundary of each subrectangle is 0, which is possible by the discussion above since the image of any such rectangle does not contain p and hence will subtend a small angle at p when this image is small enough. However, the winding number of f about p on C is the sum of the winding numbers on the small rectangle boundaries since contributions to this sum made on sides interior to R are counted twice with opposite signs.

(2) *Let $f(z)$ be continuous in a region S of Z and suppose f is differentiable at a point z_0 of S. If $f'(z_0) \neq 0$, then for any sufficiently small rectangle C enclosing z_0 we have $w_c(f, w_0) = 1$, where $w_0 = f(z_0)$.*

To show this, we write

$$(*) \qquad f(z) - w_0 = (z - z_0)[f'(z_0) - \epsilon(z)]$$

where $\epsilon(z) \longrightarrow 0$ as $z \longrightarrow z_0$. If C is taken sufficiently small, it will lie in R and neither side of Eq. (*) will vanish on C. It then follows readily from the definition and properties of the index μ that

$$\begin{aligned} w_c(f, w_0) &= w_c(z - z_0, 0) + w_c[f'(z_0) - \epsilon(z), 0] \\ &= w_c(z, z_0) + w_c[-\epsilon(z), -f'(z_0)]. \end{aligned}$$

The first term on the right here is 1 since z is the identity function, and the second is 0 for C sufficiently small since $\epsilon(C)$ lies in an arbitrarily small neighborhood of 0 and thus subtends a small angle at the point $-f'(z_0)$.

(3) *Let $f(z)$ be continuous inside and on a rectangle C with interior R and be differentiable on the inverse of a dense open subset E_0 of $E = f(R + C) - f(C)$. Then for any $p \in E$, we have $w_c(f, p) > 0$.*

The argument required here is considerably more delicate and only a brief sketch will be given. The density assumption yields a region Q in $Q_0 \cdot E_0$, where Q_0 is the component of E containing p, and a component of $f^{-1}(Q)$ on which f is not constant so that there is a point z_0 in $f^{-1}(Q)$ where $f'(z_0) \neq 0$. Then statement (2) can be applied to show that Q contains an open set in the w-plane W. From this we deduce that, for some q in Q, $f'(z)$ does not vanish on $f^{-1}(q)$ because the image of the zeros of the derivative of f cannot contain an open set in W (a fact readily provable by an elementary argument).

Then $f^{-1}(q)$ consists of just a finite sequence of points $q_1, q_2, \ldots, q_m$ in R. Next, $R + C$ is subdivided by lines parallel to the sides of C into a finite set of rectangles, m of which, $C_1, C_2, \ldots, C_m$ are disjoint and enclose $q_1, q_2, \ldots, q_m$, respectively. The winding number $w_c(f, p)$ is the sum of the winding numbers of f about p on all the subrectangles. All the latter numbers are zero by statement (1), however, except those for the rectangles $C_1, C_2, \ldots, C_m$. Each of the numbers for these is 1 by statement (2) and this gives $w_c(f, p) = m > 0$.

This proposition is a kingpin in the whole development and the fact that it is proved with differentiability assumed only on the *inverse of a dense open set* rather than on the whole region R is of paramount importance. Indeed this fact alone provides the key to the success of the entire method.

As a direct consequence of statements (1) and (3), we find

(4) THEOREM: *If* $w = f(z)$ *is continuous on a rectangle* C *and on its interior* R *and is differentiable on the inverse of a dense open subset of* $f(R + C) - f(C)$, *then* $f(R + C)$ *consists of* $f(C)$ *together with certain bounded components of* $W - f(C)$.

This in turn gives at once

(5) MAXIMUM PRINCIPLE: *If* $|f(z)| \leqq M$ *on* C, *then* $|f(z)| \leqq M$ *on* R. *In particular, if* $f(z)$ *is continuous on a rectangle* C *and on its interior* R *and is differentiable on* $R - F$ *where* F *is a finite set of points, then* $|f(z)| \leqq M$ *on* C *implies* $|f(z)| \leqq M$ *on* $R + C$.

With this landmark of classical complex analysis established, our development now takes on a decidedly more analytic character, although topological-type reasoning persists to some extent. We next define, for $w = f(z)$ continuous in a region S, the *differential quotient function*

$$h(x, y) = \frac{f(x) - f(y)}{x - y}, \quad \text{for} \quad x, y \in R, x \neq y;$$

$$h(x, x) = f'(x), \quad \text{for} \quad x \in R, \quad \text{when } f'(x) \text{ exists at } x.$$

Thus $h(x, y)$ is defined at all points of the Cartesian product space $R \times R$ except at points (x, x) of the diagonal Δ of this space where f fails to be differentiable at x. Further, $h(x, y)$ is continuous in (x, y) at all points of $R \times R - \Delta$ and is continuous in x (and in y) separately at points (x, x) of Δ where it is defined, i.e., such that $f'(x)$ exists. We note also that $h(x, y)$ is symmetric in x and y.

It is now possible to prove rather easily, using the Maximum Principle above, the remarkable result

(6) THEOREM: *Let* $w = f(z)$ *be continuous inside and on a rectangle* C *and differentiable at all points of the interior* R *of* C *except at a finite set* F *of points. Then if* K *is any compact set in* R *and*

$K_0 = K - K \cdot F$, *the function* $h(x, y)$ *is uniformly continuous on* $K_0 \times K_0$.

Details of the proof will not be given. These can be found in the references given below. (The second edition of the author's *Topological Analysis* contains a full treatment of all the results and notions entering into this discussion.)

We next apply this theorem to prove

(7) *If* $f(z)$ *is continuous in the region* S *and differentiable at all points of* $S - F$, *where* F *is a finite set of points, then* $h(x, y)$ *is defined and continuous at all points* (x, y) *of* $S \times S$. *Thus* $f'(z)$ *exists and is continuous at all points of* S.

For if z_0 is any point of S, we choose a rectangle C, with center z_0, that lies with its interior R in S. Then taking K as a circular disk centered at z_0 that lies inside R where $K_0 = K - K \cdot F$ and using statement (6), we see by a standard extension theorem that $h(x, y)$ admits a unique continuous extension to $K \times K$ since $K_0 \times K_0$ is dense in $K \times K$. In particular, at the point $z_0 \times z_0$ (which is interior to $K \times K$), this extension gives that

$$\lim_{z \to z_0} h(z, z_0) = \lim_{z \to z_0} \frac{f(z) - f(z_0)}{z - z_0} = f'(z_0)$$

exists. Thus $f'(z)$ exists everywhere in S so that $h(x, y)$ was already defined everywhere in $S \times S$. Also $h(x, y)$ is continuous at (z_0, z_0) since it is identical with its extension on $K \times K$. This gives continuity of $h(x, y)$ everywhere in $S \times S$, as (z_0, z_0) is interior to $K \times K$ and z_0 was an arbitrary point of S. Finally, $f'(z)$ is continuous everywhere in S, since $f'(z)$ is identical with $h(x, y)$ on the diagonal Δ of $S \times S$.

Our final goal is at hand and we now prove

(8) THEOREM: *If* $f(z)$ *is differentiable in a region* S, *so also is* $f'(z)$.

Proof: Let y_0 be any point of S. Then since the function $h(x, y_0)$ is continuous (in x) everywhere in R and differentiable (in x) at all points of $S - y_0$, by statement (7) it is also differentiable at y_0. Whence

$$(*)\quad h'_x(y_0, y_0) = \lim_{x \to y_0} \frac{h(x, y_0) - h(y_0, y_0)}{x - y_0}$$

$$= \lim_{x \to y_0} \frac{\dfrac{f(x) - f(y_0)}{x - y_0} - f'(y_0)}{x - y_0}.$$

Thus, since for $x \neq y_0$,

$$h'_x(x, y_0) = \frac{f'(x)(x - y_0) - [f(x) - f(y_0)]}{(x - y_0)^2}$$

and since

$$\frac{f'(x) - f'(y_0)}{x - y_0} = \frac{f'(x) - \dfrac{f(x) - f(y_0)}{x - y_0}}{x - y_0} + \frac{\dfrac{f(x) - f(y_0)}{x - y_0} - f'(y_0)}{x - y_0},$$

we have

$$\lim_{x \to y_0} \frac{f'(x) - f'(y_0)}{x - y_0} = \lim_{x \to y_0} h'_x(x, y_0) + \lim_{x \to y_0} \frac{\dfrac{f(x) - f(y_0)}{x - y_0} - f'(y_0)}{x - y_0}$$

$$= h'_x(y_0, y_0) + h'_x(y_0, y_0) = 2h'_x(y_0, y_0)$$

by continuity of $h'_x(x, y_0)$ as given in statement (7) and by Eq. (*) above. Accordingly $f''(y_0)$ exists and equals $2h'_x(y_0, y_0)$.

Thus we have the classical result that the existence of the first derivative in a region implies the existence and continuity of derivatives of all orders for a function of a complex variable.

It is now possible to continue and round out a development of the entire differential calculus for functions of a complex variable. For example, the Maximum Principle on p. 34 along with techniques introduced by Cornell and Read can be made to yield the Cauchy inequality. This in turn leads directly to standard results on power series expansion and the like. Similarly the way is made easier for the development of the integral calculus of such functions, since Cauchy's integral theorem in its general form is now obtainable as a direct application of Green's theorem because we already have continuity of the derivative.

6. CONCLUSION

We have touched but a few of the many interesting aspects of the fundamental theory of curves. The subject has an extensive literature, particularly from the topological point of view, which the explorative reader will find fascinating as well as instructive. The field is a live one and it is currently receiving important contributions. Interesting and difficult problems remain unsolved. There is much to attract and repay the student who will expend the effort necessary to acquire a knowledge of these problems and to master the methods which have been devised for attacking them.

BIBLIOGRAPHY

For further reading, the following books and articles are suggested.

I. For original formulation of definitions and more or less complete treatment of dimension theory and curve theory:

1. Hurewicz, W., and H. Wallman, "Dimension theory," *Princeton Mathematical Series*, No. 4, Princeton University Press, 1941.
2. Kuratowski, C., "Topologie I," *Monografie Matematyczne*, Warsaw, **20** (1948).
3. Menger, K., *Dimensionstheorie*. Berlin-Leipzig: B. G. Teubner, 1928.
4. ———, *Kurventheorie*. Berlin-Leipzig: B. G. Teubner, 1932.
5. Urysohn, P., "Mémoire sur les multiplicités cantoriennes," *Verhandelingen Akademie van Wetenschappen*, Amsterdam, **13** (1928), No. 4.
6. ———, "Mémoire sur les multiplicités cantoriennes," *Fundamenta Mathematicae*, **7** (1925), 29–137; **8** (1926), 225–351.

II. For treatments in which curves and sets in the plane receive special attention:

1. Hall, D. W., and G. L. Spencer, *Elementary Topology*. New York: John Wiley & Sons, Inc., 1955.
2. Kuratowski, C., "Topology II," *Monografie Matematyczne*, **21** (1950).
3. Moore, R. L., "Foundations of point set theory," *Am. Math. Soc. Coll. Publ.*, **13** (1932).

4. Newman, M. H. A., *Elements of the Topology of Plane Sets of Points.* New York: Cambridge University Press, 1939.

5. Whyburn, G. T., "Analytic topology," *Am. Math. Soc. Coll. Publ.*, **28** (1942).

6. Wilder, R. L., "Topology of manifolds," *ibid.*, **32** (1949).

III. For interesting and unexpected types of curves:

1. Anderson, R. D., and G. Choquet, "A plane continuum no two of whose subcontinua are homeomorphic," *Proc. Am. Math. Soc.*, **10** (1959), 347–53.

2. Bing, R. H., "A homogeneous indecomposable plane continuum," *Duke Math. Jour.*, **15** (1948), 729–42.

3. ———, and F. B. Jones, "Another homogeneous plane continuum," *Trans. Am. Math. Soc.*, **90** (1959), 171–92.

4. Knaster, B., "Quelques coupures singulières du plan," *Fund. Math.*, **7** (1925), 277–80. Also, "Un continu dont tout sous-continu est indécomposable," *ibid.*, **3** (1922), 247–86.

5. Moise, E. E., "An indecomposable plane continuum which is homeomorphic to each of its non-degenerate subcontinua," *Trans. Am. Math. Soc.*, **63** (1948), 581–94.

6. Whyburn, G. T., "A continuum every subcontinuum of which separates the plane," *Am. Jour. Math.*, **52** (1930), 319–30.

IV. For a complete detailed treatment of the topics discussed in § 5 concerned with a topological analysis application of the classical path-type curve, see the author's book *Topological Analysis* (2nd ed.), Princeton: Princeton University Press, 1964. References to the original sources will be found in this book, particularly to papers by Plunkett, Ursell and Eggleston, Cornell, Porcelli, Read, the author, and others who made key contributions to this development.

SOME RESULTS ON SURFACES IN 3-MANIFOLDS†

Wolfgang Haken

1. PREFACE

The term *geometric topology* has been introduced for such topological investigations which attempt to solve geometric problems rather than those of an algebraic or analytic nature. However, the *methods* used in attacking these problems may be mainly algebraic or analytic as well as combinatorial or geometric. From this point of view, there is no clearly defined border between geometric topology and algebraic and differential topology. The geometric methods have the special feature of appealing to visualization, and it is a matter of taste whether one regards this feature as an advantage or a disadvantage. If the author of a

† This research was supported by the Air Force Office of Scientific Research under grants AF-AFOSR-62-124 and AF-AFOSR-359-63 and by the National Science Foundation under grant NSF-GP-5610.

topological paper relies on pictures instead of precise verbal proofs, he may produce an especially short and understandable treatment of his topic, but at the same time this may lead to serious errors. So some special care is required in this respect. On the other hand, visualization enables one to maintain a survey over rather complicated configurations whose verbal description would be lengthy and require elaborate notation. So one may regard visualization as a valuable tool for finding topological results and attacking problems which are extremely difficult and complex.

2. HEEGAARD-SURFACES AND INCOMPRESSIBLE SURFACES IN 3-MANIFOLDS

As an example of geometric topological investigations, let us consider some results on surfaces in 3-dimensional manifolds. By a *manifold* M^m of dimension m we mean a connected, separable, metric space such that each point $p \in M^m$ possesses a neighborhood N whose closure $\overline{N}$ is homeomorphic to the closed m-dimensional unit ball; if p lies in the boundary $\dot{N}$ of N, then we call p a *boundary point* of M^m, otherwise an *interior point.* We call a 2-manifold a *surface.*

It has been proved by Moise [17] and Bing [4] that every 3-manifold admits a triangulation and that two triangulated 3-manifolds M_1^3, M_2^3 are homeomorphic if and only if they are combinatorially equivalent, i.e., if the triangulations possess isomorphic subdivisions. The corresponding statements (the latter one is named the *Hauptvermutung* of combinatorial topology) hold also for 0-, 1-, and 2-manifolds; but it is not yet known whether they hold for 4- or higher-dimensional manifolds.

One of the main problems on manifolds is the (topological) *classification problem:* to find an enumeration M_1^m, M_2^m, . . . of m-manifolds such that every homeomorphism class is represented just once, i.e., such that M_i^m and M_j^m are not homeomorphic if $i \neq j$ and such that every arbitrary m-manifold is homeomorphic to one of the enumerated manifolds M_i^m. Related to this is the *homeomorphism problem:* to find an algorithm for deciding whether or not two given m-manifolds are homeomorphic. Regarding compact manifolds, both problems are solved for $m = 2$ (see for instance [25], Kap. 6); are open for $m = 3$; and as Markov [15] has proved, the homeomorphism problem is unsolvable for $m \geqq 4$. From this point of view the 3-dimensional case is of special interest.

Regarding the classification problem of 3-manifolds, one may ask the question, How can a given 3-manifold M^3 be decomposed by surfaces into pieces which are as simple as possible?

Different approaches can be made to answer this question. One of them is the consideration of so-called *Heegaard-surfaces*, i.e., of surfaces which decompose M^3 into two handlebodies (see for instance [25], Sec. 63). If M^3 has no boundary, then there exist Heegaard-surfaces in M^3. To find a Heegaard-surface, one may take an arbitrary triangulation Δ of M^3 and consider a small neighborhood N_1 of its 1-skeleton G^1. Then N_1 is obviously a handlebody (orientable or nonorientable): Let T be a tree in G^1 that consists of all vertices $\in \Delta$ and of certain edges $\in \Delta$ and let $E_1, \ldots, E_h$ be the (open) edges $\in \Delta$ not in T. Then we can find "small," pairwise disjoint, disks $C_1, \ldots, C_h$ with boundaries in the boundary $^{\cdot}N_1$ of N_1 and interiors in the interior $^{\circ}N_1$ of N_1 such that C_i is pierced by E_i in just one point and disjoint from all E_j's with $j \neq i$. These disks C_i form a *complete system of meridian disks* of N_1; i.e., $^{\circ}N_1 - \bigcup_{i=1}^{h} C_i$ is an open 3-cell. From this we see that N_1 can be obtained from a (compact) 3-cell by identifying h pairs of disjoint disks in its boundary, i.e., that (by definition, see [25], pp. 219, 221) N_1 is a handlebody of genus h; moreover, N_1 and $^{\cdot}N_1$ are orientable if and only if all identifications are of the orientable type. The closure $N_2 = {}^{-}(M^3 - N_1)$ of the complement $M^3 - N_1$ of N_1 is also a handlebody of genus h: Let $F_1, \ldots, F_s$ be the triangles $\in \Delta$, and let D_k be the disk $F_k \cap N_2$. Then $N_2 - \bigcup_{k=1}^{s} D_k$ consists of open 3-cells (just one in each tetrahedron $\in \Delta$) such that each disk D_k lies in the boundaries of just two of them. Hence the D_k's contain a complete system of meridian disks of N_2; since $^{\cdot}N_2 = {}^{\cdot}N_1$, this system will contain just h disks, say $D_1, \ldots, D_h$, and N_2 will be orientable if and only if N_1 is orientable. This means that the common boundary $H = {}^{\cdot}N_1 = {}^{\cdot}N_2$ of N_1 and N_2 is a Heegaard-surface in M^3 and that it is orientable if and only if M^3 is orientable. The manifold M^3 is uniquely determined (up to homeomorphy) by the surface H and both systems of curves $\dot{C}_i$, $\dot{D}_i$ $(i = 1, \ldots, h)$ on H which form a so-called *Heegaard-diagram* of M^3.

It would be of great interest to find a Heegaard-surface of minimal genus h in an arbitrary given 3-manifold. But this is still an unsolved problem. In 1939 Reidemeister [20] succeeded in classifying all 3-manifolds that possess Heegaard-surfaces of genus 1.

Another approach to our problem is to consider (polyhedral) surfaces in M^3 that split M^3 into pieces which are more or less typical for M^3, i.e., which cannot be imbedded in *every* 3-manifold. The simplest examples of such surfaces are (polyhedral) 2-spheres in M^3 that are not boundaries of 3-cells in M^3—let us call them *incompressible in* M^3. The Alexander theorem [1] states that the 3-sphere S^3 does not contain incompressible 2-spheres. In 1929 H. Kneser devoted a paper [12] to the theory of incompressible 2-spheres in 3-manifolds without boundary. At first he proved a finiteness theorem: **If s pairwise disjoint, polyhedral 2-spheres $S_1^2, \ldots, S_s^2$ are given in M^3; and if s is greater than a certain number $r(M^3)$, then at least one of the connected components of $M^3 - (S_1^2 + \cdots + S_s^2)$ is an open 3-sphere with holes, i.e., homeomorphic to S^3 minus a certain number of pairwise disjoint (compact) 3-cells.**

As a consequence of this, every 3-manifold M^3 admits a certain reduction to *irreducible* 3-manifolds, where irreducible means *not containing incompressible 2-spheres:* In M^3 there exists a "maximal" system of pairwise disjoint, polyhedral 2-spheres $S_1^2, \ldots, S_t^2$ so that none of the connected components $N_1^3, \ldots, N_u^3$ $(1 \leqq u \leqq t + 1)$ of $M^3 - (S_1^2 + \cdots + S_t^2)$ is an open 3-sphere with holes; but if an arbitrary polyhedral 2-sphere S_{t+1}^2, disjoint from $S_1^2, \ldots, S_t^2$, is added, then one connected component of $M^3 - (S_1^2 + \cdots + S_{t+1}^2)$ is an open 3-sphere with holes. Now we obtain u compact, irreducible 3-manifolds $M_1^3, \ldots, M_u^3$ without boundary by "cutting M^3 in $S_1^2, \ldots, S_t^2$ and closing the holes by $2t$ 3-cells" such that M_i^3 is the union of an open 3-manifold $N_i'^3$, homeomorphic to N_i^3, and some pairwise disjoint 3-cells. The difference $t + 1 - u$ is called the *handle number* of M^3. It can be proved further (see [12, 9]) that the homeomorphism class of M^3 is uniquely determined by the homeomorphism classes of $M_1^3, \ldots, M_u^3$, the handle number, and the orientability or nonorientability of M^3 (where in the orientable case *oriented* manifolds M_i^3 are to be considered).

The concept of incompressibility can be generalized for arbitrary polyhedral surfaces M^2 in 3-manifolds M^3: If M^2 is not a 2-sphere, then it is called *incompressible in* M^3 if every 1-sphere $S^1 \subset M^2$ that bounds an (open) disk in $M^3 - M^2$ also bounds a disk in M^2. One may interpret this property by saying that M^2 possesses no "trivial handles." The Alexander theorem [1] can be generalized by a lemma of R. H. Fox [7] to the statement: *The 3-sphere does not contain incompressible surfaces.* An example of an incompressible surface would be a torus M^2 in a 3-manifold M^3 such that $M^3 - M^2$ consists of two connected components which are homeomorphic to complementary spaces of knots in the 3-sphere.

A nice feature of incompressible surfaces is that in many cases algorithms can be found to effectively determine such surfaces in a given 3-manifold, using the so-called method of normal-surfaces [8, 9, 10, 24]. Also, the finiteness theorem mentioned above can be generalized as follows: **If M^3 is irreducible and if s pairwise disjoint incompressible surfaces $M_1^2, \ldots, M_s^2$ are given in M^3, where $s > r(M^3)$, then at least two of the surfaces are topologically parallel in M^3; i.e., at least one of the connected components of $M^3 - (M_1^2 + \cdots + M_s^2)$ has its closure homeomorphic to the Cartesian product of a surface and an interval.** This theorem has been proved in [9], using the language of the theory of normal-surfaces since it was needed as an auxiliary theorem for the development of the method of normal-surfaces. However, there are several other applications possible, two of which will be presented in Secs. 5 and 6 of this article. Section 7 establishes a connection between Heegaard-surfaces and incompressible 2-spheres. In Sec. 4 we shall give a proof of a generalized finiteness theorem that is independent of the theory of normal-surfaces and is analogous to H. Kneser's proof for the 2-spheres in [12].

The finiteness theorems mentioned hold as well for 3-manifolds with boundary. But it is obvious that such a finiteness theorem cannot hold for surfaces which are not incompressible, since we may take arbitrarily many topologically parallel surfaces in M^3 and attach to each of them a trivial handle such that the surfaces remain pairwise disjoint but no two of them remain topologically parallel.†

Moreover, the finiteness theorems can be generalized to surfaces with boundaries which lie in the boundary of M^3. For this purpose we need some additional definitions. A polyhedral surface M^2 in M^3 is called *transversal in* M^3 if ${}^{\cdot}M^2 = M^2 \cap {}^{\cdot}M^3$. The surface M^2 is called *boundary-incompressible in* M^3 if it is transversal in M^3 such that no component of ${}^{\cdot}M^2$ bounds a disk in ${}^{\cdot}M^3$ and such

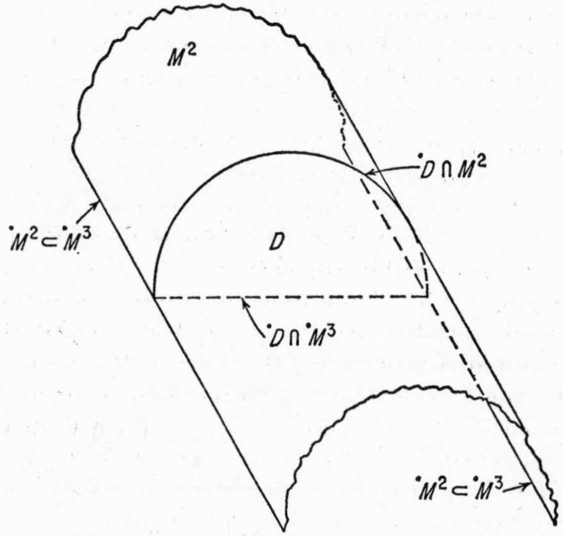

FIG. 1

that the following holds: if D is a polyhedral disk (see Fig. 1) with ${}^{\circ}D \subset {}^{\circ}M^3 - M^2$ such that each of ${}^{\cdot}D \cap {}^{\circ}M^2$ and ${}^{\cdot}D \cap$

† However, E. C. Edwards, Jr. has shown [6a] that every uncountable collection of pairwise disjoint (tame) surfaces in M^3 contains a pair of topologically parallel (in [6a] called concentric) ones.

$(\dot{M}^3 - \dot{M}^2)$ is one open arc and $\dot{D} \cap \dot{M}^2$ consists of two points, then $°M^2 - \dot{D}$ consists of two connected components and at least one of them is an open disk.

For some applications, e.g., the one presented in Sec. 6 of this article, we need the following generalization: If X is a polyhedron in $\dot{M}^3$, and M^2 is transversal in M^3, then M^2 is called *boundary-incompressible* mod X *in* M^3 if no component of $\dot{M}^2 \cap (\dot{M}^3 - X)$ bounds a disk in $\dot{M}^3$ and if the following holds: if D is a polyhedral disk with $°D \subset °M^3 - M^2$ and $\dot{D} \cap X = \varnothing$ such that each of $\dot{D} \cap °M^2$ and $\dot{D} \cap (\dot{M}^3 - \dot{M}^2)$ is an open arc and $\dot{D} \cap \dot{M}^2$ consists of two points, then $°M^2 - \dot{D}$ consists of two connected components and at least one of them is an open disk.

Finally, M^3 is called *boundary-irreducible* if it does not contain boundary-incompressible disks. It is trivial that a polyhedral surface in M^3 without boundary is always boundary-incompressible and that a 3-manifold without boundary is always boundary-irreducible. It can be shown that every 3-manifold with or without boundary admits a reduction to 3-manifolds which are irreducible and boundary-irreducible, analogous to the reduction described above.

3. THE SEMILINEAR STANDPOINT

For several investigations in geometric topology it is convenient to consider only "polyhedral" point sets in order to avoid set-theoretical difficulties such as "wild" imbeddings (compare [30, 21]).

By a *piecewise-rectilinear polyhedron* we mean a *finite* union of (compact) rectilinear simplices in some Euclidean space $\mathfrak{E}^n$ of sufficiently high dimension n. In the case of 3-dimensional manifolds one may consider them—without essential loss of generality—as piecewise-rectilinear polyhedra, since (as a consequence of the triangulability [17, 4]) every compact 3-dimensional manifold $\mathfrak{M}^3$ is homeomorphic to a piecewise-rectilinear polyhedron M^3 in $\mathfrak{E}^n$. Furthermore it is obvious that any result on (piecewise-rectilinear) polyhedral point sets in M^3 (as for instance our finiteness theorem for polyhedral surfaces in M^3) extends to a result on *tame* point sets in M^3 and in $\mathfrak{M}^3$ (a point set $\mathfrak{U}$ in M^3 or in $\mathfrak{M}^3$ is called *tame* if there exists an† epi-homeomorphism $M^3 \longrightarrow M^3$ or $\mathfrak{M}^3 \longrightarrow M^3$, respectively, that maps $\mathfrak{U}$ onto a piecewise-rectilinear polyhedral point set).

One may, of course, generalize the concept of polyhedron to point sets which are not necessarily subsets of $\mathfrak{E}^n$ and not necessarily piecewise-rectilinear (see for instance [2]).

It should be remarked that the restriction to polyhedral point sets, the so-called "combinatorial" or "semilinear" standpoint, is not necessarily the most convenient approach if manifolds of dimension greater than 3 are considered (see for instance M. Brown's treatment of the generalized Schoenflies theorem [5]).

For our purposes we may formulate the semilinear standpoint as follows:

In the subsequent part of this article capital Roman letters will always mean *piecewise-rectilinear polyhedral point sets* in $\mathfrak{E}^n$, i.e., finite unions of rectilinear *open* simplices in $\mathfrak{E}^n$ (compare [21]). (In Sec. 5 we shall have to consider some more general point sets which we shall denote by Gothic letters.) A compact polyhedral point set is called a *polyhedron*. Upper indices will denote *dimensions*. We use the notation $^{\cdot}X$, $\overline{X}$, $^{\circ}X$ for the *boundary*, *closure*, *interior* of X, respectively, and $X + Y$, $X - Y = X - (X \cap Y)$ for the *union* and the *difference* of X and Y, respectively.

By a *decomposition* of X we shall always mean a collection of *finitely many* pairwise disjoint point sets whose union is X. A decomposition Δ is called a *cell-decomposition* if the elements of Δ are open cells (i.e., homeomorphic to open simplices in $\mathfrak{E}^n$) such that for every two cells $A, B \in \Delta$ either $A \cap {}^{\cdot}B = \emptyset$ or $A \subset {}^{\cdot}B$ holds; moreover, we demand the following property: if $A, B \in \Delta$ and if a point $p \in A$ lies m times in $^{\cdot}B$ (i.e., if $p \in {}^{\cdot}B$ such that a small neighborhood N of p in X intersects B in m connected components), then every point of A lies m times in $^{\cdot}B$. We call a cell-decomposition Λ a *rectilinear triangulation* if its elements are rectilinear open simplices in $\mathfrak{E}^n$ such that the open faces of each element are also elements of Λ; we call a cell-decomposition Δ a

† Epi-homeomorphism $X \longrightarrow Y$ means homeomorphism *onto* Y.

(*piecewise-rectilinear*) *triangulation* if for each element $A \in \Delta$ the decomposition $\Delta(\overline{A})$ of $\overline{A}$ into all those elements of Δ that lie in $\overline{A}$ is isomorphic to the decomposition of a rectilinear simplex (of the same dimension as A) into its interior and its open faces.

By a (regular, polyhedral) *neighborhood of X in Y* (as defined in [29]) we mean the closure of the simplex star of X in a second barycentric subdivision Δ^{**} of a (piecewise-rectilinear) triangulation Δ of Y such that X is the union of elements of Δ; the neighborhood is called *small with respect to $Z|V| \cdots |W$* (see [8] Kap. I, 2) if $Z \cap Y, V \cap Y, \ldots, W \cap Y$ are unions of elements of Δ. For brevity, by a *small neighborhood of X in Y* we shall mean a neighborhood of X in Y which is small with respect to all point sets explicitly considered in the previous part of the section.

By an *arc*, *disk*, or 3-*cell* we mean, if not stated otherwise, a compact, nonsingular 1-, 2-, or 3-cell, respectively.

All maps denoted by lower case Greek letters are *semilinear maps* (also called *simplicial* maps; see [25], p. 114): a continuous map $\phi: A \longrightarrow B$ is called a semilinear map if there exist rectilinear triangulations Λ' of A and Λ of B such that ϕ maps each element of Λ' linearly onto an element of Λ.

We always use the concept of *isotopy* in the strong sense (ambient isotopy) as follows: two point sets A and B are called *isotopic* in a point set P if there exists a continuous family of (semilinear) epi-homeomorphisms† $\phi_t: P \longrightarrow P$ $(t \in [0, 1])$ such that ϕ_0 is the identity on P, and $\phi_1(A) = B$. We call A and B *isotopic in P with respect to point sets $X, \ldots, Z$* if the homeomorphisms ϕ_t may be chosen so that $\phi_t(P \cap X) = P \cap X, \ldots, \phi_t(P \cap Z) = P \cap Z$ for all $t \in [0, 1]$; (in this case $A \cap X$, and $B \cap X$ are obviously isotopic in $P \cap X$, etc.). We call A and B *topologically parallel in P* if there exists a connected component K of $P - (A + B)$ such that $\overline{K}$ can be represented as Cartesian product $A \times [0, 1]$ with $A \times 0 = A$ and‡ $A \times 1 = B$. Finally we call A and B

† Epi-homeomorphism $X \longrightarrow Y$ means homeomorphism *onto* Y.

‡ By this we mean that each point $q \in \overline{K}$ can be associated with a pair (p, a) of coordinates; (we express this by writing $q = p \times a$), where $p \in A$, $a \in [0, 1]$, such that the following holds: There is a semilinear homeomorphism $\lambda: A' \times I' \longrightarrow \overline{K}$ of a "standard Cartesian product," $A' \times I'$,

topologically parallel in P with respect to $X, \ldots, Z$ if the product representation of $\bar{K}$ can be chosen such that $\bar{K} \cap X = (A \cap X) \times [0, 1], \ldots, \bar{K} \cap Z = (A \cap Z) \times [0, 1]$. With these definitions it is obvious that if A and B are isotopic or topologically parallel in P, then they are isotopic or topologically parallel with respect to $\dot{P}$.

4. THE FINITENESS THEOREM ON INCOMPRESSIBLE SURFACES

We may state the extensions of H. Kneser's finiteness theorem discussed in Sec. 2 in a somewhat stronger form as follows:

FINITENESS THEOREM: *Let M^3 be a compact 3-manifold, with or without boundary, that admits a triangulation Δ into α tetrahedra and their faces. Let $X \subset \dot{M}^3$ (X may be $\varnothing$) be a union of closures of elements of Δ. Let $M_1^2, \ldots, M_s^2$ be pairwise disjoint surfaces in M^3 with $\dot{M}_i^2 = M_i^2 \cap (\dot{M}^3 - X)$ which are incompressible and boundary-incompressible* mod *X in M^3. If $s > 61\alpha$, then at least two of the M_i^2's are topologically parallel in M^3 with respect to X such that there exists a connected component K^3 of $M^3 - (M_1^2 + \cdots + M_s^2)$, with $\dot{K}^3 \cap X = \varnothing$, whose closure $\bar{K}^3$ can be represented as Cartesian product $M_i^2 \times [0, 1]$ with $M_i^2 \times 0 = M_i^2$ and $M_i^2 \times 1 = M_j^2$ for some i, j (and $\dot{M}_i^2 \times [0, 1] = \dot{K}^3 \cap \dot{M}^3$).*

We call K^3 (as described in the theorem) a *parallelity component of $M^3 - (M_1^2 + \cdots + M_s^2)$ with respect to X.*

Proof: The idea of the proof is to replace the given surfaces M_i^2 by surfaces $M_i'^2$ in a *nice position with respect to* Δ, i.e., such that the following holds: If E^d ($d = 0, 1, 2$, or 3) is an (open) d-simplex of Δ and if $M_i'^2 \cap E^d$ is not empty, then each connected component F of $M_i'^2 \cap \bar{E}^d$ is a $(d - 1)$-cell with $\dot{F} = F \cap \dot{E}^d$, and no edge of Δ intersects $\bar{F}$ in more than one point.

It follows, in particular, that if $M_i'^2$ is in nice position with

---

onto $\bar{K}$, where A' is a homeomorphic image of A in the $(n - 1)$-dimensional subspace $\mathfrak{E}^{n-1}$ of $\mathfrak{E}^n$ with coordinates $x_1, \ldots, x_{n-1}$, and I' is the unit interval of the x_n-axis of $\mathfrak{E}^n$, so that λ maps $A' \times 0$ onto A, maps $A' \times 1$ onto B, and maps each point $(p', a) \in A' \times I'$ onto $\lambda(p', 0) \times a$.

respect to Δ, then $M_i'^2$ does not contain vertices of Δ and intersects the edges of Δ at most in isolated piercing points and the triangles of Δ at most in piercing arcs.

Now let us assume that no connected component of $M^3 - (M_1^2 + \cdots + M_s^2)$ is a parallelity component with respect to X, and that $s > 61\alpha$.

Our first step is to show that among the s surfaces $M_1^2, \ldots, M_s^2$ there are t of them, say $M_1^2, \ldots, M_t^2$, with $t > 20\alpha$, that are "*independent in M^3 with respect to X.*" Surfaces $\tilde{M}_0^2, \tilde{M}_1^2, \ldots, \tilde{M}_z^2$ are said to be *dependent in M^3 with respect to X* (all surfaces polyhedral, transversal in M^3, pairwise disjoint, and disjoint from X) if there is a "*dependency component K^3 of $M^3 - (\tilde{M}_0^2 + \cdots + \tilde{M}_z^2)$ with respect to X*" i.e., a connected component of $M^3 - (\tilde{M}_0^2 + \cdots + \tilde{M}_z^2)$ such that (under proper notation) the following holds:

(i) $\tilde{M}_0^2$ and $\tilde{M}_1^2$ lie in $^{\cdot}K^3$.

(ii) The only $\tilde{M}_l^2$'s in $^{\cdot}K^3$ for $l > 1$ are 2-spheres—let us denote them by $S_1^2, \ldots, S_p^2$ (p may be zero)—and disks, $D_1^2, \ldots, D_q^2$ (q may be zero) ($\tilde{M}_0^2$ and $\tilde{M}_1^2$ may also be 2-spheres or disks).

(iii) There exists a simplicial map $\phi: K^{*3} \longrightarrow \bar{K}^3$ of a "Cartesian product with holes," K^{*3} (see Fig. 2), onto $\bar{K}^3$ with the following properties:

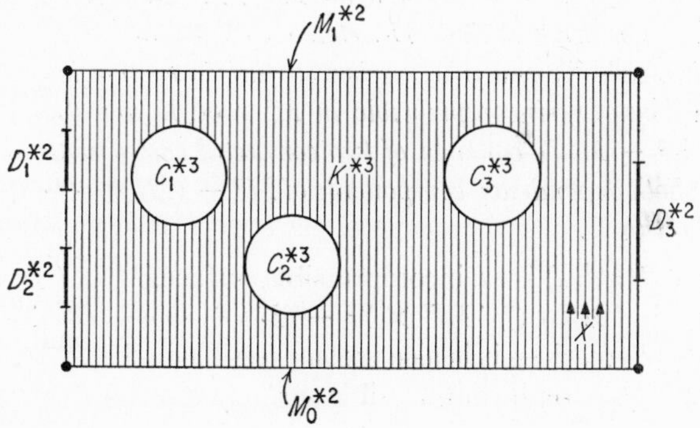

FIG. 2

(iiia) K^{*3} can be represented as $K^{*3} = (M_0^{*2} \times I) - ({}^{\circ}C_1^{*3} + \cdots + {}^{\circ}C_{p^*}^{*3})$ where M_0^{*2} is a surface homeomorphic to $\tilde{M}_0^2$, I is the unit interval $0 \leqq x \leqq 1$, $M_0^{*2} \times 0 = M_0^{*2}$, and $C_1^{*3}, \ldots, C_{p^*}^{*3}$ are pairwise disjoint 3-cells in $°(M_0^{*2} \times I)$; we denote $M_0^{*2} \times 1$ by M_1^{*2}.

(iiib) $\phi|M_0^{*2}$, $\phi|M_1^{*2}$, and $\phi|°K^{*3}$ are homeomorphisms onto $\tilde{M}_0^2$, $\tilde{M}_1^2$, and $°K^3$, respectively.

(iiic) $\phi|\dot{}C_k^{*3}$ is a homeomorphism onto one of the 2-spheres $S_1^2, \ldots, S_p^2$ or onto a 2-sphere in $\dot{}M^3$ (for all $k = 1, \ldots, p^*$); (but it may be that two different 2-spheres $\dot{}C_k^{*3}$, $\dot{}C_l^{*3}$ are mapped onto the same image S_m^2).

(iiid) There are q^* disks $D_1^{*2}, \ldots, D_{q^*}^{*2}$ (pairwise disjoint) in $\dot{}M_0^{*2} \times °I$ such that $\phi|[(\dot{}M_0^{*2} \times I) - (D_1^{*2} + \cdots + D_{q^*}^{*2})]$ is a homeomorphism into $\dot{}K^3 \cap (\dot{}M^3 - X)$ and such that $\phi|D_k^{*2}$ is a homeomorphism onto one of the disks $D_1^2, \ldots, D_q^2$ (for all $k = 1, \ldots, q^*$) (where it may be that two different disks D_k^{*2}, D_l^{*2} are mapped onto the same image D_m^2).

If K^3 has the properties stated above, then we say also that $\tilde{M}_0^2$ *is dependent on* $\tilde{M}_1^2, \ldots, \tilde{M}_z^2$ *in* M^3 *with respect to* X (and, of course, $\tilde{M}_1^2$ is dependent on $\tilde{M}_0^2, \tilde{M}_2^2, \ldots, \tilde{M}_z^2$). In the special case $p^* = q^* = 0$, $\tilde{M}_0^2$ and $\tilde{M}_1^2$ are topologically parallel in M^3 with respect to X. The surfaces $M_1^2, \ldots, M_t^2$ are called *independent in* M^3 *with respect to* X if none of them is dependent upon the others.

LEMMA 1: *If $\tilde{M}_0^2$ is dependent on $\tilde{M}_1^2, \ldots, \tilde{M}_z^2$ in M^3 with respect to X, if K^3, K^{*3}, ϕ, S_k^3, D_k^3, etc., have the same meaning as in the definition above, and if $\tilde{M}_{z+1}^2$ is a surface in K^3 that is incompressible and boundary-incompressible in M^3* mod X *and disjoint from X, then $K^3 - \tilde{M}_{z+1}^2$ consists of two connected components K'^3, K''^3 which are both dependency components of $M^3 - (\tilde{M}_0^2 + \cdots + \tilde{M}_{z+1}^2)$ with respect to X.*

Proof: $\phi^{-1}(\tilde{M}_{z+1}^2)$ is an incompressible surface, M_{z+1}^{*2} (see Fig. 3), in K^{*3} with $\dot{}M_{z+1}^{*2} \subset \dot{}M_0^{*2} \times °I - (D_1^{*2} + \cdots + D_{q^*}^{*2})$. If M_{z+1}^{*2} is not a 2-sphere, then it is also incompressible in $M_0^{*2} \times I$. Therefore, by a lemma on incompressible surfaces in Cartesian products which we prove in the appendix (Sec. 8) of this article, $M_0^{*2} \times I - M_{z+1}^{*2}$ consists of two connected components L'^3 and L''^3 such that either

Case A: (Case 1 of the lemma in Sec. 8 applies) $\overline{L}'^3 = M_0^{*2} \times I'$,

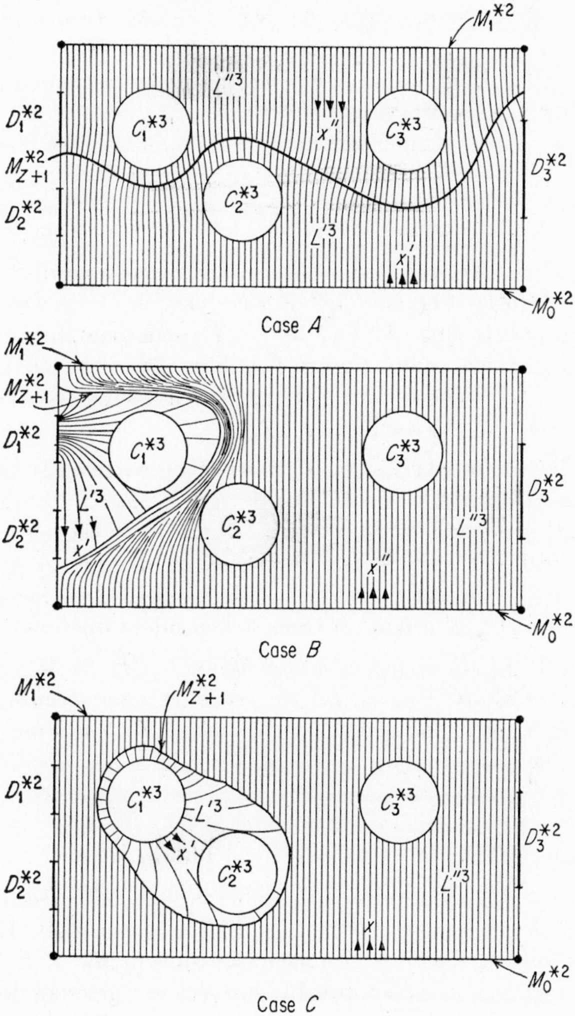

M*2 1
L''3
D*2 1
C*3 1
x''
C*3 3
M*2 Z+1
D*2 3
C*3 2
D*2 2
L'3
x'
M*2 0
Case A
M*2 1
M*2 Z+1
D*2 1
C*3 1
C*3 3
D*2 3
L'3
D*2 2
C*3 2
L''3
x'
x''
M*2 0
Case B
M*2 1
M*2 Z+1
D*2 1
C*3 1
L'3
C*3 3
D*2 3
x'
D*2 2
C*3 2
L''3
x
M*2 0
Case C

FIG. 3

$\overline{L}''^3 = M_1^{*2} \times I''$ where I', I'' are unit intervals $0 \leqq x' \leqq 1$, $0 \leqq x'' \leqq 1$ with $M_0^{*2} \times 0 = M_0^{*2}$, $M_0^{*2} \times 1 = M_{z+1}^{*2}$, $M_1^{*2} \times 0 = M_1^{*2}$, $M_1^{*2} \times 1 = M_{z+1}^{*2}$;

Case B: (Case 2 of the lemma of Sec. 8 applies) $\overline{L}'^3$ is a 3-cell and M_{z+1}^{*2} is a disk in $\dot{}L'^3$ with $\dot{}L'^3 - M_{z+1}^{*2} \subset \dot{}M_0^{*2} \times {}^\circ I$; or

Case C: (M_{z+1}^{*2} bounds a 3-cell) $\overline{L}'^3$ is a 3-cell with $\dot{}L'^3 = M_{z+1}^{*2}$. (Case 3 of the lemma in Sec. 8 cannot apply since in this case $\tilde{M}_{z+1}^2$ would be boundary-compressible in M^3 mod X.)

In every case, $\phi(\overline{L}'^3 \cap K^{*3})$ and $\phi(\overline{L}''^3 \cap K^{*3})$ are the closures of components K'^3 and K''^3, respectively, with the required properties, since $\overline{L}'^3 \cap K^{*3}$ and $\overline{L}''^3 \cap K^{*3}$ can be represented as Cartesian products minus open 3-cells in the following way (see Fig. 3): In Case A we have $\overline{L}'^3 \cap K^{*3} = M_0^{*2} \times I' -$ (the ${}^\circ C_k^{*3}$'s in L'^3) and $\overline{L}''^3 \cap K^{*3} = M_1^{*2} \times I'' -$ (the ${}^\circ C_k^{*3}$'s in L''^3). In Case B, $\dot{}L'^3 - M_{z+1}^{*2}$ contains at least one of the disks D_j^{*2}, say D_1^{*2} (since otherwise $\tilde{M}_{z+1}^2$ would be boundary-compressible in M^3 mod X); then we may write $\overline{L}'^3 = D_1^{*2} \times I'$ with $D_1^{*2} \times 0 = D_1^{*2}$, $D_1^{*2} \times 1 = M_{z+1}^{*2}$ and $\overline{L}''^3 = M_0^{*2} \times I''$ with $M_0^{*2} \times 0 = M_0^{*2}$, $M_0^{*2} \times 1 = M_1^{*2}$; hence $\overline{L}'^3 \cap K^{*3} = D_1^{*2} \times I' -$ (the ${}^\circ C_k^{*3}$'s in L'^3) and $\overline{L}''^3 \cap K^{*3} = M_0^{*2} \times I'' -$ (the ${}^\circ C_k^{*3}$'s in L''^3). In Case C, L'^3 contains at least one of the 3-cells C_i^{*3}, say C_1^{*3} (since otherwise $\tilde{M}_{z+1}^2$ would be compressible in M^3); then we may write $\overline{L}'^3 - {}^\circ C_1^{*3} = \dot{}C_1^{*3} \times I'$ with $\dot{}C_1^{*3} \times 0 = \dot{}C_1^{*3}$, $\dot{}C_1^{*3} \times 1 = M_{z+1}^{*2}$; hence $\overline{L}'^3 \cap K^{*3} = \dot{}C_1^{*3} \times I' -$ (the ${}^\circ C_k^{*3}$'s in L'^3 with $k > 1$) and $\overline{L}''^3 \cap K^{*3} = M_0^{*2} \times I - (L'^3 +$ the ${}^\circ C_k^{*3}$'s in L''^3). This proves Lemma 1.

Corollary: *If $\tilde{M}_0^2$ is dependent on $\tilde{M}_1^2, \ldots, \tilde{M}_z^2$ in M^3 with respect to X and if $\tilde{M}_{z+1}^2$ is an arbitrary surface in M^3 which is disjoint from $\tilde{M}_1^2, \ldots, \tilde{M}_z^2$, X and incompressible and boundary-incompressible in M^3* mod *X, then $\tilde{M}_0^2$ is also dependent on $\tilde{M}_1^2, \ldots, \tilde{M}_{z+1}^2$ in M^3 with respect to X.*

This is an immediate consequence of Lemma 1.

Lemma 2: *Let b denote the number of 2-spheres in $\dot{}M^3$; obviously $b \leqq \alpha$. If no connected component of $M^3 - (M_1^2 + \cdots + M_s^2)$ is a parallelity component with respect to X and if $M_1^2, \ldots, M_t^2$ form a maximal set of independent surfaces in $\{M_1^2, \ldots, M_s^2\}$; i.e., $M_1^2, \ldots,$*

M_i^2 are independent in M^3 with respect to X but every surface M_{i+t}^2 $(i = 1, \ldots, s - t)$ is dependent on $M_1^2, \ldots, M_t^2$ with respect to X, then $t > (s - b)/3 \geqq (s - \alpha)/3$.

Proof: The idea of the proof is to show that each connected component of $M^3 - (M_1^2 + \cdots + M_t^2)$ has a limited "capacity" of containing M_k^2's with $t < k \leqq s$.

Since the case $s = 0$ is trivial, we assume that $s > 0$, and hence $t > 0$.

Let us consider the connected components of $M^3 - (M_1^2 + \cdots + M_u^2)$ for some u between t and s, and let us associate to each of them a certain *capacity number* in the following way: Let K^3 be a component and let r be the number of those M_k^2's ($k = 1, \ldots, u$) that are disks or 2-spheres in $\cdot K^3$ plus the number of 2-spheres in $\cdot K^3 \cap \cdot M^3$; in the case that a disk or 2-sphere M_k^2 lies "twice" in $\cdot K^3$, i.e., that both sides of M_k^2 belong to K^3, it is counted twice.

Case a: If K^3 is not a dependency component of $M^3 - (M_1^2 + \cdots + M_u^2)$ with respect to X and at least one of the M_k^2's in $\cdot K^3$ is not a disk or a 2-sphere, then we associate to K^3 the capacity-number r.

Case b: If K^3 is not a dependency component with respect to X and all M_k^2's in $\cdot K^3$ are disks or 2-spheres, then the capacity number of K^3 is $r - 1$ (where $r > 0$ since otherwise $K^3 = M^3$ and $u = t = 0$).

Case c: If K^3 is a dependency component with respect to X and not all M_k^2's in $\cdot K^3$ are disks or 2-spheres, then the capacity number is $r - 1$ (where $r > 0$ since otherwise K^3 would be a parallelity component with respect to X).

Case d: If K^3 is a dependency component with respect to X and all M_k^2's in $\cdot K^3$ are disks or 2-spheres, then the capacity number is $r - 3$ (where $r > 2$).

By the capacity c_u of $\{M_1^2, \ldots, M_u^2\}$ we mean the sum of the capacity numbers of all connected components of $M^3 - (M_1^2 + \cdots + M_u^2)$.

Now we have $c_t < 2t + b$ (where the maximum $2t + b - 1$ is reached if all $M_1^2, \ldots, M_t^2$ are disks or 2-spheres and if $M^3 -$

$(M_1^2 + \cdots + M_t^2)$ is connected), and $c_u \geqq 0$. To prove Lemma 2, we have to show that $c_{u+1} < c_u$ for $t \leqq u < s$ (which implies $0 \leqq c_s \leqq c_t - (s - t) < 3t - s + b$).

Let K^3 be that connected component of $M^3 - (M_1^2 + \cdots + M_u^2)$ that contains M_{u+1}^2. Then, by the corollary of Lemma 1 (and since M_{u+1}^2 is dependent on $M_1^2, \ldots, M_t^2$), $K^3 - M_{u+1}^2$ consists of two connected components K'^3, K''^3 at least one of which, say K'^3, is a dependency component of $M^3 - (M_1^2 + \cdots + M_{u+1}^2)$ with respect to X. Moreover, if K^3 is a dependency component of $M^3 - (M_1^2 + \cdots + M_u^2)$ with respect to X, then, by Lemma 1, both K'^3 and K''^3 are dependency components of $M^3 - (M_1^2 + \cdots + M_{u+1}^2)$ with respect to X. In every case (a, b, c, or d) the capacity number of K^3 is greater than zero (since otherwise K'^3 or K''^3 would be a parallelity component with respect to X) and it is easy to check that the sum of the capacity numbers of K'^3 and of K''^3 is one less than the capacity number of K^3; hence $c_{u+1} = c_u - 1$. This finishes the proof of Lemma 2.

Now we can conclude that there exist $t > (s - b)/3 \geqq (s - \alpha)/3$ independent surfaces in nice position with respect to Δ:

LEMMA 3: *If the t surfaces* $M_1^2, \ldots, M_t^2$ *are independent in* M^3 *with respect to* X, *then there exist t surfaces* $M_1'^2, \ldots, M_t'^2$ *in nice position with respect to* Δ *that are also independent with respect to* X, *incompressible, boundary-incompressible* mod X, *pairwise disjoint, and disjoint from* X *in* M^3.

Proof: Step i: First we deform $M_1^2, \ldots, M_t^2$ by "small" isotopic deformations (in such a way that the surfaces remain pairwise disjoint and that their boundaries remain in $\dot{} M^3 - X$) into surfaces $M_{11}^2, \ldots, M_{1t}^2$ that do not contain vertices of Δ and intersect the edges and triangles of Δ at most in piercing points and curves, respectively, i.e., such that the following holds: If E^d ($d = 0, 1, 2,$ or 3) is an (open) d-simplex of Δ and if $M_{1i}^2 \cap E^d$ is not empty, then each connected component F of $M_{1i}^2 \cap \overline{E}^d$ is a $(d - 1)$-manifold with $\dot{}F = F \cap \dot{}E^d$.

Now it remains to transform the M_{1i}^2's in such a way that the components F become cells which intersect no edge of Δ in more than one point. For this we shall need operations that are, in general, stronger than isotopic deformations.

Step ii: If a triangle $E^2 \in \Delta$ is intersected by one of the M^2_{1i}'s in a closed curve, then we remove these intersections by the following procedure: First we remark that $E^2 \subset {}^\circ M^3$ since otherwise one of the M^2_{1i}'s would be boundary-compressible mod X. The intersection curve bounds a disk in E^2. We begin with a "smallest" disk $D^2 \subset E^2$ of that type; i.e., we may assume that ${}^{\cdot}D^2$ is disjoint from the M^2_{1i}'s and under proper notation that ${}^\circ D^2 \subset M^2_{11}$. Now we remove (see Fig. 4) a small neighborhood A^2 of ${}^{\cdot}D^2$ from M^2_{11} and we close the holes by two disks D'^2, D''^2 "parallel" to D^2

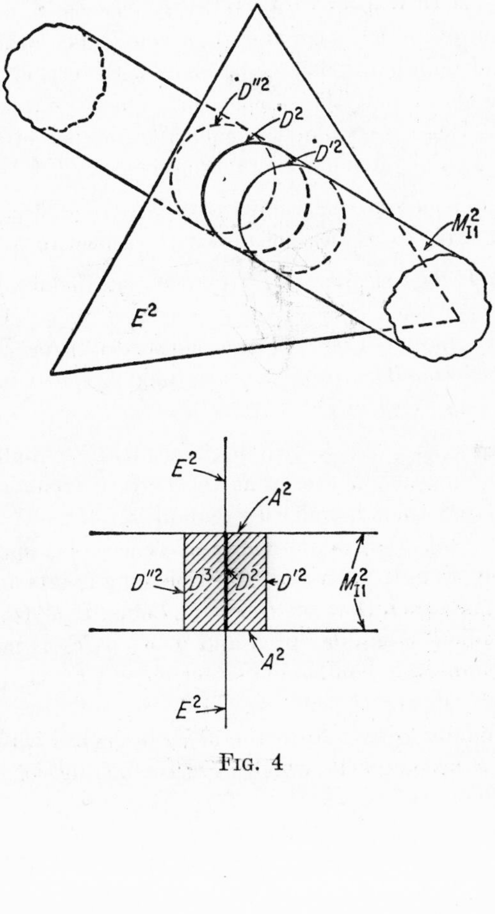

FIG. 4

(where $A^2 + D'^2 + D''^2$ bounds a 3-cell D^3 in M^3 that contains D^2); we call this operation a *ρ-operation.* Since M^2_{I1} is incompressible, $M^2_{I1} - {}^\circ A^2$ consists of two connected components at least one of which is a disk; therefore, we obtain by our ρ-operation two surfaces M'^2_{I1}, M''^2_{I1} such that (under proper notation) M'^2_{I1} is a 2-sphere.

Since M^2_{I1} is independent of $M^2_{I2}, \ldots, M^2_{It}$ with respect to X, it follows that not both M'^2_{I1} and M''^2_{I1} can be dependent with respect to X on $M^2_{I2}, \ldots, M^2_{It}$ or compressible in M^3.

To prove this, let us assume the contrary. Then M'^2_{I1} and M''^2_{I1} lie in the boundaries of components K'^3 and K''^3, respectively, of

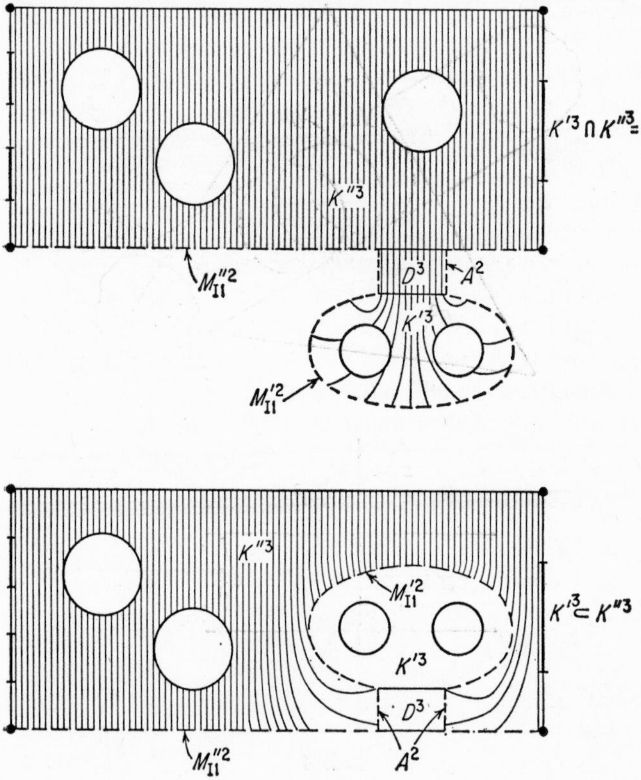

Fig. 5

$M^3 - (M'^2_{I1} + M^2_{I2} + \cdots + M^2_{It})$ and of $M^3 - (M''^2_{I1} + M^2_{I2} + \cdots + M^2_{It})$, respectively, each of which is a dependency-component with respect to X or an open 3-cell; [this follows from (1) if M''^2_{I1} is not a 2-sphere, then it is incompressible, since otherwise M^2_{I1} would not be incompressible; and (2) no surface M^2_{Ii} lies in an open 3-cell in M^3, since otherwise by the lemma of Fox [7] M^2_{Ii} would not be incompressible]. In every case, $°K'^3$ is an open 3-sphere with holes. If K''^3 and K'^3 are disjoint (see Fig. 5), then $K''^3 + (D^3 - A^2) + K'^3$ is either a dependency component of $M^3 - (M^2_{I1} + \cdots + M^2_{It})$ with respect to X or an open 3-cell; hence M^2_{I1} is dependent or not incompressible, either of which is a contradiction. If $K'^3 \subset K''^3$ (see Fig. 5), then $K''^3 - (\bar{K}'^3 + D^3)$ is either a dependency component of $M^3 - (M^2_{I1} + \cdots + M^2_{It})$ with respect to X or an open 3-cell, which means again that M^2_{I1} is dependent or not incompressible. Finally, if $K''^3 \subset K'^3$, then (by the lemma of Sec. 8) M''^2_{I1} is also a 2-sphere, and we may reduce this case by a change of notation to $K'^3 \subset K''^3$.

So we may replace M^2_{I1} by an independent, incompressible (and boundary-incompressible mod X) surface M'^2_{I1} or M''^2_{I1}. In this way we remove, step by step, all closed curves in the triangles of Δ and we call the t surfaces so obtained $M^2_{II1}, \ldots, M^2_{IIt}$.

Step iii: If a triangle $E^2 \in \Delta$ is intersected by one of the M^2_{IIi}'s in an arc with both end points in the same edge $E^1 \in \Delta$, then we remove these intersections as follows: We can find a "smallest" disk D^2 in E^2 (see Fig. 6) whose boundary consists of one arc A^1

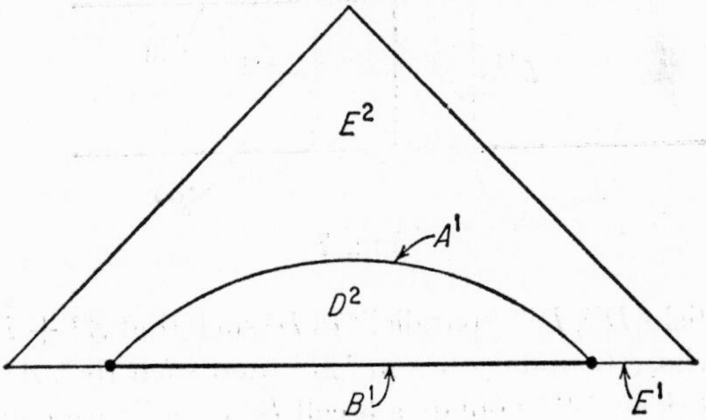

FIG. 6

in one of the $M^2_{\mathrm{II}i}$'s, say $M^2_{\mathrm{II}1}$, and of one arc B^1 in E^1 such that $°D^2$ is disjoint from the $M^2_{\mathrm{II}i}$'s. We have to distinguish

Case A: Both E^2 and E^1 lie in $°M^3$.

Case B: Both E^2 and E^1 lie in $^{\cdot}M^3 - X$.

Case C: $E^2 \subset °M^3$, $E^1 \subset {}^{\cdot}M^3 - X$.

In the Cases A and B we remove the intersection arc A^1 by a simple isotopic deformation of $M^2_{\mathrm{II}1}$ that changes $M^2_{\mathrm{II}1}$ only in a small neighborhood of D^2 in M^3 (where, in Case *B*, $^{\cdot}M^2_{\mathrm{II}1}$ is deformed within $^{\cdot}M^3$). In Case C we remove (similar to Step ii—see Fig. 7) a small neighborhood A^2 of A^1 from $M^2_{\mathrm{II}1}$ and replace

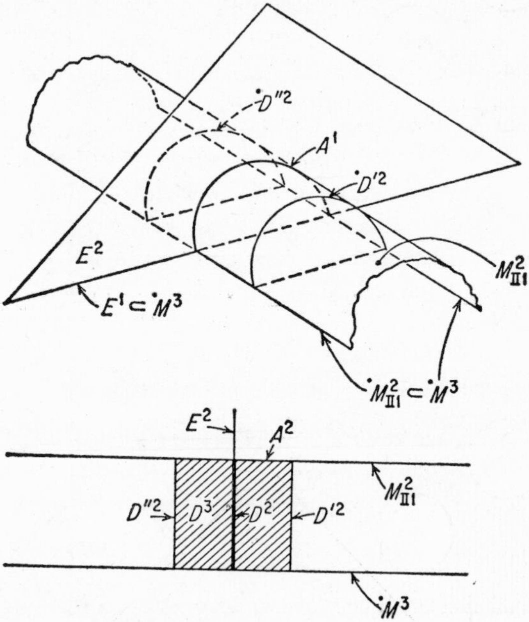

FIG. 7

it by two disks D'^2, D''^2 "parallel" to D^2 such that $A^2 + D'^2 + D''^2$ is a disk whose boundary lies in $^{\cdot}M^3$ (and such that $A^2 + D'^2 + D''^2$ + a disk in $^{\cdot}M^3$ bounds a 3-cell D^3 in M^3); we call this procedure a $^{\cdot}\rho$*-operation.* Since $M^2_{\mathrm{II}1}$ is boundary-incompressible mod X, $^-(M^2_{\mathrm{II}1} - A^2)$ consists of two connected components at least one of which is a disk whose boundary intersects $^\cdot M^3$ in just one arc. Hence the $^\cdot\rho$-operation yields two surfaces $M'^2_{\mathrm{II}1}$, $M''^2_{\mathrm{II}1}$ such that $M'^2_{\mathrm{II}1}$ is a transversal disk in $M^3 - X$. Since $M^2_{\mathrm{II}1}$ is independent of $M^2_{\mathrm{II}2}, \ldots, M^2_{\mathrm{II}t}$ with respect to X, it follows, again, that at least one of the surfaces $M'^2_{\mathrm{II}1}$, $M''^2_{\mathrm{II}1}$ is also independent, incompressible, and boundary-incompressible mod X. (See Fig. 8.

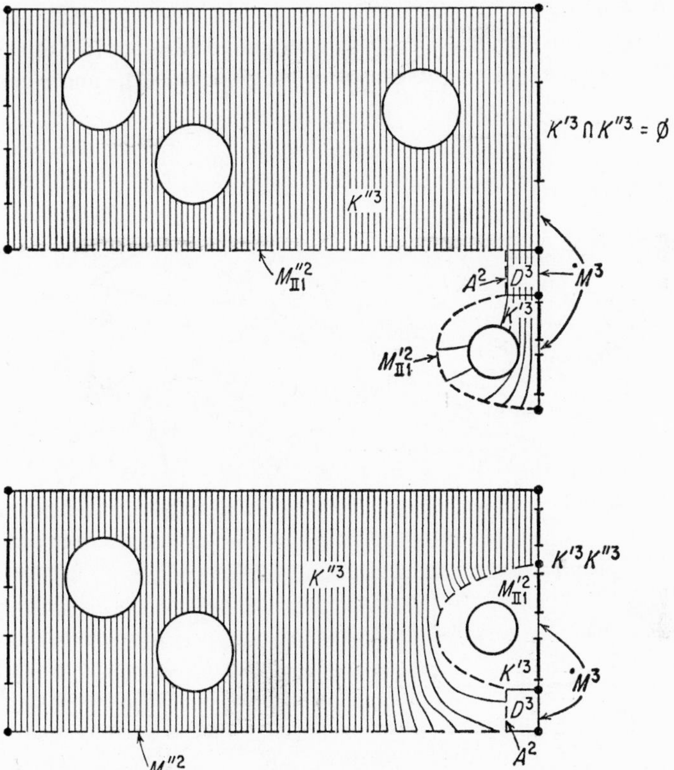

FIG. 8

For a proof of this, read the corresponding proof in Step ii, replacing "2-sphere" by "transversal disk," "incompressible" by "incompressible and boundary-incompressible mod X," "open

3-cell" by "3-cell minus a disk in its boundary," subscript "I" by subscript "II," and "Fig. 5" by "Fig. 8.") Hence we may replace $M^2_{\mathrm{II}1}$ by this surface.

It may be that our removing of A^1 created closed intersection curves in triangles of Δ. We then have to reapply Step ii (which will *not* create new intersection arcs with the triangles of Δ). In this way we remove, step by step, all intersection arcs with triangles of Δ that have both end points in the same edge of Δ and we denote the surfaces so obtained by $M^2_{\mathrm{III}1}, \ldots, M^2_{\mathrm{III}t}$.

Step iv: Let E^3 be a tetrahedron of Δ and F^2 a connected component of $M^2_{\mathrm{III}i} \cap \overline{E}^3$. Then F^2 is a disk with or without holes; for F^2 is orientable and if it were a 2-sphere or would possess a handle, then one could conclude (by the Alexander theorem [1] or the lemma of Fox [7], respectively) that $M^2_{\mathrm{III}i}$ was compressible in M^3. If F^2 possesses more than one boundary curve, then we can find a disk D^2 in E^3 with $\dot{D}^2$ in F^2 parallel to one of the boundary curves of F^2 such that D^2 is disjoint from all those components of $\overline{E}^3 \cap (M^2_{\mathrm{III}1} + \cdots + M^2_{\mathrm{III}t})$ that are disks. Then we take a "smallest" disk $\tilde{D}^2$ in D^2 with $^\circ\tilde{D}^2$ disjoint from the $M^2_{\mathrm{III}i}$'s and $\dot{\tilde{D}}^2$ in one of the $M^2_{\mathrm{III}i}$'s, and we perform a ρ-operation in a neighborhood of $\tilde{D}^2$ (compare Step ii). In this way we obtain, step by step, finally t surfaces $M^2_{\mathrm{IV}1}, \ldots, M^2_{\mathrm{IV}t}$ that intersect the tetrahedra of Δ only in disks.

Step v: If a component F^2 of $M^2_{\mathrm{IV}i} \cap \overline{E}^3$, $E^3 \in \Delta$, intersects an edge $E^1 \in \Delta$ in more than one point (in $\dot{F}^2$), then there is a disk $D^2 \subset \overline{E}^3$ such that $\dot{D}^2$ is the union of an arc $A^1 \subset F^2$ and of an arc $B^1 \subset E^1$ (compare Step iii); F^2 and D^2 can be found such that $^\circ D^2$ is disjoint from the $M^2_{\mathrm{IV}i}$'s. Then we remove two intersections with E^1—as in Step iii—by an isotopic deformation if $E^1 \subset {}^\circ M^3$, and by a $\dot{\rho}$-operation if $E^1 \subset \dot{M}^3$, such that $M^2_{\mathrm{IV}i}$ is changed only in a small neighborhood of D^2. After this we may have to reapply Steps ii, iii, and iv, but we can repeat the whole procedure only a limited number of times since the number of intersections of the surfaces and the edges of Δ is decreased by the operations of Steps iii and v, and it is not increased by the operations of Steps ii and iv. Hence we obtain finally t surfaces $M_1'^2, \ldots, M_t'^2$ with the required properties and the proof of Lemma 3 is finished.

Now it is sufficient to prove the finiteness theorem for surfaces in nice position with respect to Δ:

LEMMA 4: *If t surfaces $M_1'^2, \ldots, M_t'^2$ are pairwise disjoint, disjoint from X, and in nice position with respect to Δ and if $t > 20\alpha$, then there exists a parallelity component of $M^3 - (M_1'^2 + \cdots + M_t'^2)$ with respect to X.*

Proof: The proof bases on the following

REMARK: If E^3 is a tetrahedron of Δ (see Fig. 9) and if $\overline{E}^3 \cap (M_1'^2 + \cdots + M_t'^2)$ consists of more than five connected components, then at least two of them, say F_0^2, F_1^2, are topologically parallel *with respect to* Δ; i.e., there is a connected component F^3 of $\overline{E}^3 - (F_0^2 + F_1^2)$ whose closure can be represented as Cartesian product $\overline{F}^3 = F_0^2 \times I$, with $F_0^2 \times 0 = F_0^2$, $F_0^2 \times 1 = F_1^2$, and such that for each face $G \in \Delta$ of E^3, $G \cap {}^{\cdot}F^3 = (G \cap {}^{\cdot}F_0^2) \times I$; in this case we call F^3 a *prism* with respect to Δ.

To prove this remark, let P_1, P_2, P_3, P_4 be the vertices of E^3 (see Fig. 9); then the boundary of a component, say F_0^2, separates

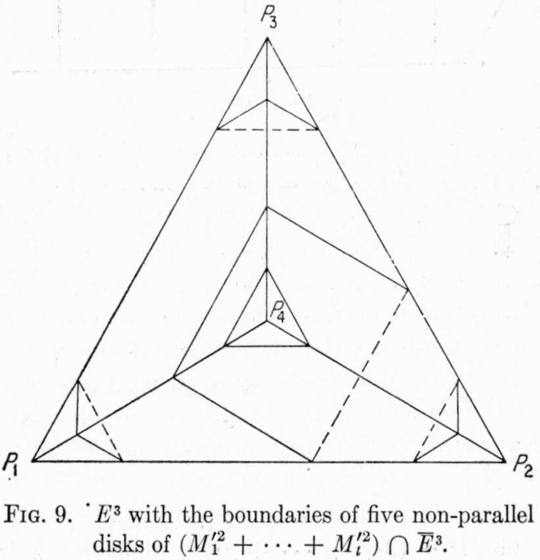

FIG. 9. ${}^{\cdot}E^3$ with the boundaries of five non-parallel disks of $(M_1'^2 + \cdots + M_t'^2) \cap \overline{E}^3$.

the set $\{P_1, P_2, P_3, P_4\}$ in $\dot{}E^3$ into two nonempty subsets; there are six different separations possible, but two of them, $\{P_1, P_2\}$, $\{P_3, P_4\}$ and $\{P_1, P_3\}$, $\{P_2, P_4\}$, cannot be produced by disjoint disks. Now, if the boundary of some other component, say F_1^2, separates $\{P_1, P_2, P_3, P_4\}$ in the same way as F_0^2, then F_0^2 and F_1^2 are already topologically parallel with respect to Δ (since $\dot{}F_0^2$ and $\dot{}F_1^2$ intersect each edge of E^3 at most in one point).

We call a connected component F^2 of $(M_1'^2 + \cdots + M_t'^2) \cap \bar{E}^3$ *escorted* (see Fig. 10) if there are four other connected components

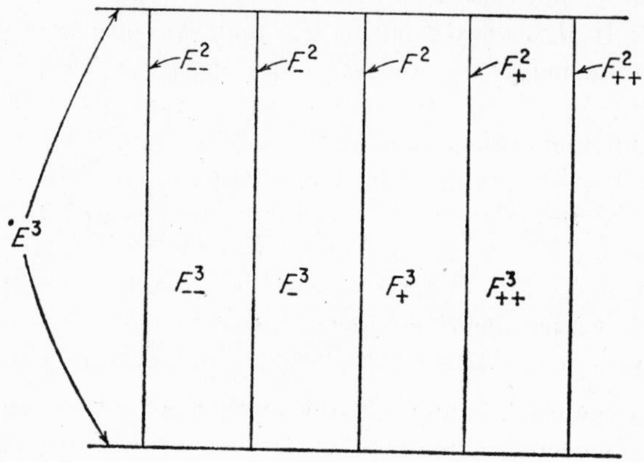

FIG. 10

F^2_-, F^2_{--}, F^2_+, F^2_{++} of $(M_1'^2 + \cdots + M_t'^2) \cap \bar{E}^3$ and four prisms F^3_-, F^3_{--}, F^3_+, F^3_{++} in $E^3 - (M_1'^2 + \cdots + M_t'^2)$ such that $F^2_{--} + F^2_- \subset \dot{}F^3_{--}$, $F^2_- + F^2 \subset \dot{}F^3_-$, $F^2 + F^2_+ \subset \dot{}F^3_+$, $F^2_+ + F^2_{++} \subset \dot{}F^3_{++}$. We call F^2_-, F^2_+ the *next neighbors* and F^2_{--}, F^2_{++} the *overnext neighbors* of F^2. It follows from our remark that at most 20 of the connected components of $(M_1'^2 + \cdots + M_t'^2) \cap \bar{E}^3$ are not escorted and hence that at least one of the $M_i'^2$'s, say $M_1'^2$, is a union of escorted disks (since by hypothesis $t > 20\alpha$).

Let K_1^3 be the union of all those prisms (with respect to Δ) in $M^3 - (M_1'^2 + \cdots + M_t'^2)$ that contain points of $M_1'^2$ in their boundaries.

Case 1: If $M_1'^2$ is one-sided in M^3, then K_1^3 is a connected component of $M^3 - (M_1'^2 + \cdots + M_t'^2)$. Since $\bar{K}_1^3 \neq M^3$, there is a two-sided surface among the $M_i'^2$'s, say $M_2'^2$, in $^{\cdot}(\bar{K}_1^3)$; it is the union of all the disks which are next neighbors of disks in $M_1'^2$. Now let K_2^3 be the union of all those prisms in $M^3 - (M_1'^2 + \cdots + M_t'^2)$ that contain points of $M_2'^2$ in their boundaries, but do not lie in K_1^3. Then K_2^3 is a connected component of $M^3 - (M_1'^2 + \cdots + M_t'^2)$. Again, since $\bar{K}_1^3 + \bar{K}_2^3 \neq M^3$, there is a two-sided surface, say $M_3'^2$ (different from $M_2'^2$) in $^{\cdot}(\bar{K}_2^3)$; this is the union of all the overnext neighbors of disks in $M_1'^2$. Hence, K_2^3 is a parallelity component of $M^3 - (M_1'^2 + \cdots + M_t'^2)$ with respect to X, and Case 1 is settled.

Case 2: If $M_1'^2$ is two-sided in M^3, then K_1^3 consists of two connected components K_+^3 and K_-^3, and these are also connected components of $M^3 - (M_1'^2 + \cdots + M_t'^2)$. Since $\bar{K}_1^3 \neq M^3$, there are two different surfaces among the $M_i'^2$'s—let us denote them by M_+^2 and M_-^2 (one of them may be identical with $M_1'^2$)—in $^{\cdot}K_+^3$ and in $^{\cdot}K_-^3$, respectively; $M_+^2 + M_-^2$ is the union of all the next neighbors of disks in $M_1'^2$. Moreover, since $\bar{K}_1^3 \neq M^3$, at least one of M_+^2, M_-^2, say M_+^2, is different from $M_1'^2$ and is two-sided in M^3; hence K_+^3 is a parallelity component of $M^3 - (M_1'^2 + \cdots + M_t'^2)$ with respect to X. This settles Case 2, and Lemma 4 is proved.

From Lemmas 2, 3, and 4 it follows that our initial assumption that no connected component of $M^3 - (M_1'^2 + \cdots + M_t'^2)$ is a parallelity component with respect to X, and $s > 61\alpha$ (hence $t > 20\alpha$) leads to a contradiction. This proves the finiteness theorem.

5. APPLICATION 1: A CONJECTURE ON OPEN HOMOTOPY 3-CELLS

The Poincaré conjecture [19] states that every homotopy 3-sphere, i.e., every simply connected, compact 3-manifold without boundary, is a 3-sphere. This is still an open question. It is remarkable that the generalization of the Poincaré conjecture to n-dimensional (compact, triangulable) manifolds has been proved for all $n \geqq 5$, see [26, 27, 31].

On the other hand, the generalization to *open* 3-manifolds does not hold: In 1935, J. H. C. Whitehead [28] constructed an open homotopy 3-cell $\mathfrak{W}$, i.e., a noncompact, simply connected, 3-manifold with trivial second homology group and without boundary, which is not homeomorphic to Euclidean 3-space $\mathfrak{E}^3$. He constructed $\mathfrak{W}$ as the union of an "ascending sequence" $\mathfrak{T}_1^3, \mathfrak{T}_2^3, \ldots, \mathfrak{T}_i^3, \ldots$ of solid tori in $\mathfrak{E}^3$ where $\mathfrak{T}_i^3$ lies in $\mathfrak{T}_{i+1}^3$ as shown in Fig. 11

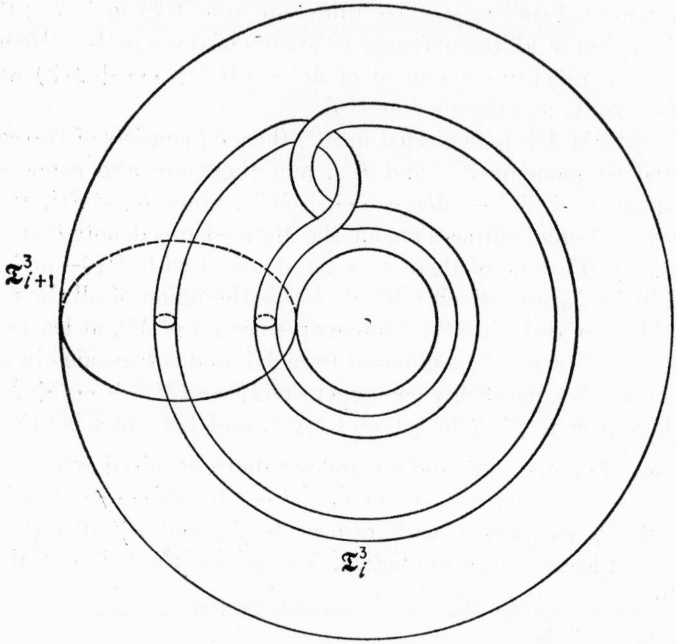

FIG. 11

(for all $i = 1, 2, \ldots$), $\mathfrak{W} = \bigcup_{i=1}^{\infty} \mathfrak{T}_i^3$. This space $\mathfrak{W}$ is simply connected: every closed curve $\mathfrak{C} \subset \mathfrak{W}$ lies in a solid torus $\mathfrak{T}_r^3$ (r sufficiently large) since $\mathfrak{C}$ is compact and therefore intersects at most finitely many tori $\mathfrak{T}_i^3$; but $\mathfrak{T}_r^3$ is contractible in $\mathfrak{T}_{r+1}^3$ and hence $\mathfrak{C}$ is contractible in $\mathfrak{T}_{r+1}^3 \subset \mathfrak{W}$. That $\mathfrak{W}$ is not homeomorphic to $\mathfrak{E}^3$ follows from the fact that $\mathfrak{W}$ contains a simple closed curve that does not lie in a compact 3-cell $\mathfrak{C}^3 \subset \mathfrak{W}$, e.g., the median curve $\mathfrak{C}_1^1$ of $\mathfrak{T}_1^3$. From the assumption that $\mathfrak{C}_1^1$ lies in a compact

3-cell $\mathfrak{C}^3 \subset \mathfrak{W}$, it would follow that $\mathfrak{C}^3 \subset {}^\circ\mathfrak{T}_r^3$ (r sufficiently large) and further that there exists a compact 3-cell $\mathfrak{C}_1^3 \subset {}^\circ\mathfrak{T}_r^3$ with $\mathfrak{T}_1^3 \subset {}^\circ\mathfrak{C}_1^3$ such that the 2-sphere ${}^\cdot\mathfrak{C}_1^3$ intersects the tori ${}^\cdot\mathfrak{T}_2^3, \ldots, {}^\cdot\mathfrak{T}_{r-1}^3$ at most in piercing curves; then no connected component of ${}^\cdot\mathfrak{C}_1^3 \cap \mathfrak{T}_2^3$ could be a meridian disk of $\mathfrak{T}_2^3$; hence one could isotopically deform ${}^\cdot\mathfrak{C}_1^3$ out of $\mathfrak{T}_2^3$ and in this way obtain a compact 3-cell $\mathfrak{C}_2^3 \subset {}^\circ\mathfrak{T}_r^3$ with $\mathfrak{T}_2^3 \subset {}^\circ\mathfrak{C}_2^3$; continuing in this way, one would finally obtain a 3-cell $\mathfrak{C}_{r-1}^3 \subset {}^\circ\mathfrak{T}_r^3$ with $\mathfrak{T}_{r-1}^3 \subset {}^\circ\mathfrak{C}_{r-1}^3$, which is a contradiction.

A remarkable property of $\mathfrak{W}$ is that it can be imbedded in $\mathfrak{E}^3$. The initial solid torus $\mathfrak{T}_1^3$ may be chosen unknotted in $\mathfrak{E}^3$ (as $\mathfrak{T}_i^3$ appears in Fig. 11); then $\mathfrak{T}_2^3$ will also be unknotted; then one can construct $\mathfrak{T}_3^3$, also unknotted in $\mathfrak{E}^3$, (without changing $\mathfrak{T}_1^3$ and $\mathfrak{T}_2^3$), and so on; i.e., the whole sequence $\mathfrak{T}_1^3, \mathfrak{T}_2^3, \ldots, \mathfrak{T}_i^3, \ldots$ can be imbedded in $\mathfrak{E}^3$.

Another interesting property of $\mathfrak{W}$ has been proved by McMillan [13]: $\mathfrak{W} \times \mathfrak{E}^1$, the Cartesian product of $\mathfrak{W}$ and the Euclidean line, is homeomorphic to Euclidean 4-space $\mathfrak{E}^4$. The proof uses results of M. Brown [6] and J. Stallings [27]; the idea is to show that every product $\mathfrak{T}_i^3 \times [a, b]$, where $[a, b]$ is an arbitrary closed interval in $\mathfrak{E}^1$, lies in a 4-cell in $\mathfrak{W} \times \mathfrak{E}^1$ and, hence, that $\mathfrak{W} \times \mathfrak{E}^1$ can be represented as the union of an ascending sequence of 4-cells.

In [13] it was proved further that $\mathfrak{W} \times \mathfrak{W}$ is homeomorphic to $\mathfrak{E}^6$ and, in [14] by a modification of Whitehead's construction, that there exist uncountably many topologically different spaces with the properties of $\mathfrak{W}$ stated above.

Another question in this context was raised by R. H. Bing: Do there exist open homotopy 3-cells that cannot be imbedded in $\mathfrak{E}^3$? He proposed a space $\mathfrak{W}' = \bigcup_{i=1}^\infty \mathfrak{T}_i'^3$, obtained by a modification of Whitehead's construction as shown in Fig. 12 (to obtain $\mathfrak{T}_i'^3$ in $\mathfrak{T}_{i+1}'^3$, a "local" knot, in a cube $\mathfrak{P}_i^3 \subset \mathfrak{T}_{i+1}'^3$, is tied in Whitehead's $\mathfrak{T}_i^3$). Kister and McMillan proved in [11] that $\mathfrak{W}'$ cannot be imbedded in $\mathfrak{E}^3$ (but each compact subset of $\mathfrak{W}'$ can be imbedded in $\mathfrak{E}^3$) and they conjectured that $\mathfrak{W}'$ cannot be imbedded in a closed 3-manifold.

As an application of our finiteness theorem, we prove that $\mathfrak{W}'$

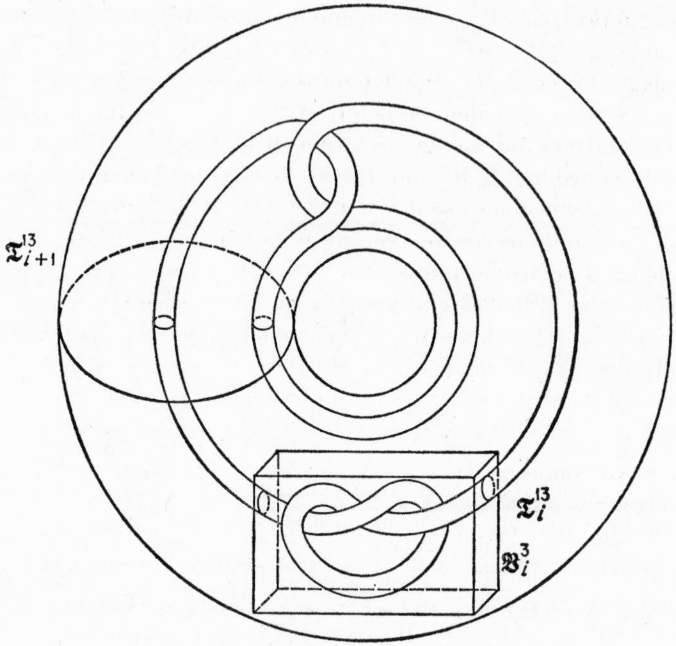

FIG. 12

cannot be imbedded in a compact 3-*manifold* (*with or without boundary*):

Let us assume that $\mathfrak{W}'$ could be imbedded in a compact 3-manifold; then, by [17, 4] $\mathfrak{W}'$ can be imbedded in a compact, polyhedral 3-manifold M^{*3}; i.e., there exists a homeomorphism $h: \mathfrak{W}' \longrightarrow M^{*3}$. First we consider the point set $h(\mathfrak{T}'^3_1)$ which is semilocally tamely imbedded (see [17]) in M^{*3}; i.e., there exists a (topological) neighborhood $\mathfrak{U}$ of $h(\mathfrak{T}'^3_1)$ in M^{*3} which is homeomorphic to a piecewise-rectilinear polyhedron in M^{*3} ($\mathfrak{U}$ may be found as the image under h of a neighborhood $\mathfrak{U}'$ of $\mathfrak{T}'^3_1$ in $\mathfrak{W}'$ which is a solid torus). Therefore, by a result of Moise (theorem 5 in [17]), $h(\mathfrak{T}'^3_1)$ is tamely imbedded in M^{*3}; i.e., there is a homeomorphism $g: M^{*3} \longrightarrow M^{*3}$ of M^{*3} onto itself such that $gh(\mathfrak{T}'^3_1)$ is a piecewise-rectilinear polyhedron T'^3_1.

To apply our finiteness theorem, we consider the compact 3-manifold $M^3 = M^{*3} - {}^\circ T_1'^3$ and a (piecewise rectilinear) triangulation Δ of M^3. We denote the number of tetrahedra of Δ by α. Now we consider the point set $\mathfrak{L} = \bigcup_{i=1}^{s} gh({}^\cdot\mathfrak{T}_{i+1}'^3)$ where s is an arbitrary integer greater than 61α. Then $\mathfrak{L}$ is semilocally tamely imbedded in M^3 and, hence, tamely imbedded in M^3; i.e., there is a homeomorphism $f'\colon M^3 \longrightarrow M^3$ of M^3 onto itself such that $f'(\mathfrak{L})$ is a piecewise rectilinear polyhedron; f' may be extended to a homeomorphism $f\colon M^{*3} \longrightarrow M^{*3}$ which is the identity on $T_1'^3$. Now $f(\mathfrak{L})$ is the disjoint union of s tori $M_i^2 = fgh({}^\cdot\mathfrak{T}_{i+1}'^3)$ $(i = 1, \ldots, s)$, where M_i^2 is the boundary of the (polyhedral) solid torus $T_{i+1}'^3 = fgh(\mathfrak{T}_{i+1}'^3)$ in M^{*3}.

To obtain a contradiction to the finiteness theorem, we have to prove

(1) No connected component of $M^3 - (M_1^2 + \cdots + M_s^2)$ is a parallelity component.

(2) The M_i^2's are incompressible in M^3 (the boundary-incompressibility is trivial, since the M_i^2's do not have boundaries).

Proof of 1: If there did exist a parallelity component K^3 of $M^3 - (M_1^2 + \cdots + M_s^2)$, then K^3 would be equal to ${}^\circ T_{i+1}'^3 - T_i'^3$ for some i between 2 and s; but then $\mathfrak{T}_{i+1}'^3 - {}^\circ\mathfrak{T}_i'^3$ would be a Cartesian product of a torus and an interval in contradiction to the hypothesis (see Fig. 12).

Proof of 2: If M_j^2 were compressible in M^3, there would exist a disk $D^2 \subset M^3$ with ${}^\cdot D^2 \subset M_j^2$ and ${}^\circ D^2 \subset M^3 - M_j^2$ such that ${}^\cdot D^2$ did not bound a disk in M_j^2. Then, by small isotopic deformations of D^2, we may obtain a disk D_*^2 with ${}^\cdot D_*^2 = {}^\cdot D^2$ and ${}^\circ D_*^2 \subset {}^\circ M^3 - M_j^2$ that intersects the surfaces $M_1^2, \ldots, M_{j-1}^2, M_{j+1}^2, \ldots, M_s^2$ at most in simple piercing curves. We may remove, step by step, all those intersection curves that bound disks in the M_i^2's (replacing disks in D_*^2 by disks close to disks in the M_i^2's); this yields finally a disk D_{**}^2 with ${}^\cdot D_{**}^2 = {}^\cdot D^2$ and ${}^\circ D_{**}^2 \subset {}^\circ M^3 - M_j^2$ such that no curve in $D_{**}^2 \cap M_i^2$ bounds a disk in M_i^2 (for all $i = 1, \ldots, s$).

D_{**}^2 cannot lie in $T_{j+1}'^3$, for otherwise it would be a meridian disk of $T_{j+1}'^3$; but then it would contain meridian disks of $T_j'^3$ (compare

Fig. 12); consequently it would contain meridian disks of T'^3_{j-1}, . . . , and finally of T'^3_1, in contradiction to $\dot{}T'^3_1 \subset \dot{}M^3$.

Now it follows that $\dot{}D^2_{**}$ must be a "longitude" of T'^3_{j+1} that intersects a (properly chosen) meridian curve of T'^3_{j+1} in just one piercing point. Otherwise a small neighborhood N^3 of $T'^3_{j+1} + D^2_{**}$ in M^{*3} would be either a lens space minus an open 3-cell or homeomorphic to $S^2 \times S^1$ minus an open 3-cell; hence, a longitude C^1 of T'^3_{j+1} would not be contractible in N^3; then C^1 would not be contractible in M^{*3} (since if C^1 were to bound a singular disk in M^{*3}, it would lie in the boundary of a singular disk with holes in N^3 and these holes could be closed by singular disks in the 2-sphere $\dot{}N^3$). This is a contradiction, since C^1 lies in the simply connected space $fgh(\mathfrak{W}') \subset M^{*3}$.

It follows that we can deform $\dot{}D^2_{**}$ isotopically within M^2_j into a curve that intersects the image-cube $P^3_{j+1} = fgh(\mathfrak{P}^3_{j+1})$ (see Figs. 12, 13) in just one arc A^1 with $^\circ A^1 \subset {}^\circ P^3_{j+1}$. This curve bounds

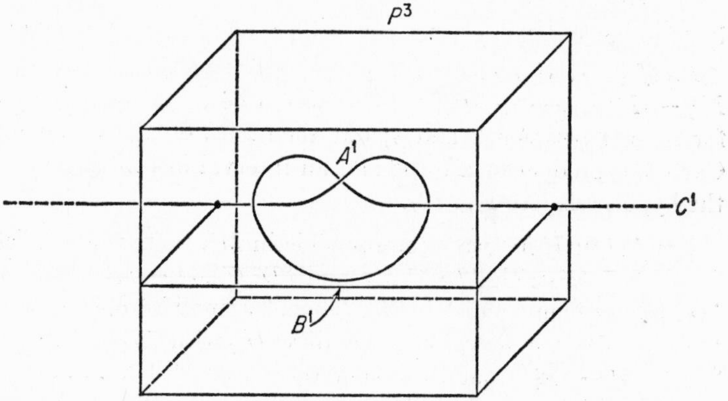

FIG. 13

a disk $D^2_\#$ (isotopic to D^2_{**} in $M^3 - {}^\circ T'^3_{j+1}$) that intersects $\dot{}P^3_{j+1}$ only in simple piercing curves. One of these piercing curves is an arc B^1 with $\dot{}B^1 = \dot{}A^1$, and the other ones are closed curves, bounding disks in $\dot{}P^3_{j+1} - T'^3_{j+1}$; but we may remove the closed piercing curves, step by step (replacing disks in $D^2_\#$ by disks close to disks in $\dot{}P^3_{j+1} - T'^3_{j+1}$), and we obtain in this way a disk $D^2_{\#\#}$

that intersects $P^3_{j+1} - {}^\circ T'^3_{j+1}$ in a disk $\tilde{D}^2$ with ${}^\cdot\tilde{D}^2 = B^1 + A^1$. But this is a contradiction to the fact that A^1 is a *knotted* chord in P^3_{j+1}. This finishes the proof.

6. APPLICATION 2: ON CELL-DECOMPOSITIONS OF 3-MANIFOLDS

If a 3-manifold M^3 contains a (polygonal) simple closed curve C^1 such that C^1 does not lie in a 3-cell in M^3, then M^3 is not a 3-sphere. R. H. Bing proved in [3] that the converse is also true: If M^3 is compact and without boundary and every polygonal simple closed curve in M^3 lies in a 3-cell in M^3, then M^3 is a 3-sphere. This shows that simple closed curves in M^3 which do not lie in 3-cells in M^3 may be characteristic of the homeomorphism class of M^3. So one may seek curves of this kind that are "especially simple" and without "local complications." For instance, if a curve C^1 intersects a certain 3-cell $P^3 \subset M^3$ in a knotted chord A^1 (as in Fig. 13), then one may consider this as a local complication of the curve and simplify it by replacing A^1 by an (unknotted) arc B^1 in ${}^\cdot P^3$; the "simpler" curve so obtained will not lie in a 3-cell in M^3 if C^1 does not lie in a 3-cell in M^3 and our simplification preserved those "global" properties of C^1 which are typical for M^3.

In general, we shall say that a polygonal, simple closed curve C^1 is *elementary with respect to 3-cells in* M^3 if the following holds: If P^3 is an arbitrary (compact) 3-cell in ${}^\circ M^3$ such that $C^1 \cap {}^\cdot P^3$ consists of (at least two) isolated piercing points, then (at least) one of the following two cases applies (compare Figs. 14, 15):

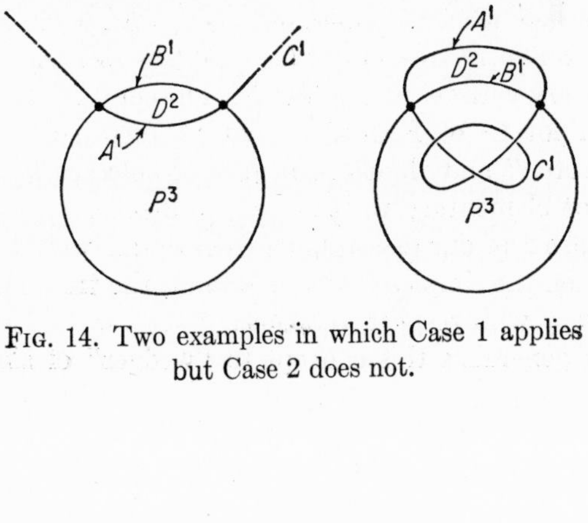

FIG. 14. Two examples in which Case 1 applies but Case 2 does not.

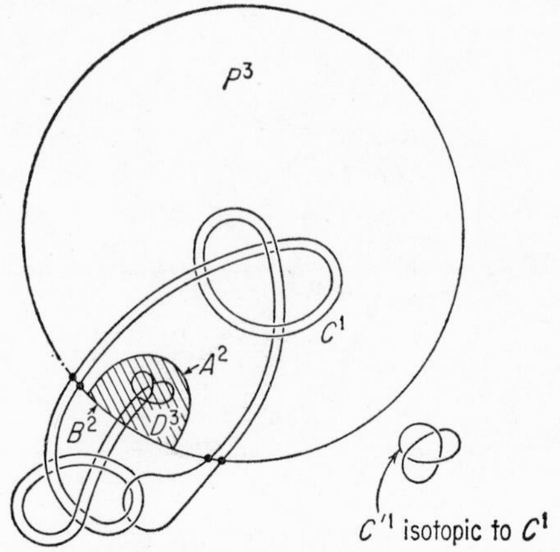

FIG. 15. Case 2 applies but Case 1 does not; C^1 is a trefoil knot.

Case 1: At least one connected component, say A^1, of $C^1 - \dot{}P^3$ is "*trivial in* $M^3 - \dot{}P^3$ *with respect to* C^1"; i.e., there exists a disk D^2 (see Fig. 14) with $^\circ D^2 \subset M^3 - (\dot{}P^3 + C^1)$ such that $\dot{}D^2$ is the union of A^1 and an arc $B^1 \subset \dot{}P^3$ with $^\circ B^1 \cap C^1 = \emptyset$.

Case 2: $C^1 - \dot{}P^3$ is "*splittable in* $M^3 - \dot{}P^3$"; i.e., there exists a 3-cell D^3 (see Fig. 15) with $^\circ D^3 \subset M^3 - \dot{}P^3$ such that $\dot{}D^3$ is the union of an open disk $A^2 \subset {}^\circ M^3 - \dot{}P^3$ and a disk $B^2 \subset \dot{}P^3$ with $\overline{A}^2 \cap C^1 = \emptyset$, $B^2 \cap C^1 \neq \emptyset$, and $(\dot{}P^3 - B^2) \cap C^1 \neq \emptyset$ (we call D^3 a *splitting* 3-*cell with respect to* P^3, C^1).

To illustrate the meaning of this definition, let us consider Figs. 15, 16, 17 which show examples of knots in S^3. If C^1 is a product knot (of two nontrivial factors) (see [22]) as in Fig. 16, then it is not elementary with respect to 3-cells. The converse does not hold, since the knot C^1 of Fig. 17 cannot be factored (since it is a "Schlingknoten" and therefore a prime knot; see [23], Sec. 20) but it is not elementary with respect to 3-cells. Figure 15 shows that the Case 2 of our definition is essential: if we would omit it, then not even the simplest nontrivial knot, the trefoil knot, would be elementary with respect to 3-cells.

We may generalize this concept to "wedges" of simple closed

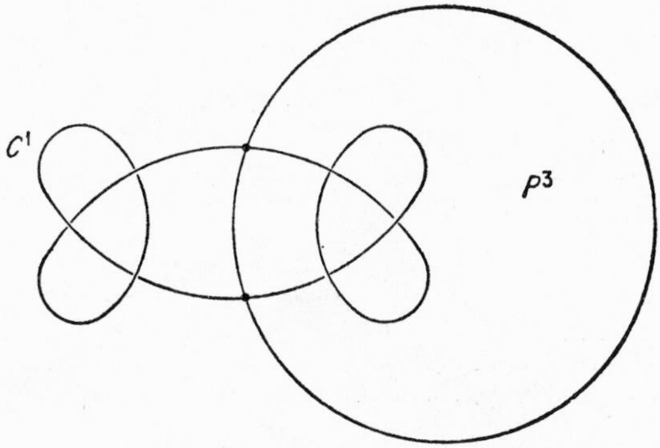

FIG. 16

curves that have an important meaning for combinatorial presentations of 3-manifolds. Every compact 3-manifold without boundary possesses a cell-decomposition Ω that contains just one 3-dimensional element (see [25], Sec. 60; Ω may be derived from an arbitrary cell-decomposition Δ of M^3 by deleting, step by step, such 2-dimensional elements of Δ that lie in the boundaries of two different 3-dimensional elements of Δ). From Ω we may derive (by contracting a maximal tree in the 1-skeleton of Ω—as described in Sec. 2—to one vertex) a cell-decomposition Γ of M^3 that con-

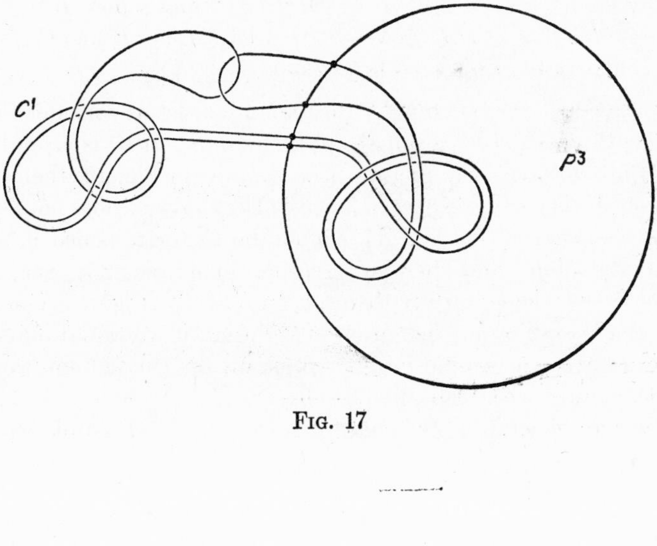

FIG. 17

tains just one 3-dimensional element C^3 and just one vertex p. Since the Euler characteristic of M^3 is zero, Γ contains as many, say h, 2-dimensional elements $C^2_1, \ldots, C^2_h$ as 1-dimensional elements $C^1_1, \ldots, C^1_h$. Such a simplified cell-decomposition Γ may serve as a convenient presentation of M^3.

Now the closures $\overline{C}^1_j$ of the 1-dimensional elements of Γ are simple closed curves with just one point, p, in common; i.e., the 1-skeleton $G^1 = \overline{C}^1_1 + \cdots + \overline{C}^1_h$ of Γ is a so-called wedge of closed curves, $\overline{C}^1_1, \ldots, \overline{C}^1_h$. We shall say that a wedge $\overline{C}^1_1 + \cdots + \overline{C}^1_h$, $h \geqq 2$, with common vertex p, $(\overline{C}^1_i = C^1_i + p)$ is *elementary with respect to 3-cells in* M^3 if the following holds: If P^3 is an arbitrary (compact) 3-cell in $^\circ M^3$ such that $(\overline{C}^1_1 + \cdots + \overline{C}^1_h) \cap {}^\cdot P^3$ consists of (at least two) isolated piercing points and $p \in {}^\circ P^3$, then (at least) one of the following three cases applies:

Case 1: At least one connected component, say A^1, of $(C^1_1 + \cdots + C^1_h) - {}^\cdot P^3$ (N.B., $p \notin A^1$) is *trivial in* $M^3 - {}^\cdot P^3$ *with respect to* $\overline{C}^1_1 + \cdots + \overline{C}^1_h$, i.e., there exists a disk D^2 with $^\circ D^2 \subset M^3 - ({}^\cdot P^3 + \overline{C}^1_1 + \cdots + \overline{C}^1_h)$ such that ${}^\cdot D^2$ is the union of A^1 and an arc $B^1 \subset {}^\cdot P^3$ with $^\circ B^1 \cap (C^1_1 + \cdots + C^1_h) = \emptyset$.

Case 2: $(\overline{C}^1_1 + \cdots + \overline{C}^1_h) - {}^\cdot P^3$ is *splittable in* $M^3 - {}^\cdot P^3$; i.e., there exists a *splitting* 3-*cell* D^3 with $^\circ D^3 \subset M^3 - {}^\cdot P^3$, $p \notin D^3$, such that ${}^\cdot D^3$ is the union of an open disk $A^2 \subset {}^\circ M^3 - {}^\cdot P^3$ and a disk $B^2 \subset {}^\cdot P^3$ with $\overline{A}^2 \cap (\overline{C}^1_1 + \cdots + \overline{C}^1_h) = \emptyset$, $B^2 \cap (\overline{C}^1_1 + \cdots + \overline{C}^1_h) \neq \emptyset$, and $({}^\cdot P^3 - B^2) \cap (\overline{C}^1_1 + \cdots + \overline{C}^1_h) \neq \emptyset$.

Case 3: (See Fig. 18.) P^3 is a neighborhood of p in M^3 which is small with respect to $\overline{C}^1_1 + \cdots + \overline{C}^1_h$.

Now one may ask the following

QUESTION: *If* $\overline{C}^1_1 + \cdots + \overline{C}^1_h$ *is elementary with respect to 3-cells in* M^3, *then is each single* $\overline{C}^1_j$ *also elementary with respect to 3-cells in* M^3*?*

We shall prove that the answer is *yes, if* $\overline{C}^1_1 + \cdots + \overline{C}^1_h$ *does not lie in a 3-cell in* M^3 and that the answer is also *yes, if* M^3 *is a 3-sphere.* We leave it to the reader to investigate the case that $\overline{C}^1_1 + \cdots + \overline{C}^1_h$ lies in a 3-cell in M^3, where M^3 is an arbitrary 3-manifold.

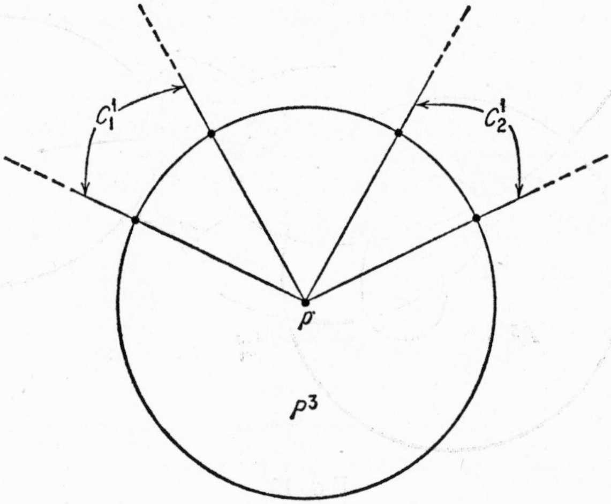

FIG. 18

Proof: Let us assume that $\overline{C}_1^1$ is not elementary with respect to 3-cells in M^3. Then by definition there exists a 3-cell $P^3 \subset {}^\circ M^3$ such that

(1) $\overline{C}_1^1 \cap {}^{\cdot}P^3$ consists of at least two isolated piercing points.

(2) No component of $\overline{C}_1^1 - {}^{\cdot}P^3$ is trivial in $M^3 - {}^{\cdot}P^3$ with respect to $\overline{C}_1^1$.

(3) $\overline{C}_1^1 - {}^{\cdot}P^3$ is not splittable in $M^3 - {}^{\cdot}P^3$.

Our target is to derive from P^3, step by step, a 3-cell $P^{\prime 3}$ which shows that $\overline{C}_1^1 + \cdots + \overline{C}_h^1$ is also not elementary with respect to 3-cells in M^3, in contradiction to the hypothesis.

Step a: If $p \notin {}^\circ P^3$, then there is an arc $Q^1 \subset \overline{C}_1^1 - {}^\circ P^3$ (see Fig. 19) that joins p to a point in ${}^{\cdot}P^3$ (Q^1 degenerates to the point p if $p \in {}^{\cdot}P^3$); then we choose a small neighborhood Q^3 of Q^1 in M^3 and let $P^{*3} = P^3 + Q^3$; then P^{*3} also has the properties (1) to (3), and moreover

(4) $p \in {}^\circ P^{*3}$.

If $p \in {}^\circ P^3$, then we take $P^{*3} = P^3$.

Step b: From P^{*3} we derive by small deformations a 3-cell $P^{\prime 3}$ which also has properties (1) to (4), and moreover

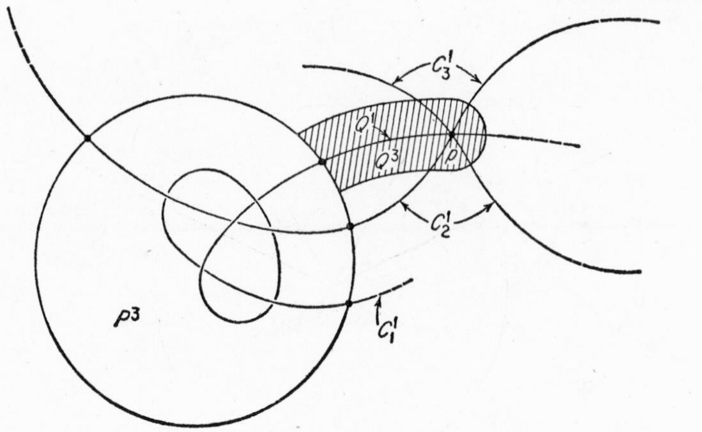

FIG. 19

(5) ${}^{\cdot}P'^3 \cap (C_1^1 + \cdots + C_h^1)$ consists of isolated piercing points only.

Step c: If in M^3 there exists a splitting 3-cell D'^3 with respect to P'^3, $\overline{C}_1^1 + \cdots + \overline{C}_h^1$, then we distinguish the following four cases (see Fig. 20), denoting ${}^{\cdot}P'^3 \cap {}^{\cdot}D'^3$ by B'^2:

Case α: $D'^3 \subset P'^3$.

Case β: $D'^3 \subset {}^{\circ}M^3 - {}^{\circ}P'^3$, and $B'^2 \cap C_1^1 = \varnothing$.

Case γ: $D'^3 \subset {}^{\circ}M^3 - {}^{\circ}P'^3$, $B'^2 \cap C_1^1 \neq \varnothing$, and M^3 is a 3-sphere.

Case δ: $D'^3 \subset {}^{\circ}M^3 - {}^{\circ}P'^3$, $B'^2 \cap C_1^1 \neq \varnothing$, and $\overline{C}_1^1 + \cdots + \overline{C}_h^1$ does not lie in a 3-cell in M^3.

In each case we construct a 3-cell P''^3 with similar properties as P'^3 but such that the number u'' of points in ${}^{\cdot}P''^3 \cap (C_1^1 + \cdots + C_h^1)$ is smaller than the number u' of points in ${}^{\cdot}P'^3 \cap (C_1^1 + \cdots + C_h^1)$.

In Case α we have $p \in {}^{\circ}P'^3 - D'^3$ and hence $\overline{C}_1^1 \cap D'^3 = \varnothing$ (since otherwise D'^3 would be a splitting 3-cell with respect to P'^3, $\overline{C}_1^1$); then we take for P''^3 the 3-cell ${}^{-}(P'^3 - D'^3)$ which has properties (1) to (5). In Case β we take $P''^3 = P'^3 + D'^3$, preserving properties (1) to (5). In Case γ we take $P''^3 = M^3 - {}^{\circ}D'^3$

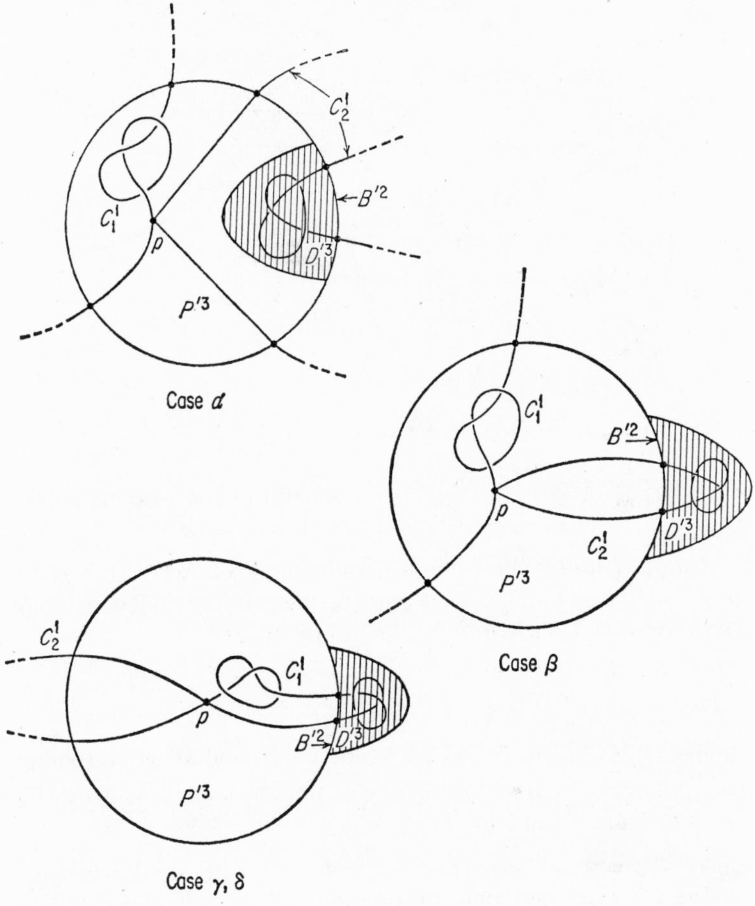

FIG. 20

with properties (1) to (5). In Case δ we take $P''^3 = P'^3 + D'^3$; then P''^3 has properties (2) to (5) and instead of (1) the property

(1*) $\overline{C}_1^1 \subset {}^\circ P''^3$, and $\overline{C}_1^1 + \cdots + \overline{C}_h^1$ does not lie in a 3-cell in M^3.

Step d: We repeat the procedure of Step c as often as possible and obtain in this way (in less than u' steps) a 3-cell $P^{\#3}$ with properties (1) or (1*) and (2) to (5), and

(6) $(\overline{C}_1^1 + \cdots + \overline{C}_h^1) - {}^{\cdot}P^{\#3}$ is not splittable in $M^3 - {}^{\cdot}P^{\#3}$.

Now $P^{\#3}$ also has the property

(7) No component of $(C_1^1 + \cdots + C_h^1) - {}^{\cdot}P^{\#3}$ is trivial in $M^3 - {}^{\cdot}P^{\#3}$ with respect to $\overline{C}_1^1 + \cdots + \overline{C}_h^1$.

For otherwise, if A'^1 were a trivial component, then $A'^1 \cap \overline{C}_1^1 = \varnothing$ and there would exist a disk D'^2 with ${}^{\circ}D'^2 \subset M^3 - ({}^{\cdot}P^{\#3} + \overline{C}_1^1 + \cdots + \overline{C}_h^1)$, $A'^1 \subset {}^{\cdot}D'^2$, and ${}^{\cdot}D'^2 - \overline{A}'^1 \subset {}^{\cdot}P^{\#3} - (C_1^1 + \cdots + C_h^1)$; then a small neighborhood D'^3 of D'^2 in $M^3 - {}^{\circ}P^{\#3}$ or in $P^{\#3}$ would be a splitting 3-cell with respect to $P^{\#3}$, $\overline{C}_1^1 + \cdots + \overline{C}_h^1$, in contradiction to property (6).

Moreover, we have

(8) $P^{\#3}$ is not a neighborhood of p in M^3 which is small with respect to $\overline{C}_1^1 + \cdots + \overline{C}_h^1$.

For otherwise ${}^{\circ}P^{\#3} \cap \overline{C}_1^1$ would be trivial in $M^3 - {}^{\cdot}P^{\#3}$ with respect to $\overline{C}_1^1$, in contradiction to the fact that $P^{\#3}$ has property (2).

Since $P^{\#3}$ has properties (1) or (1*) and (4) to (8), $\overline{C}_1^1 + \cdots + \overline{C}_h^1$ is not elementary with respect to 3-cells in M^3, in contradiction to the hypothesis. Therefore our initial assumption is wrong and $\overline{C}_1^1$ is elementary with respect to 3-cells in M^3, Q.E.D.

On the other hand, if each single $\overline{C}_j^1$ is elementary, then the wedge $\overline{C}_1^1 + \cdots + \overline{C}_h^1$ need not be elementary as Fig. 21 shows.

We shall prove the following

THEOREM: *Every compact, irreducible* 3-*manifold* M^3 *without boundary possesses a cell-decomposition* Γ *that contains just one* 3-*dimensional and just one* 0-*dimensional element such that*

(a) *The* 1-*skeleton of* Γ *is elementary with respect to* 3-*cells in* M^3.
(b) *No* 1-*dimensional element of* Γ *lies in a* (*compact*) 3-*cell in* M^3.

If M^3 is a 3-sphere, then the decomposition Γ of the theorem does not contain 1- or 2-dimensional elements, but just one open 3-cell and one vertex.

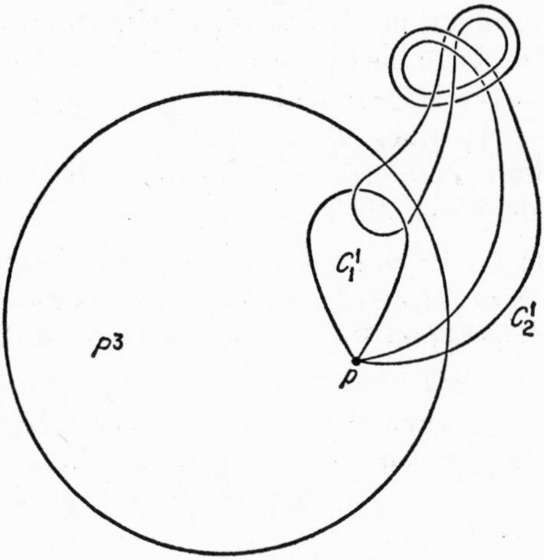

FIG. 21

REMARK: *If M^3 is not a 3-sphere, then condition* (b) *is a consequence of condition* (a).

Proof: Let us assume that a 1-dimensional element C_1^1 of Γ lies in a 3-cell $R^3 \subset M^3$. Then we can find a 3-cell $P'^3 \subset M^3$ that contains $\overline{C}_1^1$ in its interior such that the 1-skeleton G^1 of Γ intersects $^{\cdot}P'^3$ in at least two isolated piercing points. If there exists a splitting 3-cell D'^3 in M^3 with respect to P'^3, G^1, then we consider the 3-cell

$$P''^3 = \begin{cases} P'^3 + D'^3 & \text{if} \quad D'^3 \subset M^3 - {}^{\circ}P'^3 \\ {}^{-}(P'^3 - D'^3) & \text{if} \quad D'^3 \subset P'^3. \end{cases}$$

$^{\cdot}P''^3$ intersects G^1 in at least two points less than $^{\cdot}P'^3$, but still $\overline{C}_1^1 \subset {}^{\circ}P''^3$. We repeat this operation as often as possible and we obtain finally a 3-cell $P^{\#3}$ with $\overline{C}_1^1 \subset {}^{\circ}P^{\#3}$, but $G^1 \not\subset P^{\#3}$ (since otherwise M^3 would be a 3-sphere; see [3]). From this we conclude, as in the proof given above, that G^1 is not elementary with respect to 3-cells in M^3, Q.E.D.

In the case that M^3 is a homotopy 3-sphere it is remarkable that M^3 possesses also a cell-decomposition Γ^* that contains just one

3-dimensional and just one 0-dimensional element, with properties contrary to those of Γ: the closure of each 1-dimensional element of Γ^* lies in a 3-cell in M^3 and, moreover, bounds a nonsingular disk in M^3 (this is proved in [10a]).

We may also state a certain extension of Bing's result [3] on conditions under which M^3 is a 3-sphere as a

COROLLARY: *Let M^3 be a compact, irreducible, 3-manifold without boundary. If every polygonal, simple closed curve that is elementary with respect to 3-cells in M^3 is contained in a 3-cell in M^3, then (and only then) M^3 is a 3-sphere.*

Proof: Let us assume the contrary: every polygonal, simple closed curve that is elementary with respect to 3-cells in M^3 is contained in a 3-cell in M^3, but M^3 is not a 3-sphere. Then we may apply the theorem and conclude that there exists a cell-decomposition Γ of M^3 that possesses just one vertex such that the 1-skeleton G^1 of Γ is elementary with respect to 3-cells in M^3 and such that no 1-dimensional element of Γ lies in a 3-cell in M^3. Since M^3 is not a 3-sphere, Γ possesses at least one 1-dimensional element C^1. Then $\overline{C}^1$ is not contained in a 3-cell in M^3 and (because of the affirmative answer to our "question") $\overline{C}^1$ is elementary with respect to 3-cells in M^3. This is a contradiction to our assumption, and the corollary is proved.

Proof of theorem: We may assume that M^3 is not a 3-sphere.

Let Γ_0 be a cell-decomposition of M^3 that contains just one vertex p and just one 3-dimensional element; we denote the 1-skeleton of Γ_0 by G_0^1 and the 2-skeleton by G_0^2. Let P_0^3 be a small neighborhood of p in M^3 (see Fig. 22). Let H^3 be a small neighborhood of G_0^1 in M^3 (small with respect to $P_0^3|G_0^2$). Then H^3 is a handlebody and the connected components of $H^3 \cap {}^{\boldsymbol{\cdot}}P_0^3$ are meridian disks of H^3; we denote the union of their boundaries, ${}^{\boldsymbol{\cdot}}(H^3 \cap {}^{\boldsymbol{\cdot}}P_0^3)$, by X_0. Further we denote the handlebody $H^3 + P_0^3$ by H_0^3. Then $M^3 - {}^{\circ}H_0^3$ is also a handlebody, denoted by M_0^3 (since ${}^{\boldsymbol{\cdot}}H_0^3$, which is isotopic to ${}^{\boldsymbol{\cdot}}H^3$ in M^3, is a Heegaard-surface in M^3).

If G_0^1 is elementary with respect to 3-cells in M^3, then (because of our "remark") we may take Γ_0 for Γ and the proof is finished.

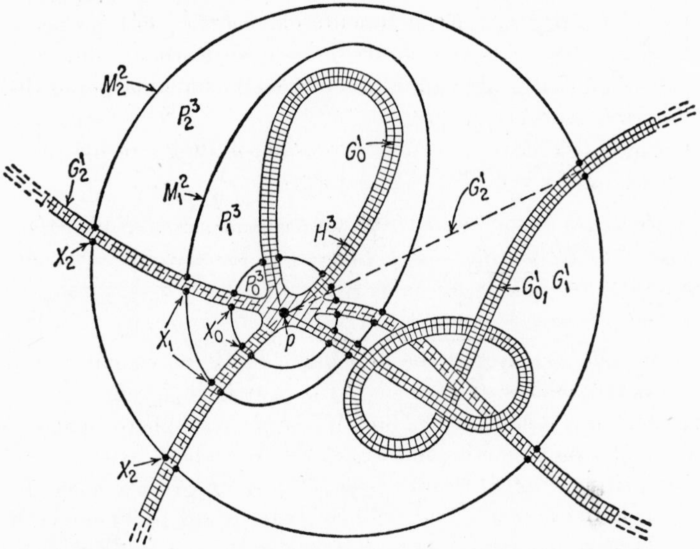

FIG. 22

If G_0^1 is not elementary, then by definition there exists a 3-cell $P^3 \subset M^3$ such that

(i) $G_0^1 \cap {}^{\bullet}P^3$ consists of at least two isolated piercing points, and $p \in {}^{\circ}P^3$.

(ii) No connected component of $(G_0^1 - p) - {}^{\bullet}P^3$ is trivial in $M^3 - {}^{\bullet}P^3$ with respect to G_0^1.

(iii) $G_0^1 - {}^{\bullet}P^3$ is not splittable in $M^3 - {}^{\bullet}P^3$.

(iv) P^3 is not a neighborhood of p in M^3 which is small with respect to G_0^1.

From P^3 we shall derive a 3-cell $P_1^3 \subset M^3$ (see Fig. 22) that also has properties (i) to (iv) and, moreover,

(v) $P_0^3 \subset {}^{\circ}P_1^3$.

(vi) The connected components of $H^3 \cap {}^{\bullet}P_1^3$ are meridian disks of H^3.

(vii) The connected components of $(G_0^2 - G_0^1) \cap {}^{\bullet}P_1^3$ are open piercing arcs (with boundaries in G_0^1).

(viii) The connected components of $\dot{P}^3_{\mathrm{I}} - G^2_0$ are open disks.

(ix) As a consequence of properties (i) to (vi), the 2-manifold $\dot{P}^3_{\mathrm{I}} - {}^{\circ}H^3$, denoted by M^2_{I}, is incompressible and boundary-incompressible mod X_0 in M^3_0.

We may obtain P^3_{I} in five steps as follows:

Step 1: We take a neighborhood P^3_* of p in M^3 which is small with respect to $P^3|G^1_0$ and a self-homeomorphism† $\alpha\colon M^3 \longrightarrow M^3$ such that $\alpha(P^3_*) = P^3_0$ and $\alpha(G^1_0) = G^1_0$. Then $\alpha(P^3)$ is a 3-cell, denoted by P^3_{I}, with properties (i) to (v).

Step 2: We take a neighborhood H^3_* of G^1_0 in M^3 which is small with respect to $P^3_0|P^3_{\mathrm{I}}$ and a self-homeomorphism $\beta\colon M^3 \longrightarrow M^3$ such that $\beta(H^3_*) = H^3$, $\beta(P^3_0) = P^3_0$, and $\beta|G^1_0 = \text{identity}$. Then $\beta(P^3_{\mathrm{I}})$ is a 3-cell, denoted by P^3_{II}, with properties (i) to (vi).

Step 3: From P^3_{II} we derive by small deformations a 3-cell P^3_{III}, also with properties (i) to (vi), such that $\dot{P}^3_{\mathrm{III}}$ intersects $G^2_0 - G^1_0$ only in normal piercing curves.

Step 4: If certain connected components of $\dot{P}^3_{\mathrm{III}} - G^2_0$ are not open disks, then these components are disks with holes [since $\dot{P}^3_{\mathrm{III}} \cap G^2_0 \neq \varnothing$ because of property (i)], and we claim there exists an open disk $A^2 \subset ({}^{\circ}M^3_0 - G^2_0) - \dot{P}^3_{\mathrm{III}}$ with $\dot{A}^2 \subset \dot{P}^3_{\mathrm{III}} - (G^2_0 + H^3)$ such that $\dot{A}^2$ does not bound a disk in $\dot{P}^3_{\mathrm{III}} - G^2_0$. To find A^2, we use the fact that ${}^{\circ}M^3_0 - G^2_0$ is an open 3-cell, i.e., that there exists a map $\gamma\colon R^3 \longrightarrow M^3_0$ of a 3-cell R^3 onto M^3_0 such that $\gamma|{}^{\circ}R^3$ is a homeomorphism onto ${}^{\circ}M^3_0 - G^2_0$; now the connected components of $\gamma^{-1}(\dot{P}^3_{\mathrm{III}} - {}^{\circ}H^3)$ are 3-spheres with holes, the boundaries of which lie in $\dot{R}^3$, and some of which, say $Y^2_1, \ldots, Y^2_v$, are not disks. We can find a disk $A'^2 \subset {}^{\circ}R^3$ with ${}^{\circ}A'^2 \subset {}^{\circ}R^3 - \gamma^{-1}(\dot{P}^3_{\mathrm{III}})$ such that $\dot{A}'^2$ lies in ${}^{\circ}Y^2_k$ (for some $k = 1, \ldots, v$) and is parallel to a boundary curve of Y^2_k; then $A^2 = \gamma({}^{\circ}A'^2)$ has the demanded properties.

Now (since M^3 is irreducible by hypothesis) $\dot{A}^2$ bounds a disk $B^2 \subset \dot{P}^3_{\mathrm{III}}$ such that the 2-sphere $A^2 + B^2$ bounds a 3-cell $D^3 \subset M^3$ with either $D^3 \subset P^3_{\mathrm{III}} - p$ or $D^3 \subset M^3 - {}^{\circ}P^3_{\mathrm{III}}$. Then [since P^3_{III} has property (iii)] either $B^2 \cap G^1_0$ or $(\dot{P}^3_{\mathrm{III}} - {}^{\circ}B^2) \cap G^1_0$

† The existence of such a self-homeomorphism is rather obvious; for a proof, see [8], Folgerung 3, p. 259.

is empty. If $D^3 \subset P_{\text{III}}^3$, then D^3 is disjoint from G_0^1, and $^-(P_{\text{III}}^3 - D^3)$—denoted by P_{IV}^3—is a 3-cell with properties (i) to (vi) such that the number of connected components of $^\cdot P_{\text{IV}}^3 \cap G_0^2$ is smaller than the corresponding number u of $^\cdot P_{\text{III}}^3 \cap G_0^2$. If $D^3 \subset M^3 - {}^\circ P_{\text{III}}^3$, then again D^3 is disjoint from G_0^1 (since otherwise G_0^1 would lie in the 3-cell $P_{\text{III}}^3 + D^3$ in contradiction to the hypothesis that M^3 is not a 3-sphere); then we choose $P_{\text{III}}^3 + D^3$ for P_{IV}^3; it has properties (i) to (vi), and $^\cdot P_{\text{III}}^3 \cap G_0^2$ consists of less than u connected components.

Step 5: We repeat the procedure of Step 4 as often as possible and obtain in this way (after less than u steps) a 3-cell P_1^3 with properties (i) to (vi) and (viii). Now P_1^3 has also property (vii) since if Q^1 were a closed curve in $^\cdot P_1^3 \cap (G_0^2 - G_0^1)$, then, because of property (viii), $^\cdot P_1^3 - Q^1$ would consist of two open disks which are disjoint from G_0^2, in contradiction to the fact that P_1^3 has property (i). It remains to prove that P_1^3 has also property (ix): If M_1^2 were compressible in M_0^3, then (by definition) there would exist an open disk $A^2 \subset {}^\circ M_0^3 - M_1^2$ such that $^\cdot A^2$ lies in ${}^\circ M_1^2$ but does not bound a disk in M_1^2; i.e., both connected components of $^\cdot P_1^3 - {}^\cdot A^2$ are intersected by G_0^1; then (since M^3 is irreducible) there would exist a splitting 3-cell D^3 in M^3 with respect to P_1^3, G_0^1 (with $A^2 \subset {}^\cdot D^2$) in contradiction to property (iii); hence M_1^2 is incompressible in M_0^3. If M_1^2 were boundary-compressible mod X_0 in M_0^3, then (by definition) there would exist a disk D^2 with ${}^\circ D^2 \subset {}^\circ M_0^3 - M_1^2$ such that $^\cdot D^2$ is the union of an arc $A^1 \subset M_1^2$ and an open arc $B^1 \subset {}^\cdot M_0^3 - ({}^\cdot M_1^2 + X_0)$, $^\cdot D^2 \cap {}^\cdot M_1^2 = {}^\cdot A^1 = {}^\cdot B^1$, where no connected component of ${}^\circ M_1^2 - A^1$ is an open disk. Moreover, no connected component of $^\cdot M_0^3 - ({}^\cdot M_1^2 + B^1)$ would be the interior of a disk D_*^2 [since otherwise we could conclude that M_1^2 is compressible in M_0^3, for $D^2 + D_*^2$ would be a disk F^2 with $^\cdot F^2 \subset {}^\cdot M_1^2$, where $^\cdot F^2$ does not bound a disk in M_1^2]. Now we observe that those connected components of $^\cdot M_0^3 - ({}^\cdot M_1^2 + X_0)$ which contain curves of $^\cdot M_1^2$ in their boundaries are open annuli (compare Fig. 22), and consequently B^1 would lie in the boundary of a connected component K^3 of $H^3 - {}^\cdot P_1^3$ which does not contain p, where $\bar{K}^3$ is a 3-cell and $^\cdot K^3 \cap {}^\cdot P_1^3$ consists of just two meridian disks of H^3 whose boundaries are joined by $\bar{B}^1$. Then, if D^3 is a small neighborhood of $\overline{D}^2 + \overline{K}^3$ in P_1^3 or in $M^3 - {}^\circ P_1^3$, the disk $A^2 = {}^-({}^\cdot D^3 - {}^\cdot P_1^3)$ would have its boundary in M_1^2, and ${}^\cdot A^2$ would not bound a disk in M_1^2 [since K^3 cannot be the only component of $H^3 \cap {}^\circ P_1^3$ or of $H^3 \cap (M^3 - P_1^3)$]; hence, M_1^2 would be compressible in M_0^3 in contradiction to our last result. Hence P_1^3 has property (ix).

Now we use P_1^3 for deriving a new cell-decomposition Γ_1 of M^3 from Γ_0.

The connected components of $(M^3 - G_0^2) - P_1^3$ are open 3-cells [because of property (viii)], and the connected components of $(G_0^2 - G_0^1) - P_1^3$ are open disks [because of property (vii)]; now, if $(M^3 - G_0^2) - P_1^3$ is not connected, we may remove from $G_0^2 - {}^\circ P_1^3$ certain connected components of $(G_0^2 - G_0^1) - {}^\circ P_1^3$ such that the remaining polyhedron G_1^{*2} has the property that $(M^3 - G_1^{*2}) - P_1^3$ is an open 3-cell. Now we choose in P_1^3 a "cone" $p \cdot (G_1^{*2} \cap {}^\cdot P_1^3)$, i.e., a polyhedron such that there exists a homeomorphism f of P_1^3 onto the unit ball in $\mathfrak{E}^3$ that maps p onto the origin O and $p \cdot (G_1^{*2} \cap {}^\cdot P_1^3)$ onto the rectilinear cone over $f(G_1^{*2} \cap {}^\cdot P_1^3)$ with vertex O. We then take for Γ_1 the cell-decomposition with 2-skeleton $G_1^2 = G_1^{*2} + p \cdot (G_1^{*2} \cap {}^\cdot P_1^3)$, with 1-skeleton $G_1^1 = (G_0^1 - {}^\circ P_1^3) + p \cdot {}^\cdot(G_0^1 - {}^\circ P_1^3)$, and with the single vertex p. Finally we denote ${}^\cdot(H^3 \cap {}^\cdot P_1^3)$ by X_1 and $M^3 - {}^\circ(H^3 + P_1^3)$ by M_1^3.

If G_1^1 is elementary with respect to 3-cells in M^3, then we take Γ_1 for Γ, and the proof is finished. If G_1^1 is not elementary, then we repeat the procedure described above (just replacing the subscript 0 by 1, and 1 by 2) in order to obtain a cell-decomposition Γ_2 of M^3, and so on. Now we apply our finiteness theorem in order to prove that this procedure cannot be repeated arbitrarily often, i.e., that it must yield a certain cell-decomposition Γ_r whose 1-skeleton G_r^1 is elementary with respect to 3-cells in M^3 as demanded for Γ. For this it is sufficient to show the following.

If the procedure above yields cell-decompositions $\Gamma_1, \ldots, \Gamma_s$ of M^3, then the corresponding 2-manifolds $M_1^2, \ldots, M_s^2$ are

(I) Incompressible in M_0^3.

(II) Boundary-incompressible mod X_0 in M_0^3.

respectively, i.e., systems such that $°H'^3 - (N_1'^2 + \cdots + N_h'^2)$ and $°H''^3 - (N_1''^2 + \cdots + N_h''^2)$ are open 3-cells C'^3 and C''^3, respectively.

Step 1: We replace $S_{01}^2, \ldots, S_{0t_0}^2$ by a system of isotopic 2-spheres $S_{11}^2, \ldots, S_{1t_0}^2$ such that for all $i = 1, \ldots, t_0$, $H''^3 \cap S_{1i}^2$ consists of disks only, $H^2 \cap S_{1i}^2 = \dot{}(H''^3 \cap S_{1i}^2) = \dot{}(H'^3 \cap S_{1i}^2)$, and S_{1i}^2 intersects the meridian disks $N_j'^2, N_j''^2$ $(j = 1, \ldots, h)$ at most in normal piercing curves.

We may do this as follows: We choose a "wedge" of h simple closed curves (see Fig. 23) $G_1^1, \ldots, G_h^1$ in $°H''^3$ that have just one

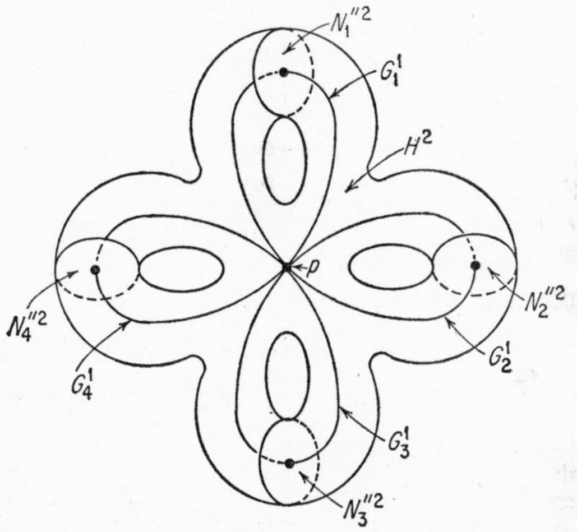

FIG. 23

point $p \in C''^3$ in common and such that H''^3 may be regarded as a neighborhood of $G_1^1 + \cdots + G_h^1$ in M^3; we choose the G_j^1's such that they intersect the S_{0i}^2's at most in isolated piercing points, different from p, and such that $G_j^1 \cap N_k''^2$ is empty if $j \neq k$ and is just one point if $j = k$. Then we take a neighborhood H^{*3} of $G_1^1 + \cdots + G_h^1$ in H''^3 which is small with respect to the S_{0i}^2's and to the $N_j''^2$'s. There exists a self-homeomorphism† δ: $M^3 \longrightarrow M^3$,

† See footnote on p. 80.

isotopic to the identity, such that $\delta | G_1^1 + \cdots + G_h^1 =$ identity, $\delta(H^{*3}) = H''^3$, and $\delta(H^{*3} \cap N_j''^2) = N_j''^2$. Now the 2-spheres $\delta(S_{0i}^2)$ intersect H''^3 in disks only, and we may transform them by small isotopic deformations into 2-spheres S_{Ii}^2 that intersect the $N_j'^2$'s, $N_j''^2$'s normally and have the demanded properties.

We denote by $c(S_{I1}^2, \ldots, S_{It_0}^2)$, abbreviated c_I, the number of intersection curves $(S_{I1}^2 + \cdots + S_{It_0}^2) \cap H^2$. Obviously $c_I \geqq t_0$ (since otherwise at least one of the S_{Ii}^2's would lie in one of the handlebodies H'^3, H''^3 and hence would be compressible in M^3). Our objective is to transform the S_{Ii}^2's in such a way that c becomes equal to the number of the 2-spheres.

Step 2: If $(S_{I1}^2 + \cdots + S_{It_0}^2) \cap H'^3$ is compressible in H'^3, then, as we shall prove, we may transform $S_{I1}^2, \ldots, S_{It_0}^2$ into a system $S_{II1}^2, \ldots, S_{IIt_{II}}^2$ of pairwise disjoint, incompressible 2-spheres in M^3 such that for all $i = 1, \ldots, t$, $S_{IIi}^2 \cap H'^3$ is incompressible in H'^3, such that $(S_{II1}^2 + \cdots + S_{IIt_{II}}^2) \cap H''^3 \subset (S_{I1}^2 + \cdots + S_{It_0}^2) \cap H''^3$, and such that $c(S_{II1}^2, \ldots, S_{IIt_{II}}^2)$, abbreviated c_{II}, is smaller than or equal to c_I. If all $S_{Ii}^2 \cap H'^3$'s are incompressible in H'^3, we take $S_{IIi}^2 = S_{Ii}^2$ and $c_{II} = c_I$.

The transformation may be done by ρ-operations and isotopic deformations as follows: We may find a disk D^2 with interior in $^\circ H'^3 - (S_{I1}^2 + \cdots + S_{It_0}^2)$ and with boundary in one of the S_{Ii}^2's, say in S_{I1}^2, such that $^\cdot D^2$ does not bound a disk in $S_{I1}^2 \cap H'^3$. We then replace a small annular neighborhood of $^\cdot D^2$ in S_{I1}^2 by two disjoint disks "parallel" to D^2 in H'^3 (ρ-operation); in this way we obtain from S_{I1}^2 two 2-spheres S_{II}^{*2}, S_{II}^{**2}. If one of these 2-spheres, say S_{II}^{**2}, is compressible in M^3, then S_{II}^{*2} is isotopic to S_{I1}^2 in M^3; in this case we replace S_{I1}^2 by S_{II}^{*2} in our system of 2-spheres (isotopic deformation). If both S_{II}^{*2} and S_{II}^{**2} are incompressible, then we replace S_{I1}^2 by $S_{II}^{*2} + S_{II}^{**2}$. We repeat this procedure as often as possible in order to obtain the system $S_{II1}^2, \ldots, S_{IIt_{II}}^2$.

Now we denote by $a'(S_{II1}^2, \ldots, S_{IIt_{II}}^2)$, abbreviated a'_{II}, the number c_{II} of boundary curves minus the number of connected components of $(S_{II1}^2 + \cdots + S_{IIt_{II}}^2) \cap H'^3$. Furthermore, we denote by $b'(S_{II1}^2, \ldots, S_{IIt_{II}}^2)$, abbreviated b_{II}, the number a'_{II} minus the number of those connected components of $(S_{II1}^2 + \cdots + S_{IIt_{II}}^2) \cap H'^3$ which are not disks. Analogously we define a''_{II} and b''_{II}. Obviously we have $a'_{\rm II} \geqq 0$ (since otherwise at least one of the $S^2_{{\rm II}i}$'s would lie in H'^3 and hence be compressible in M^3) and $a''_{\rm II} = 0$ (since all components of $S^2_{{\rm II}i} \cap H''^3$ are disks).

Step 3: If $a'_{\rm II} > 0$, then not all connected components of $S^2_{{\rm II}i} \cap H'^3$ are disks; hence $a'_{\rm II} > b'_{\rm II} \geqq 0$. Then, as we shall prove, we may transform the system $S^2_{\rm II1}, \ldots, S^2_{{\rm II}t_{\rm II}}$ into an isotopic system $S^2_{\rm III1}, \ldots, S^2_{{\rm III}t_{\rm II}}$ such that either

$$\textit{Case } \alpha\text{:} \begin{cases} c_{\rm III} = c_{\rm II} - 1, \\ a'_{\rm III} = a'_{\rm II} - 1, \\ b'_{\rm III} \leqq b'_{\rm II}, \end{cases}$$

or

$$\textit{Case } \beta\text{:} \begin{cases} c_{\rm III} = c_{\rm II} + 1, \\ a'_{\rm III} = a'_{\rm II}, \\ b'_{\rm III} = b'_{\rm II} - 1, \end{cases}$$

where $c_{\rm III}$ stands for $c(S^2_{\rm III1}, \ldots, S^2_{{\rm III}t_{\rm II}})$, etc.

If $a'_{\rm II} = 0$, we take $S^2_{{\rm III}i} = S^2_{{\rm II}i}$ and we have $c_{\rm III} = c_{\rm II} = t_{\rm II}$ (since in this case all $S^2_{{\rm II}i} \cap H'^3$'s are disks).

The isotopic deformation of $S^2_{{\rm II}i}$ into $S^2_{{\rm III}i}$ may be done as follows.

First we prove that (if $a'_{\rm II} > 0$) there exists a disk D^2 in H'^3 (compare Fig. 26) such that (1) $°D^2 \subset °H'^3 - (S^2_{\rm II1} + \cdots + S^2_{{\rm II}t_{\rm II}})$; (2) $^{\bullet}D^2$ intersects a connected component K^2 of some $S^2_{{\rm II}i} \cap H'^3$, say $S^2_{\rm II1} \cap H'^3$, in one arc A^1 in such a way that $°A^1 \subset °K^2$ and no connected component of $°K^2 - A^1$ is the interior of a disk; (3) $^{\bullet}D^2 - A^1$ is an open arc B^1 in $H^2 - (S^2_{\rm II1} + \cdots + S^2_{{\rm II}t_{\rm II}})$.

To find D^2, we consider the meridian disks N'^2_j of H'^3; we may assume that they intersect the $S^2_{{\rm II}i}$'s at most in normal piercing curves. We shall transform the meridian disks into "better" meridian disks that contain a disk D^2 as demanded. If one of the intersection curves, say C^1 of $N'^2_k \cap S^2_{{\rm II}i}$, is closed, then it bounds a disk C^2 in N'^2_k (see Fig. 24), and we can find an intersection curve, say C^{*1}, that bounds a disk $C^{*2} \subseteq C^2$ such that $°C^{*2}$ is disjoint from the $S^2_{{\rm II}i}$'s; then we may remove C^{*1} by isotopic deformations of the N'^2_j's, since C^{*1} bounds a disk C^{**2} in one of the $S^2_{{\rm II}i} \cap °H'^3$'s (since the $S^2_{{\rm II}i} \cap H'^3$'s are incompressible in H'^3); hence (by the Alexander theorem) $C^{*2} + C^{**2}$ bounds a 3-cell C^3 in $°H'^3$ (see Fig. 24). In this way we may obtain, step by step, a

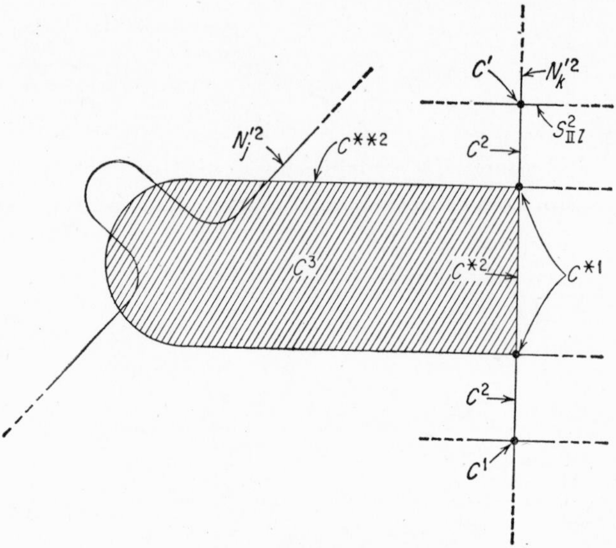

FIG. 24. (Section)

system of meridian disks N'^2_{*j} ($j = 1, \ldots, h$) such that all intersection curves $N'^2_{*j} \cap S^2_{IIi}$ are arcs. Now, if one of the intersection arcs, say F^1 of $N'^2_{*k} \cap S^2_{IIl}$, lies in a connected component L^2 of $S^2_{IIl} \cap H'^3$ (see Fig. 25) in such a way that a component G^2 of $^\circ L^2 - F^1$ is the interior of a disk, then we can find an intersection arc F^{*1} in $\overline{G}^2$, say in $\overline{G}^2 \cap N'^2_{*1}$, such that a connected component $G^{*2} \subseteq G^2$ of $^\circ L^2 - F^{*1}$ is an open disk and is disjoint from the N'^2_{*k}'s; then we remove a small neighborhood F^{*2} of F^{*1} from N'^2_{*1} and replace it by two disks G^{*2}_1, G^{*2}_2 in $H'^3 - (N'^2_{*2} + \cdots + N'^2_{*h} + S^2_{II1} + \cdots + S^2_{IIt_{II}})$, "close" to G^{*2} (see Fig. 25), such that we obtain two disks $N'^2_{\#1}$, $N'^2_{\#\#1}$, with interiors in $^\circ H'^3$ and boundaries in $^\cdot H'^3$. Now, under proper notation, $H'^3 - (N'^2_{\#1} + N'^2_{*2} + \cdots + N'^2_{*h})$ is connected and $H'^3 - (N'^2_{\#\#1} + N'^2_{*2} + \cdots + N'^2_{*h})$ is not [since $^\circ H'^3 - (N'^2_{*1} + \cdots + N'^2_{*h})$ is an open 3-cell]; i.e., $N'^2_{\#1}$, $N'^2_{*2}, \ldots, N'^2_{*h}$ is a new complete system of meridian disks of H'^3 and intersects the S^2_{IIi}'s in a smaller number of arcs than $N'^2_{*1} + \cdots + N'^2_{*h}$. Repeating this procedure as often as possible,

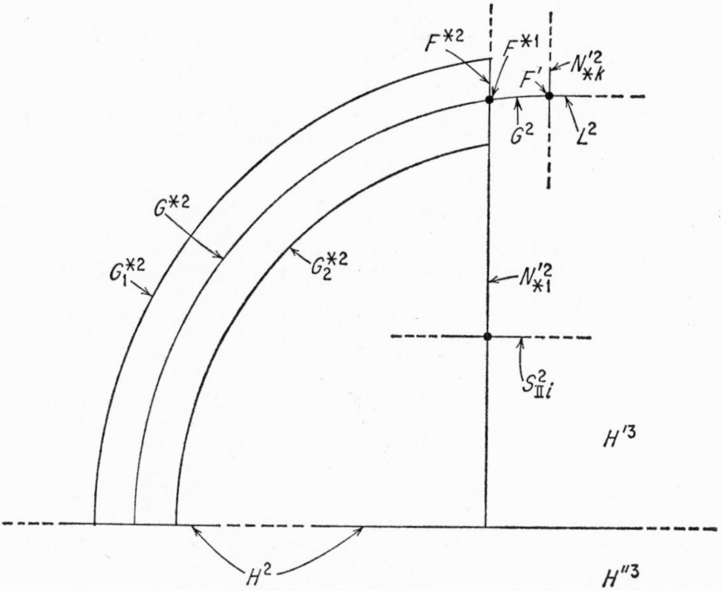

FIG. 25. (Section)

we finally obtain a complete system of meridian disks $N'^2_{**1}, \ldots, N'^2_{**h}$ of H'^3. Then there exists at least one intersection arc, say $\tilde{A}^1$ of $N'^2_{**k} \cap S^2_{\mathrm{II}l}$ (for some k, l), since otherwise all $S^2_{\mathrm{II}i} \cap {}^\circ H'^3$'s would lie in an open 3-cell in ${}^\circ H'^3$; hence those connected components of $S^2_{\mathrm{II}i} \cap H'^3$ which are not disks would be compressible in H'^3. Therefore N'^2_{**k} contains a disk D^2 with the required properties (see Fig. 26) (under proper notation).

Now we choose a small neighborhood U^3 of D^2 in M^3, and we replace the open disk ${}^\circ(S^2_{\mathrm{II}1} \cap U^3)$ by that connected component $D^2_\#$ of ${}^\cdot U^3 - S^2_{\mathrm{II}1}$ whose closure intersects H'^3 in two disjoint disks "parallel" to D^2. This is an isotopic deformation of $S^2_{\mathrm{II}1}$ into a 2-sphere which we denote by $S^2_{\mathrm{III}1}$; furthermore, we denote $S^2_{\mathrm{II}2}, \ldots, S^2_{\mathrm{II}m_{\mathrm{II}}}$ by $S^2_{\mathrm{III}2}, \ldots, S^2_{\mathrm{III}m_{\mathrm{II}}}$, respectively. Now the conditions of Case α are fulfilled if the end points of the arc A^1 lie in different components of ${}^\cdot K^2$ (see Fig. 27), and the conditions of Case β are fulfilled if ${}^\cdot A^1$ lies in one connected component of ${}^\cdot K^2$.

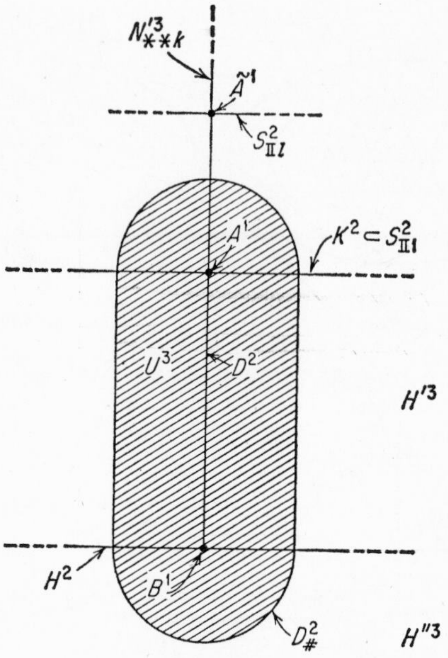

FIG. 26. (Section)

Step 4: We repeat the procedure of Step 3 as often as possible. This yields a system $S^2_{IV1}, \ldots, S^2_{IVt_{II}}$ of 2-spheres, isotopic to $S^2_{II1}, \ldots, S^2_{IIt_{II}}$, such that (under analogous notation) $a'_{IV} = b'_{IV} = 0$. This means that the deformations of the S^2_{IIIi}'s into the S^2_{IVi}'s required just a'_{II} steps under the conditions of Case α and at most b'_{II} steps under the conditions of Case β; but this means that we have either $c_{IV} < c_{II}$ (if $a'_{II} > 0$) or $c_{IV} = c_{II} = t_{II}$ (if $a'_{II} = 0$). We may have $a''_{IV} > 0$.

Step 5: Now we repeat Steps 2, 3, and 4 "in the direction from H''^3 to H'^3," i.e., exchanging the rôles of H'^3 and H''^3, of a' and a'', and of b' and b''. This yields a system $S^2_{V1}, \ldots, S^2_{Vt_V}$ ($t_V \geqq t_{II}$) with

(1) $a''_V = 0$.

(2) $c_V < c_{IV}$ or $c_V = t_V$.

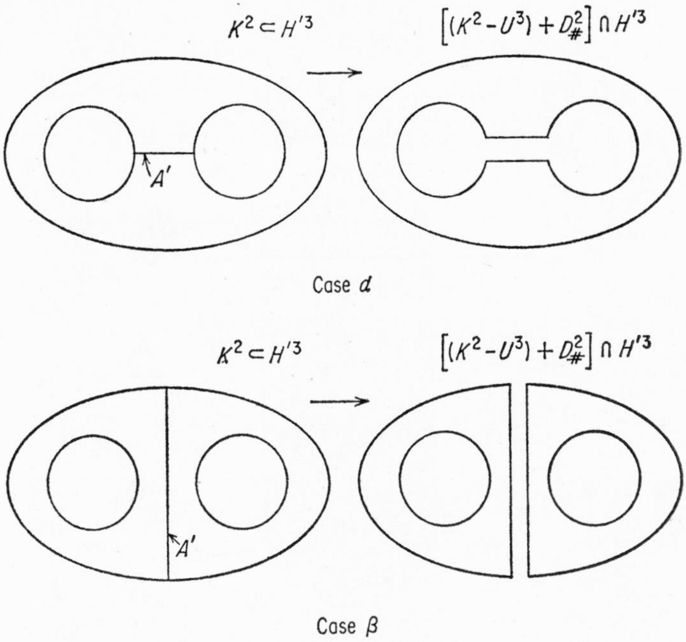

FIG. 27

Step 6: We repeat Steps 2, 3, 4, and 5 as often as possible and obtain in this way a system $S_1^2, \dots, S_t^2$ with $c = t \geqq t_0$, i.e., such that $S_i^2 \cap H^2$ is just one closed curve S_i^1 (for all $i = 1, \dots, t$), where the S_i^2's are incompressible in M^3.

This finishes the proof of the theorem.

8. APPENDIX

For the proof of Lemma 1 in Sec. 4 we need the following

LEMMA: *If M^2 is an incompressible surface in a Cartesian product $M_0^2 \times I$, where M_0^2 is an arbitrary compact 2-manifold with or without boundary and I is the unit interval $0 \leqq x \leqq 1$ with $M_0^2 \times 0 = M_0^2$, $M_0^2 \times 1$ denoted by M_1^2, and with $\dot{M}^2 = M^2 \cap (\dot{M}_0^2 \times {}^\circ I)$, then*

$M_0^2 \times I - M^2$ *consists of two connected components* L'^3, L''^3, *such that (under proper notation) one of the three following cases holds:*

Case 1: M^2 *is "parallel" to* M_0^2; *i.e.,* $\overline{L}'^3$ *and* $\overline{L}''^3$ *are Cartesian products* $\overline{L}'^3 = M_0^2 \times I'$, $\overline{L}''^3 = M_1^2 \times I''$, *where* I', I'' *are unit intervals* $0 \le x' \le 1$, $0 \le x'' \le 1$, *with* $M_0^2 \times 0 = M_0^2$, $M_0^2 \times 1 = M^2$, $M_1^2 \times 0 = M_1^2$, $M_1^2 \times 1 = M^2$.

Case 2: M^2 *is a disk "close" to a disk in* $\cdot M_0^2 \times {}^\circ I$; *i.e.,* $\overline{L}'^3$ *is a 3-cell and* $\cdot L'^3 - {}^\circ M^2$ *is a disk in* $\cdot M_0^2 \times {}^\circ I$.

Case 3: M^2 *is an annulus "close" to an annulus in* $\cdot M_0^2 \times {}^\circ I$; *i.e.,* $\overline{L}'^3$ *is a solid torus and* $\cdot L'^3 - {}^\circ M^2$ *is an annulus in* $\cdot M_0^2 \times {}^\circ I$ *such that there is a meridian disk* N^2 *of* $\overline{L}'^3$ *with* $\cdot N^2 \cap M^2$ *and* $\cdot N^2 \cap (\cdot L'^3 - {}^\circ M^2)$ *each just one arc.*

Proof: First we prove the lemma for the special case that M_0^2 is a 2-sphere. In this case M^2 is a 2-sphere separating M_0^2 from M_1^2 (since otherwise we could conclude by means of the lemma of Fox [7] and the Alexander theorem [1] that M^2 is compressible in $M_0^2 \times I$). From this it follows that Case 1 of the assertion holds.

In the following part of the proof we assume that M_0^2 is not a 2-sphere.

We choose simple, polygonal curves $V_1^1, \ldots, V_r^1$ in M_0^2 such that (1) V_k^1 is either a closed curve in ${}^\circ M_0^2$ or an arc with interior in ${}^\circ M_0^2$ and boundary in $\cdot M_0^2$; (2) $V_k^1 \cap V_l^1$ ($k \ne l$) consists at most of isolated piercing points in ${}^\circ M_0^2$; (3) the connected components of ${}^\circ M_0^2 - (V_1^1 + \cdots + V_r^1)$ and of $\cdot M_0^2 - (\cdot V_1^1 + \cdots + \cdot V_r^1)$ are open 2-cells and open 1-cells, respectively. We consider the cell-decomposition Λ_0 of M_0^2 "produced" by the V_k^1's: the vertices of Λ_0 are the points in the $\cdot V_k^1$'s and in the $V_k^1 \cap V_l^1$'s ($k \ne l$); the (open) edges of Λ_0 are the connected components of $(\cdot M_0^2 + V_1^1 + \cdots + V_r^1)$ − (all vertices of Λ_0); the (open) disks of Λ_0 are the connected components of ${}^\circ M_0^2 - (V_1^1 + \cdots + V_r^1)$. We choose the curves V_k^1 such that each edge $W^1 \in \Lambda_0$ has two different boundary points and if $W^1 \subset {}^\circ M_0^2$, then at least one point of $\cdot W^1$ lies in ${}^\circ M_0^2$ and such that each 2-dimensional element of Λ_0 has a closure that is a disk and contains at most one edge in $\cdot M_0^2$. Let Λ be the cell-decomposition of $M_0^2 \times I$ into the elements of Λ_0, the elements $W \times {}^\circ I$ with $W \in \Lambda_0$, and the elements $W \times 1$ with $W \in \Lambda_0$.

First we prove

(a) *If* S^2 *is a polyhedral 2-sphere in* $°(M_0^2 \times I)$, *then* S^2 *bounds a 3-cell in* $°(M_0^2 \times I)$; *i.e.,* $M_0^2 \times I$ *is irreducible (N.B.,* M_0^2 *is not a 2-sphere).*

Proof:† Let us assume that S^2 does not bound a 3-cell in $°(M_0^2 \times I)$. Then, by isotopic deformations and ρ-operations (by the same procedure as described in the proof of Lemma 3 in Sec. 4), we may derive from S^2 a 2-sphere S'^2 that intersects the 3-dimensional elements of Λ in open disks, intersects the 2-dimensional elements of Λ in open piercing arcs, each of which has its end points in two different 1-dimensional elements of Λ, and intersects the 1-dimensional elements of Λ in isolated piercing points. This 2-sphere S'^2 can be found such that it does not bound a 3-cell in $°(M_0^2 \times I)$ since a ρ-operation transforms a 2-sphere which does not bound a 3-cell into two 2-spheres, not both of which bound 3-cells.

Now we observe that those 2-dimensional elements of Λ that lie in $M_0^2 \times °I$ are open rectangles $W^1 \times °I$ $(W^1 \in \Lambda_0)$; hence, we may conclude that S'^2 intersects all edges $p \times °I (p \in \Lambda_0)$ in the same number, say s, of points and that it intersects each 2-dimensional element $W^1 \times °I (W^1 \in \Lambda_0)$ in s open arcs; from this it follows that S'^2 intersects each 3-dimensional element $W^2 \times °I (W^2 \in \Lambda_0)$ in s open disks and, furthermore, that S'^2 itself consists of s connected components, each of which is homeomorphic to M_0^2. This is a contradiction to our hypothesis that M_0^2 is not a 2-sphere; hence, our assumption that S^2 does not bound a 3-cell is wrong, and statement (a) is proved.

Now, as we shall show in the next paragraph, we may derive from M^2 an isotopic surface M'^2 with the following properties:

(α) M'^2 is isotopic to M^2 in $M_0^2 \times I$ with respect to $\dot{}M_0^2 \times I$.

(β) If K is a connected component of $M'^2 \cap (\overline{W}^1 \times °I)$, where $W^1 \in \Lambda_0$, then (see Fig. 28) $°K \subset W^1 \times °I$ and either

---

† For another proof, see [6a], Lemma 15.

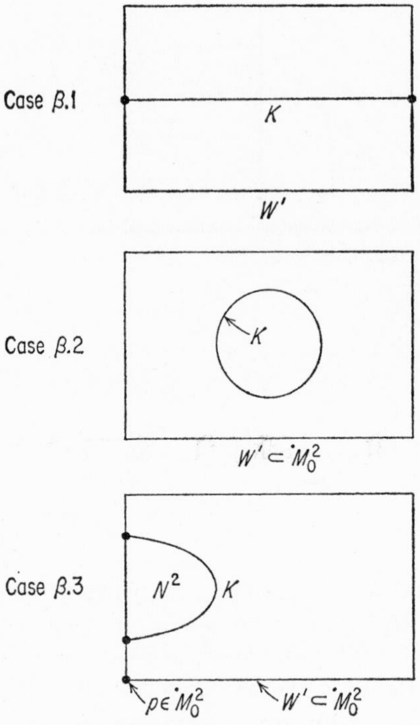

FIG. 28

Case β.1: K is an arc with end points in different 1-dimensional elements of Λ,

Case β.2: W^1 lies in $\dot{}M_0^2$, and K is a simple closed curve, or

Case β.3: W^1 lies in $^\circ M_0^2$, a point $p \in \dot{}W^1$ lies in $\dot{}M_0^2$, and K is an arc with $\dot{}K \subset p \times {}^\circ I$.

(γ) If K is a connected component of $M'^2 \cap (\overline{W}^2 \times {}^\circ I)$, where $W^2 \in \Lambda_0$, then K is a disk with $^\circ K \subset W^2 \times {}^\circ I$ such that either

Case γ.1: $\dot{}K$ intersects each $\overline{W}^1 \times {}^\circ I$, with $W^1 \subset \dot{}W^2$, $W^1 \in \Lambda_0$, in just one arc (corresponding to Case β.1),

Case γ.2: $\dot{}K$ lies in $^\circ(\dot{}W^2 \cap \dot{}M_0^2) \times {}^\circ I$ (and is a closed curve corresponding to Case β.2), or

Case γ.3: (See Fig. 29.) $\dot{}W^2 \cap \dot{}M_0^2$ is the closure of an edge

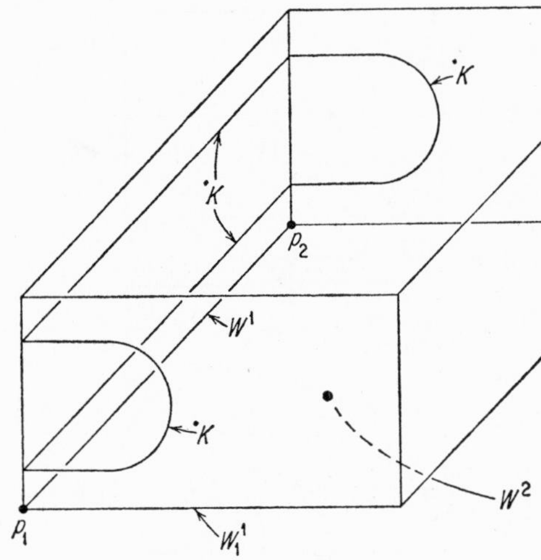

FIG. 29

$W^1 \in \Lambda_0$ with end points p_1 and p_2, there are two edges W_1^1, W_2^1 of Λ_0 in $\dot{W}^2 - \dot{M}_0^2$ incident to p_1, p_2, respectively, and $\dot{K} \cap (\overline{W}_1^1 \times {}^\circ I)$, $\dot{K} \cap (\overline{W}_2^1 \times {}^\circ I)$ are arcs with end points in $p_1 \times {}^\circ I$, $p_2 \times {}^\circ I$, respectively (corresponding to Case β.3); and $\dot{K} \cap (\overline{W}^1 \times {}^\circ I)$ consists of two arcs (corresponding to Case β.1).

We may obtain M'^2 from M^2 by the same procedure as described in the proof of Lemma 3 in Sec. 4, with the exception that we do not carry out the $\dot{\rho}$-operations and consequently do not achieve the "nice position with respect to Λ" in all details. We carry out Steps i and ii as in the proof of Lemma 3, the only exception being that we may have closed curves in disks of Λ that lie in $\dot{M}_0^2 \times {}^\circ I$ (since M^2 is not necessarily boundary-incompressible). We remove by ρ-operations only those closed curves that lie in disks in ${}^\circ M_0^2 \times {}^\circ I$. Since $M_0^2 \times I$ is irreducible [see statement (a)], a ρ-operation yields a surface which is isotopic to M^2 and a compressible 2-sphere; hence, Step ii yields a surface isotopic to M^2. We carry out Step iii in the Cases A and B which are treated by isotopic deformations, but not in Case C which requires $\dot{\rho}$-operations. After these steps, the 2-dimensional elements of Λ are intersected in three possible types of curves as described under (β). Then we carry out Step iv as in the proof of Lemma 3. In this way we obtain M'^2. If W^2 is an element of Λ_0, then $M'^2 \cap (\dot{W}^2 \times {}^\circ I)$ consists of closed curves of three possible types as described under (γ); hence, M'^2 has the required properties.

If M'^2 contains a disk, corresponding to Case γ.1, then we may conclude (since M'^2 is connected) that it intersects each 3-dimensional element of Λ in just one open disk corresponding to Case γ.1 [compare the second paragraph of the proof of statement (a)] and, hence, that Case 1 of the assertion holds.

If M'^2 contains a disk corresponding to Case γ.2, then (since M'^2 is connected) M'^2 is equal to this disk and Case 2 of the assertion holds.

If M'^2 contains a disk corresponding to Case γ.3 (Fig. 29), then M'^2 is a union of disks of that type. Hence M'^2 is an annulus, and the closure of that connected component of $(M_0^2 \times I) - M'^2$ that is disjoint from M_0^2 is a solid torus T^3. If $W^1 \in \Lambda_0$ lies in ${}^\circ M_0^2$ and possesses an end point $p \in \dot{M}_0^2$ (see Fig. 28, Case β.3), then $T^3 \cap (W^1 \times I)$ is a meridian disk N^2 of T^3 whose boundary intersects each of M'^2 and $\dot{T}^3 - {}^\circ M'^2$ in just one arc. Hence Case 3 of the assertion holds. This finishes the proof of the lemma.

BIBLIOGRAPHY

[1] Alexander, J. W., "On the subdivision of polyhedra in 3-space," *Proc. Nat. Acad. Sci.*, **10** (1924), 6–8.

[2] Alexandroff, P., and H. Hopf, *Topologie* I. Berlin: Z. Springer-Verlag, 1935.

[3] Bing, R. H., "Necessary and sufficient conditions that a 3-manifold be S^3," *Ann. Math.*, **68** (1958), 17–37.

[4] ———, "An alternative proof that 3-manifolds can be triangulated," *Ann. Math.*, **69** (1959), 37–65.

[5] Brown, M., "A proof of the generalized Schoenflies theorem," *Bull. Am. Math. Soc.*, **66** (1960), 74–76.

[6] ———, "The monotone union of open n-cells is an open n-cell," *Notices Am. Math. Soc.*, **7** (1960), 478.

[6a] Edwards, C. H., Jr., "Concentricity in 3-manifolds," *Trans. Am. Math. Soc.*, **113** (1964), 406–23.

[7] Fox, R. H., "On the imbedding of polyhedra in 3-space," *Ann. Math.*, **49** (1948), 462–70.

[8] Haken, W., "Theorie der Normalflächen," *Acta Math.*, **105** (1961), 245–375.

[9] ———, "Ein Verfahren zur Aufspaltung einer 3-Mannigfaltigkeit in irreduzible 3-Mannigfaltigkeiten," *Math. Zeit.*, **76** (1961), 427–67.

[10] ———, "Über das Homöomorphieproblem der 3-Mannigfaltigkeiten I," *Math. Zeit.*, **80** (1962), 89–120.

[10a] ———, "Trivial loops in homotopy 3-spheres," *Illinois J. Math.*, **11** (1967), 547–554.

[11] Kister, J. M., and D. R. McMillan, Jr., "Locally Euclidean factors of E^4 which cannot be imbedded in E^3," *Ann. Math.*, **76** (1962), 541–46.

[12] Kneser, H., "Geschlossene Flächen in dreidimensionalen Mannigfaltigkeiten," *Jber. D.M.V.*, **38** (1929), 248–60.

[13] McMillan, D. R., Jr., "Cartesian products of contractible open manifolds," *Bull. Am. Math. Soc.*, **67** (1961), 510–14.

[14] ———, "Some contractible open 3-manifolds," *Trans. Am. Math. Soc.*, **102** (1962), 373–82.

[15] Markov, A. A., "Insolvability of the problem of homeomorphy," *Proc. Intern. Cong. Math.*, 1958, Cambridge, 300–306.

[16] Milnor, J. W., "A unique decomposition theorem for 3-manifolds," *Am. Jour. Math.*, **84** (1962), 1–7.

[17] Moise, E. E., "Affine structures in 3-manifolds V: The triangulation theorem and Hauptvermutung," *Ann. Math.*, **56** (1952), 96–114.

[18] Papakyriakopoulos, C. D., "On Dehn's lemma and the asphericity of knots," *Ann. Math.*, **66** (1957), 1–26.

[19] Poincaré, H., "Cinquième complément à l'Analysis Situs," *Rend. Circ. Mat. Palermo*, **18** (1904), 45–110.

[20] Reidemeister, K., "Homotopieringe und Linsenräume," *Abh. Math. Sem. Hambg.*, **11** (1935), 102–109.

[21] ———, *Topologie der Polyeder und kombinatorische Topologie der Komplexe*. Leipzig, Akad. Verlagsgesellschaft, 1953.

[22] Schubert, H., "Die eindeutige Zerlegbarkeit eines Knotens in Primknoten," *Sitzungsber. Heidelbg. Akad. Wiss., Math.-Naturw. Kl.*, **3** (1949), 57–104.

[23] ———, "Knoten und Vollringe," *Acta Math.*, **90** (1953), 131–286.

[24] ———, "Bestimmung der Primfaktorzerlegung von Verkettungen," *Math. Zeit.*, **76** (1961), 116–48.

[25] Seifert, H., and W. Threlfall, *Lehrbuch der Topologie*. Leipzig: Akad. Verlagsgesellschaft, B. G. Teubner, 1934.

[26] Smale, S., "Generalized Poincaré's conjecture in dimensions greater than four," *Ann. Math.*, **74** (1961), 391–406.

[27] Stallings, J. W., "Polyhedral homotopy spheres," *Bull. Am. Math. Soc.*, **66** (1960), 485–88.

[28] Whitehead, J. H. C., "A certain open manifold whose group is unity," *Quart. Jour. Math. Oxford*, **6** (1935), 268–79.

[29] ———, "Simplicial spaces, nuclei, and *m*-groups," *Proc. London Math. Soc.*, **45** (1939), 243–327.

[30] Zeeman, E. C., "Polyhedral *n*-manifolds: I. Foundations, II. Embeddings," *Topology of 3-Manifolds and Related Topics*. Englewood Cliffs, N.J. Prentice-Hall, Inc., 1962, 57–64 and 64–70.

[31] ———, "The Poincaré conjecture for $n \geqq 5$," *ibid.*, 198–204.

SEMISIMPLICIAL HOMOTOPY THEORY

V. K. A. M. Gugenheim

INTRODUCTION

In the following article, I have tried to give an account of some of the principal results of semisimplicial homotopy theory. I have given few proofs, but I have tried to arrange the theorems in such a way that the logical sequence should be reasonably clear; and references to the original papers are always given.

The account is far from complete, even for the subjects taken up; I have entirely omitted the theory of spectra—and the interesting applications to differential and combinatorial topology.

Apart from the published papers, I am very much indebted to Daniel Kan, both for verbal and written suggestions, as well as a mimeographed set of his recent lectures at Massachusetts Institute of Technology.

1. FOUNDATIONS

When one constructs the homology theory of a simplicial complex or of a topological space using either the singular theory, the Čech theory, or one of its variants, then one inevitably encounters a certain combinatorial scheme associated with the idea of "taking the faces" of a simplex.

The idea of a c.s.s. (complete semisimplicial) complex is the result of abstracting this scheme.

We begin, however, with an even more general definition in which the underlying "objects" are not necessarily sets, but the objects of an arbitrary category.

The use of a variety of categories—sets, groups, abelian groups—will turn out to be essential in the development of our subject.

1.1 DEFINITIONS AND NOTATIONS (cf. Kan [4]) For each integer $n \geq 0$, let $[n]$ denote the ordered set $(0, 1, 2, \ldots, n)$. We consider the category $\mathcal{V}$ whose objects are $[n]$ for each $n \geq 0$ and whose maps are all monotonic functions

$$\alpha : [m] \longrightarrow [n], \quad \text{i.e., such that } i \leq j \text{ implies } \quad \alpha(i) \leq \alpha(j).$$

Let $\mathcal{C}$ be any category. By $\mathcal{C}^v$ we denote the category of all contravariant functors $\mathcal{V} \longrightarrow \mathcal{C}$. In other words, an object K of $\mathcal{C}^v$ is a contravariant functor $K : \mathcal{V} \longrightarrow \mathcal{C}$; a map $f: K \longrightarrow L$ of $\mathcal{C}^v$ is a transformation of functors. We shall invariably write K_n for $K[n]$ and f_n for $f[n]$. A map $\alpha: [m] \longrightarrow [n]$ induces $K(\alpha): K_n \longrightarrow K_m$.

Mostly, we shall be concerned with the following categories:

$\mathfrak{M}$, the category of sets;
$\mathcal{G}$, " groups;
$\mathcal{A}$, " abelian groups;
$\mathcal{A}_\Lambda$, " Λ-modules;

where Λ is a commutative ring with unit. We write Z for the ring of integers, so that $\mathcal{A}_Z = \mathcal{A}$.

It will be convenient to take the view that every abelian group is a group and every group is a set; in other words, we shall consider

$$\mathcal{A} \subset \mathcal{G} \subset \mathfrak{M}.$$

The last "inclusion" is really a "forgetful" functor. Accordingly, we shall also consider

$$\mathfrak{A}^v \subset \mathfrak{G}^v \subset \mathfrak{M}^v.$$

The objects of $\mathfrak{M}^v$, $\mathfrak{G}^v$, $\mathfrak{A}^v$ will be called *set-complexes, group-complexes,* and *commutative group-complexes,* respectively.

The structure of the category $\mathcal{V}$ is best examined by considering the maps

$$\epsilon_n^i : [n] \longrightarrow [n+1] \qquad (0 \le i \le n+1) \qquad (n \ge 0)$$

$$\eta_n^i : [n] \longrightarrow [n-1] \qquad (0 \le i \le n-1) \qquad (n > 0)$$

defined as follows: ϵ_n^i is the strictly increasing map which omits the value i; η_n^i is strictly increasing except for repeating the value i.

Let $K \in \mathcal{C}^v$. We write

$$\partial_i = K(\epsilon_n^i) : K_{n+1} \longrightarrow K_n$$

$$s_i = K(\eta_n^i) : K_{n-1} \longrightarrow K_n.$$

The notation ∂_i, s_i is, or course, highly elliptical; we should write $\partial_i^n(K)$ or at least ∂_i^n, but the shortened notation causes no ambiguities.

The maps ϵ_n^i, η_n^i satisfy certain identities when compositions of two such maps are considered; these lead to the following set of c.s.s. *identities:*

$$\left.\begin{aligned} \partial_i \partial_j &= \partial_{j-1} \partial_i && \text{when } i < j \\ \partial_i s_j &= s_{j-1} \partial_i && \text{" } i < j \\ &= \text{identity} && \text{" } i = j, j+1 \\ &= s_j \partial_{i-1} && \text{" } i > j+1 \\ s_i s_j &= s_j s_{i-1} && \text{" } i > j \end{aligned}\right\} \quad \text{(c.s.s.)}$$

It is clear that any map of $\mathcal{V}$ can be expressed as a composition of maps of type ϵ_n^i, η_n^i for suitable i, n. Hence $K \in \mathcal{C}^v$ is determined if we are given the functions ∂_i, s_i. This leads to a second definition of the category $\mathcal{C}^v$.

An object of $\mathcal{C}^v$ is a sequence $\{K_n\}$ $(n \ge 0)$, where K_n is an object of $\mathcal{C}$, together with maps

$$\partial_i : K_n \longrightarrow K_{n-1} \quad (0 \leq i \leq n, n > 0),$$
$$s_i : K_n \longrightarrow K_{n+1} \quad (0 \leq i \leq n, n \geq 0)$$

satisfying the identities (c.s.s.).

A map $F : K \longrightarrow L$ is a sequence $\{F_n : K_n \longrightarrow L_n\}$ of maps of $\mathcal{C}$ such that $\partial_i F_n = F_{n-1}\partial_i$, $s_i F_n = F_{n+1}s_i$.

The maps ∂_i are called *face operators,* the maps s_i, *degeneracy operators,* and if $a \in K_n$, $\partial_i a (0 \leq i \leq n)$ are called the *faces* of a. An element which can be written as $s_i b$ for some i and some b is called *degenerate.*

The new definition is easier to visualize and frequently the most useful one to deal with; it was essentially the original definition of $\mathfrak{M}^v$ in Eilenberg and Zilber [1]. This was obtained from the two classical examples, the *ordered* complex of a simplicial complex and the *singular theory.* In the former the objects are ordered sets of "vertices," and δ_i and s_i defined by omitting or repeating a vertex; the latter we shall consider formally in Sec. 1.3.

1.2 Let Λ be a commutative ring with unit. We shall define the functor $\Lambda: \mathfrak{M}^v \to \mathfrak{A}_\Lambda^v$ as follows: If $K \in \mathfrak{M}^v$, $(\Lambda K)_n$ is the free Λ-module generated by K_n; and ∂_i, s_i are the maps of Λ-modules induced by the corresponding maps of $\mathfrak{M}$.

1.3 THE SINGULAR COMPLEX For each $n \geq 0$, let us choose, once and for all, a fixed Euclidean n-simplex $|\Delta|^n$ with the vertices ordered in a certain way. Then, corresponding to ϵ_n^i, η_n^i (cf. Sec. 1.1), there are affine maps

$$|\epsilon^i| : |\Delta^n| \longrightarrow |\Delta^{n+1}|$$
$$|\eta^i| : |\Delta^n| \longrightarrow |\Delta^{n-1}|$$

Let X be a topological space. We define S_nX as the set of all (continuous) maps $|\Delta^n| \longrightarrow X$; and the functions

$$\partial_i : S_nX \longrightarrow S_{n-1}X, \qquad s_i : S_nX \longrightarrow S_{n+1}X$$

by

$$\partial_i T = T\epsilon^i \qquad s_i T = T\eta^i.$$

It is clear that SX, namely $\{S_nX\}$ together with the functions thus defined, is an object of $\mathfrak{M}^v$; and S is easily seen to define a functor

$$S : \mathfrak{J} \longrightarrow \mathfrak{M}^v$$

where $\mathfrak{T}$ is the category of topological spaces. S is called the *singular functor.*

1.4 HOMOLOGY By $d\mathcal{A}_\Lambda$ (or $d\mathcal{A}$ if $\Lambda = Z$) we denote the category of positive graded differential Λ-modules. Thus, an object $A = \{A_n, d_n\}$ of $d\mathcal{A}$ is a sequence of Λ-modules A_n such that $A_n = 0$ for $n < 0$ together with homomorphisms of Λ-modules $d_n : A_n \longrightarrow A_{n-1}$ such that $d_n d_{n+1} = 0$. A map $F = \{F_n : A_n \longrightarrow B_n\}$ is a sequence of maps such that $d_n f_n = f_n d_{n+1}$.

In a well-known manner there is defined the homology functor

$$H : d\mathcal{A} \longrightarrow \mathcal{A}_\Lambda^+$$

where $\mathcal{A}_\Lambda^+$ denotes the category of positive graded Λ-modules. We regard this construction as known, together with its familiar extension to pairs.

1.5 We now define, classically, a functor

$$T : \mathcal{A}_\Lambda^v \longrightarrow d\mathcal{A}_\Lambda$$

(T stands for *total,* cf. Sec. 6).

For $A \in \mathcal{A}_\Lambda^v$, $(TA)_n = A_n$ and d_n: $(TA)_n \longrightarrow (TA)_{n-1}$ is defined by

$$d_n = \sum_{i=0}^{n} (-1)^i \partial i.$$

Then

$$d_{n+1} d_n = 0$$

follows from Sec. 1.1 (c.s.s.).

1.51 We shall use the following customary abbreviations:

If $A \in \mathfrak{M}^v$, $\qquad H(A; \Lambda) = HT\Lambda A$

If $X \in \tau$, $\qquad H(X; \Lambda) = H(SX; \Lambda) = HT\Lambda SX$

and, finally,

$$H(A) = H(A; Z), \qquad H(X) = H(X; Z).$$

2. PSEUDOGEOMETRIC HOMOTOPY THEORY

2.1 THE MODELS In the category $\mathfrak{M}^v$ we define certain objects Δ^n which are analogous to the simplexes $|\Delta^n|$ in the category of spaces; for an explanation of our notation Δ^n, $|\Delta^n|$, see Sec. 3.

Thus Δ^n is the contravariant functor $\mathcal{V} \longrightarrow \mathfrak{M}$ defined by letting $\Delta^n[p] = \Delta^n_p$ be the set of all maps $[p] \longrightarrow [n]$ of $\mathcal{V}$. If $\alpha : [p] \longrightarrow [q]$ is a map of $\mathcal{V}$, $\Delta^n(\alpha)$ is defined by $\Delta^n(\alpha)\phi = \phi\alpha$ for $\phi \in \Delta^n_q$. We denote by $\delta^n \in \Delta^n_n$ the identity $[n] \longrightarrow [n]$; since $\phi = \delta^n\phi$, we see that Δ^n is "freely generated" by applying c.s.s. operators, cf. Sec. 1.1, to δ^n. If A is an object of $\mathfrak{M}^v$, $a \in A_n$ defines a unique map $\tilde{a} : \Delta^n \longrightarrow A$ by $\tilde{a}\,\delta^n = a$. The maps ϵ^i_n, η^i_n of Sec. 1.1 induce maps

$$\epsilon^i_n : \Delta^n \longrightarrow \Delta^{n+1}$$

$$\eta^i_n : \Delta^n \longrightarrow \Delta^{n-1}.$$

2.11 LEMMA:

$$\begin{aligned} H_i(T\Lambda\Delta^n) &= 0 \quad \textit{if} \quad i > 0 \\ &= \Lambda \quad \textit{if} \quad i = 0. \end{aligned}$$

2.2 THE CARTESIAN PRODUCT Let K, $L \in \mathfrak{M}^v$. We define $K \times L \in \mathfrak{M}^v$ by

$$(K \times L)_n = K_n \times L_n \quad \text{with} \quad \partial_i(k, l) = (\partial_i k, \partial_i l),$$
$$s_i(k, l) = (s_i k, s_i l), \quad \text{if} \quad f{:}\,K \longrightarrow K',\ g{:}\,L \longrightarrow L'$$

are maps of $\mathfrak{M}^v$, we define

$$f \times g{:}\,K \times L \longrightarrow K' \times L' \quad \text{by} \quad f \times g(k, l) = (fk, gl).$$

If X, Y are topological spaces, then, with an evident identification, $S(X \times Y) = S(X) \times S(Y)$.

2.3 HOMOTOPY Let us write $I = \Delta^1$, cf. Sec. 2.1. It is easily seen that Δ^1_0 consists of two elements, which we denote by $0 = \partial_1\,\delta^1$, $1 = \partial_0\,\delta^1$. We shall denote also by 0, 1 the elements of $\Delta^1_p = I_p$ obtained from these by degeneracy; i.e. $0 = s^p_0 0$, $1 = s^p_0 1$.

Let $F : I \times A \longrightarrow B$ be a map of $\mathfrak{M}^v$. We define the maps $F_0, F_1 : A \longrightarrow B$, also of $\mathfrak{M}^v$, as follows: If $a \in A_p$,

$$F_0 a = F(0, a), \qquad F_1(a) = F(1, a).$$

2.31 DEFINITION: *Let f, $g : A \longrightarrow B$ be maps of $\mathfrak{M}^v$. We say that f, g are homotopic, $f \sim g$, if there is a map $F : I \times A \longrightarrow B$, called "a homotopy" such that $F_0 = f$, $F_1 = g$.*

Unfortunately, the relation $\sim$ is not an equivalence relation. To understand the source of the difficulty, let us examine the question of transitivity in the simplest possible case, $A = \Delta^0$. We are given, in effect, maps $F, G : I \longrightarrow B$ such that $F(1) = G(0)$. This, cf. Sec. 2.1, is to be given $F(\delta^1) = b \in B_1$ and $G(\delta^1) = b' \in B_1$ such that $\partial_0 b = \partial_1 b'$. What transitivity requires is the existence of $b'' \in B_1$ such that

$$\partial_1 b'' = \partial_1 b, \qquad \partial_0 b'' = \partial_0 b'.$$

In general, no such element exists.

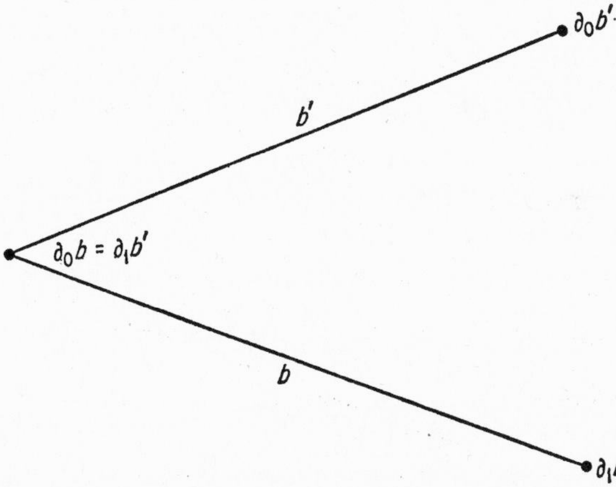

It was first observed by Daniel M. Kan that this difficulty is best overcome by adding an axiom assuring the existence, in this situation, of an element $c \in B_2$ such that $b = \partial_2 c$, $b' = \partial_0 c$. In this case, $\partial_1 c = b''$ satisfies the required condition:

$$\partial_1 b'' = \partial_1 \partial_1 c = \partial_1 \partial_2 c = \partial_1 b$$

$$\partial_0 b'' = \partial_0 \partial_1 c = \partial_0 \partial_0 c = \partial_0 b'.$$

What we have introduced is a property which the singular complex SX of a space X owes to the fact that two sides of a triangle are a retract of that triangle. Similarly, n faces of an n-simplex are a retract of that simplex; hence SX satisfies the following:

2.32 KAN CONDITION: *Given, in a set-complex* $A \in \mathfrak{M}^v$, *elements* $a_0, \ldots, a_{i-1}, a_{i+1}, \ldots, a_n \in A_{n-1}$ *such that*

$$\partial_k a_l = \partial_{l-1} a_k \qquad (k < l; k, l \neq i);$$

then there exists $a \in A_n$ *such that*

$$a_j = \partial_i a \qquad (j \neq i).$$

2.33 DEFINITION: *An object of* $\mathfrak{M}^v$ *satisfying Sec.* 2.32 *is called a "Kan complex."* $\mathfrak{M}_E^v \subset \mathfrak{M}^v$ *denotes the full subcategory whose objects are Kan complexes: E stands for "extension."*

The effect of the "extension condition," Sec. 2.32, is to make the relation of homotopy, Sec. 2.31, an equivalence relation and, indeed, to make possible analogues of all the geometric constructions of elementary homotopy theory. For instance, the example we discussed shows how to "add" paths, i.e., 1-simplexes, in a Kan complex and, thus, to construct the fundamental group.

More generally, let $A \in \mathfrak{M}_E^v$ and $a_0 \in A_0$. The set of all homotopy classes of maps $\Delta^n \longrightarrow A$ such that Δ_p^n for $p < n$ is mapped into a_0 and its degeneration is denoted by $\pi_n(A, a_0)$. If $n > 0$, it is a group; if $n > 1$, the group is abelian.

The proofs are easy analogues of the geometric case—the Kan condition providing all necessary extensions of maps; cf., for example, Moore [2] and Gugenheim [1].

Note: When the base point is irrelevant or evident from the context, we shall write $\pi_n(A)$ for $\pi_n(A, a_0)$. If $A \in A^v$ or G^v, the notation $\pi_n(A)$ will mean $\pi_n(A, 0)$ or $\pi_n(A, 1)$, A being interpreted as a set complex; cf. Secs. 2.35 and 1.1.

Fibre spaces are defined by replacing the "extension" condition of Sec. 2.31 by a "lifting" condition; namely,

2.34 DEFINITION: *The map* $\pi : E \longrightarrow B$ *of* $\mathfrak{M}^v$ *is called a fiber map if*

(i) *It is onto, i.e.,* π_n *is onto for all* $n \geq 0$.

(ii) *Given* $e_0, \ldots, e_{i-1}, e_{i+1}, \ldots, e_n \in E_{n-1}$, *and* $b \in B_n$ *such that*

$$\partial_k e_j = \partial_{j-1} e_k \qquad (k < j)$$

$$\pi e_j = \partial_j b,$$

then there exists $e \in E_n$ *such that*

$$\partial_j e = e_j, \qquad \pi e = b.$$

2.35 PROPOSITION (Moore):

(i) *All group complexes satisfy the Kan condition.*

(ii) *Every epimorphism of* G^v *is a fiber map in the sense of Sec. 2.34.*

Proof: This is proved by an induction on dimension: Using group operations and degeneracies, it is possible to write down the required elements.

If $E' \longrightarrow B'$ is a fibration in the sense of Serre, then $S(E') \longrightarrow S(B')$ is a fibration in the sense of Sec. 2.34.

If $\pi: E \longrightarrow B$ is a fiber map and $E, B \in \mathfrak{M}_E^v$, then all the customary properties of fibrations, in particular the exact homotopy sequence and the spectral sequence for homology, can be deduced by easy analogy with the geometric proofs.

If X is a topological space and $x_0 \in X$, it is almost obvious from our definitions that $\pi_p(X, x_0) = \pi_p(SX, x_0)$, where x_0 on the right-hand side is regarded as an element of $(SX)_0$.

2.4 A useful notion in the pseudogeometric theory which has no analogue in the geometric one is that of a *minimal complex.*

Suppose $a_0, a_1 \in A_n$ are two elements of a set-complex such that $\partial_i a_0 = \partial_i a_1$ for $0 \leq i \leq n$. We say that a_0, a_1 are homotopic if there is a map $F : I \times \Delta^n \longrightarrow A$ such that (cf., Secs. 2.1 and 2.3) $F_0 \delta^n = a_0$, $F_1 \delta^n = a_1$, and F is "constant on the boundary"; i.e., $F(t, x) = F_0(x)$ if $t \in I_p$, $x \in \Delta_p^n$ and x is contained in the subcomplex of Δ^n generated by its faces.

2.41 DEFINITION: $M \in \mathfrak{M}^v$ *is called minimal if homotopic elements are identical.*

2.42 PROPOSITION: *If* $A \in \mathfrak{M}_E^v$, *there is a subcomplex* M *which is minimal and a deformation retract of* A.

Note that in view of the remarks in Sec. 2.3 we can use words like *deformation retract, homotopy type*, etc., without difficulty in the category $\mathfrak{M}_E^v$.

Proof: To prove this proposition one proceeds by induction on dimension and simply removes, step by step, "redundant" simplexes.

2.43 Proposition: *Let M, N be minimal complexes of $\mathfrak{M}_E^v$, and $f : M \longrightarrow N$ a map which induces isomorphisms in all homotopy groups. Then f is an isomorphism.*

This is fairly obvious; from the point of homotopy, neither M nor N contains anything "unnecessary."

Hence minimal complexes are of the same homotopy type if and only if they are isomorphic. We obtain easily the c.s.s. analogue of a theorem of J. H. C. Whitehead:

2.44 Corollary: *Let $M, N \in \mathfrak{M}_E^v$ and $f : M \longrightarrow N$ induce isomorphisms of all homotopy groups. Then f is a homotopy equivalence.*

2.5 Let $\pi : E \rightarrow B$ be a fiber space in the sense of Sec. 2.34, and let $E \in \mathfrak{M}_E^v$. We can define for elements $e_0, e_1 \in E_n$ such that $\pi e_0 = \pi e_1$ and $\partial_i e_0 = \partial_i e_1$ a similar notion of *homotopy* by adding the condition that $\pi F : I \times \Delta^n \longrightarrow B$ should be "constant," i.e., independent of the first coordinate. Using this definition as in Sec. 2.41, we obtain the idea of a "minimal fiber space"; and an analogue of Sec. 2.42 allows us to replace every fiber space by a minimal deformation retract; see Barratt, Gugenheim, and Moore [1]. It turns out that minimal fiber spaces have a particularly simple structure, they are "twisted Cartesian products":

2.51 Definition: *(E, B, F, ξ, Γ) is called a "twisted Cartesian product" if*

(i) $E, B, F \in \mathfrak{M}^v$, $\quad \Gamma \in \mathcal{G}^v$.
(ii) $E_n = B_n \times F_n$ $\quad$ *as a set.*
(iii) $\xi : B_n \longrightarrow \Gamma_{n-1}$ $\quad (n \geq 1)$

is a set of functions satisfying

$$\partial_i \xi = \xi \partial_{i+1} \qquad (i > 0)$$

$$\partial_0 \xi(b) = [\xi(\partial_0 b)]^{-1} [\xi(\partial_1 b)]$$

$$s_i \xi = \xi s_{i+1} \qquad (i \geq 0)$$

$$\xi s_0 b = 1 \qquad (\textit{i.e., the identity element of the group}).$$

(iv) Γ *operates on F; i.e., there is given a map $\Gamma \times F \longrightarrow F$ of*

$\mathfrak{M}^v$, *written* $\gamma \times f \longrightarrow \gamma f$, *such that* $1f = f$ *and* $\gamma'(\gamma F) = (\gamma'\gamma)F$.

(v) *The face and degeneracy operations in* E *are given by*

$$\partial_0(b, f) = (\partial_0 b,\ \xi(b)\ \partial_0 F)$$

$$\partial_i(b, f) = (\partial_i b, \partial_i f) \qquad (i > 0)$$

$$s_i(b, f) = (s_i b,\ s_i f) \qquad (i \leq 0)$$

A brief and convenient notation for this situation is $E = B \times F$.

If $F = \Gamma$ and the operation of condition (iv) is the group operation of Γ, we refer to a *principal* twisted Cartesian product.

2.52 Proposition: *If* F *is a Kan complex, the map* $E \longrightarrow B$ *given by* $(b, f) \longrightarrow b$ *is a fiber map.*

For all details of this theory, see Barratt, Gugenheim, and Moore [1].

Since the homotopy and homology of a fiber space are those of its singular complex—which is that of a minimal subfiber space which is a twisted Cartesian product—these products form a convenient tool in the study of fiber spaces. See, for example, Gugenheim [2], Shih-Weishuh [1].

3. THE REALIZATION

(The theory of the present chapter is due to J. Milnor [1].)

Let A be a set-complex; i.e. $A \in \mathfrak{M}^v$. If for each $a \in A_n$ we choose a Euclidean n-simplex and then use the face and degeneracy relations of A to make identifications, we find a CW-complex $|A|$ called the *realization* of A. [A CW-complex is a cell complex topologized by the requirement that a set is closed if its intersection with each cell is (relatively) closed (cf. Whitehead [1]). A map $f : A \longrightarrow B$ of $\mathfrak{M}^v$ leads to a continuous (indeed a "cellular") map $|f| : |A| \longrightarrow |B|$. We then have a covariant functor

$$|\ \ | : \mathfrak{M}^v \longrightarrow \mathfrak{I}$$

where $\mathfrak{I}$ is the category of topological spaces; for all details, see Milnor [1] or Puppe [1].

Let $A \in \mathfrak{M}^v$ and $X \in \mathfrak{I}$. For every map $A \longrightarrow S(X)$ of $\mathfrak{M}^v$, it is easy to construct a map $|A| \longrightarrow X$, and vice versa. We thus find a natural equivalence

3.0 $$\text{Hom}(A, SX) = \text{Hom}(|A|, X)$$

expressing the fact that the functors S and $|\ \ |$ are "adjoint"; cf. Kan [5]. It follows that each of S, $|\ \ |$ uniquely determines the other.

Let $A, B \in \mathfrak{M}^v$ and $p_1 : A \times B \longrightarrow A$, $p_2 : A \times B \longrightarrow B$ the projections. Then we define

$$\eta : |A \times B| \longrightarrow |A| \times |B|$$

by $\eta x = (|p_1|x, |p_2|x)$.

3.1 Proposition: *If either A, B are countable or one of A,B is a locally finite* CW-*complex, then η is a homeomorphism.*

For a slightly more general statement, see Puppe [1], Satz 5.

3.11 Corollary: *A homotopy $F : I \times A \longrightarrow B$ of $\mathfrak{M}^v$ induces a homotopy*

$$|I| \times |A| \longrightarrow |B| \quad \textit{of} \quad \mathfrak{J}.$$

3.12 Corollary: *If A is a countable object of $\mathcal{G}^v$ or $\mathfrak{A}^v$ (i.e., a countable group-complex or a countable commutative group-complex) then $|A|$ is a topological group or commutative topological group, respectively.*

The elements of $A \in \mathfrak{M}^v$ can be regarded (using the identity maps of the simplexes used for the realization) as elements of $S(|A|)$. We thus obtain an injection

$$i : A \longrightarrow S(|A|).$$

If X is a topological space, every point of $|S(X)|$ determines in an evident way a point of X. We thus find a continuous map

$$j : |S(X)| \longrightarrow X.$$

It is easily seen that

$$S(j)i : S(X) \longrightarrow S(X)$$

is the identity.

3.2 Proposition:

(i) *i induces an isomorphism of homology groups.*

(ii) *If A is a Kan complex, i induces an isomorphism of homotopy groups.*

(iii) *j induces an isomorphism of singular homology and homotopy groups.*

3.3 Let $A \in \mathfrak{M}^v$. Then $S(|A|) \in \mathfrak{M}^v_E$. We thus obtain a functor

$$S|\quad| : \mathfrak{M}^v \longrightarrow \mathfrak{M}^v_E$$

and we can define, for any $A \in \mathfrak{M}^v$ and $a_0 \in A_0$,

$$\pi_n(A, a_0) = \pi_n(S|A|, S(a_0)) = \pi_n(|A|, |a_0|)$$

It follows from condition (ii) in Sec. 3.2 that if A is a Kan complex, this definition is consistent with the earlier one.

Note: Another functor $\mathfrak{M}^v \longrightarrow \mathfrak{M}^v_E$ accomplishing the same thing and constructed by purely combinatorial means is given in Kan [3].

4. MOORE-POSTNIKOV SYSTEMS

The theory of the present chapter is due to J. A. Zilber (unpublished), M. M. Postnikov [1], and J. C. Moore [1]; we present the theory in the form given by Moore.

4.1 Definition: *Let X be an object of $\mathfrak{M}^v$. For $n \geq 0$, $X^{(n)} \in \mathfrak{M}^v$ is defined as follows:*

(i) *A q-simplex of $X^{(n)}$ is an equivalence class of q-simplexes of X, two q-simplexes being equivalent if their faces of* dim $\leq n$ *agree.*

(ii) *The faces degeneracy operations are the induced ones. Also, we write $X = X^{(\infty)}$ and let $p^n_k : X^{(n)} \longrightarrow X^{(k)}$ for $n > k$ be the natural projection.*

4.2 Proposition: *Let X be a Kan complex; i.e., $X \in \mathfrak{M}^v_E$.*

(i) *$X^{(n)} \in \mathfrak{M}^v_E$ for every n.*

(ii) *$p : X^{(n)} \longrightarrow X^{(k)}$ for $n > k$ is a fiber map.*

(iii) *If $x \in X_0$, then $\pi_q(X^{(n)}, x) = 0$ for $q > n$ and the induced homomorphism*

$$p^\# : \pi(X^{(n)}, x) \longrightarrow \pi(X^{(k)}, x)$$

is an isomorphism if $q \leq k$.

By examining the homotopy sequence of $X^{(n+1)} \longrightarrow X^{(n)}$, we see that its fiber, F_{n+1} say, satisfies

$$\begin{aligned} \pi_q(F_{n+1}) &= 0 \quad \text{if} \quad q \neq n+1 \\ &= \pi_{n+1}(X) \quad \text{if} \quad q = n+1. \end{aligned}$$

Thus, F_{n+1} is an Eilenberg and MacLane (EM) complex of type $(\pi_{n+1}(X), n+1)$, cf. Eilenberg and MacLane [1], and Sec. 5.8. We thus obtain the following diagram:

4.3

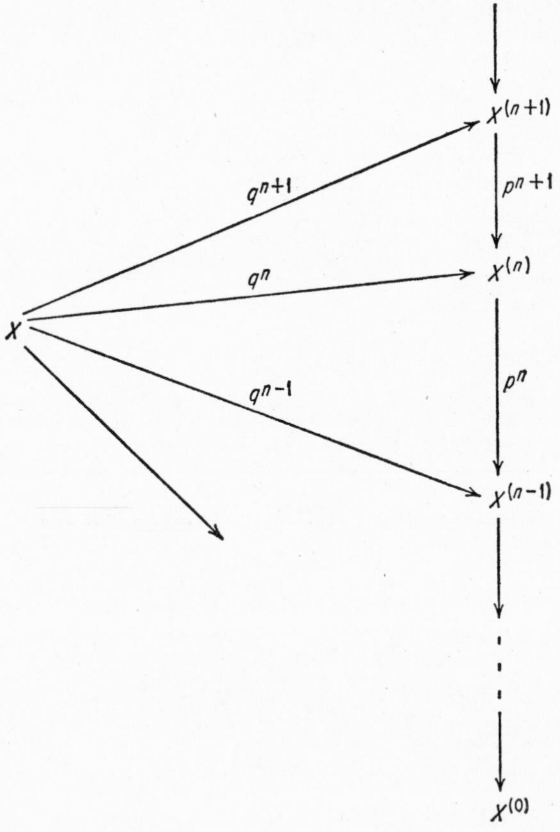

in which (i) p^n is a fibration with fiber an EM-space of type $(\pi_n(X), n)$.

(ii) $\pi_i(X^{(n)}) = 0$ for $i > n$.

(iii) q^n induces isomorphisms in π_i for $i \leq n$.

The diagram thus shows how the complex X can be built up from EM-spaces, adding one homotopy group at a time. This "resolution" of a complex—and, hence, via $S(X)$, of a space—has been much used, for instance, in the computational side of homotopy theory.

In a certain sense it also provides a means of classifying homotopy types; but this has been found less useful.

In Moore [1], the construction is generalized to the decomposition of a fiber map.

5. GROUP COMPLEXES

The algebraic structure present in a group-complex—it is a Kan complex, Sec. 2.35—can be used to give a much more "algebraic" analysis of its homotopy theory. The principal tool for this is the "Moore complex":

5.1 DEFINITION: (Moore [1].) *Let $G \in \mathcal{G}^v$. We define the graded differential group $MG = \{(MG)_n, d_n\}$ by*

$$(MG)_n = \bigcap_{i=1}^{n} (\text{kernel } \partial_i : G_n \longrightarrow G_{n-1}) \qquad (n > 0)$$

$$= G_0 \qquad (n = 0)$$

and observe that $\partial_0(MG)_n \subset (MG)_{n-1}$ so that we can define

$$d_n = \partial_0 \mid (MG)_n : (MG)_n \longrightarrow (MG)_{n-1}.$$

$d_n(MG)_n$ is a normal subgroup of the kernel of d_{n-1} so that we can define the "homology group"

$$H_n(MG) = \frac{(\text{kernel } d_n)}{\text{Image } d_{n+1}}.$$

It is not hard to see the following

5.2 PROPOSITION:

$$\pi_n(G) = \pi_n(G, 1) = H_n(MG) \qquad (n \geq 0).$$

Let us denote by $\mathfrak{M}_*^v \subset \mathfrak{M}^v$ the subcategory whose objects A contain only a single element in A_0; for connected $A \in \mathfrak{M}_E^v$, there always is a deformation retract with this property, cf., Sec. 2.42. We shall write

$$\mathfrak{M}_{E*}^v = \mathfrak{M}_E^v \cap \mathfrak{M}_*^v.$$

Following Kan [1], we now introduce a functor $G: \mathfrak{M}_*^v \longrightarrow \mathcal{G}^v$—it is the c.s.s. analogue of the *loop-space*—which permits us to exploit Sec. 5.2 for set-complexes.

5.3 Definition: *Let the principal twisted Cartesian product* $(E, B, \Gamma, \xi, \Gamma)$—*cf. Sec.* 2.51—*be such that* $\pi_i(E) = 0$ *for* $i \geq 0$. (*"E is contractible."*)

Then we say that Γ *is a loop-complex for* B *and* B *a classifying complex for* Γ.

Since the map $E \longrightarrow B$ is a fiber map, by Secs. 2.52 and 2.34, the homotopy sequence shows that

$$\pi_{i+1}(B) \approx \pi_i(\Gamma) \qquad i \geq 0.$$

5.4 Definition: *Let* $K \in \mathfrak{M}_*^v$. *We define* $GK \in \mathcal{G}^v$ *as follows:* $(GK)_n$ *is the free group with*

(i) *One generator* Gk *for every* $k \in K_{n+1}$.
(ii) *One relation* $Gs_0k = 1$ *for every* $k \in K_n$.

The face and degeneracy operators in GK are given by the relations (iii) in Sec. 2.51, with $\xi = G$.

A map $f: K \longrightarrow L$ of $\mathfrak{M}_*^v$ induces a map

$$Gf: GK \longrightarrow GL \quad \text{of } \mathcal{G}^v \quad \text{by} \quad (Gf)Gk = Gfk.$$

It is clear now that for $E = K \times_G GK$, (E, K, GK, G, GK) is a principal twisted Cartesian product, Sec. 2.51.

5.41 Proposition: *All homotopy groups of* $E = K \times_G GK$ *are trivial.*

For the proof, it is far from trivial, see Kan [1].

It follows that GK is a loop-complex for K, and $\pi_i(K) = \pi_{i-1}(GK)$ $(i > 0)$ together with Sec. 5.2 gives a purely group-theoretical definition of the homotopy groups of K.

5.5 There is, conversely, a functor $(\overline{W}: \mathcal{G}^v \rightarrow \mathfrak{M}_*^v$ which assigns to every group-complex Γ a classifying-complex $\overline{W}\Gamma$; the construction is due to MacLane [1].

Let $\Gamma \in \mathcal{G}^v$. We define $W\Gamma \in \mathfrak{M}^v$ as follows:

$$W_0(\Gamma) = \Gamma_0, \qquad W_{q+1}(\Gamma) = W_q(\Gamma) \times \Gamma_{q+1}$$

Γ_q acts on the right of $W_q(\Gamma)$ by $(w_{q-1}, \gamma_q)\gamma'_q = (w_{q-1}, \gamma_q\gamma'_q)$; the semisimplicial operators are defined inductively as follows: Let $w \in W_q(\Gamma)$, $\gamma \in \Gamma_{q+1}$;

$$\partial_0(w, \gamma) = w\, \partial_0\gamma, \qquad \partial_{i+1}(w, \gamma) = (\partial_i w, \partial_{i+1}\gamma)$$

$$s_0(w, \gamma) = (w, 1, s_0\gamma), \qquad s_{i+1}(w, \gamma) = (s_i w, s_{i+1}\gamma)$$

where 1 denotes the unit of Γ_{q+1}.

We next define $\overline{W}(\Gamma) \in \mathfrak{M}_*^v$ as follows:

$\overline{W}_0(\Gamma)$ contains a single element denoted by [ ].

$\overline{W}_{q+1}(\Gamma) = \overline{W}_q \times \Gamma_q$.

There is thus an isomorphism (in the category of sets!) $W_q(\Gamma) \longrightarrow \overline{W}_{q+1}(\Gamma)$ which we denote by $w \longrightarrow [w]$. We now define

$$p : W_q(\Gamma) \longrightarrow \overline{W}_q(\Gamma)$$

by $p(w, \gamma) = [w]$, $p\gamma = [\ \ ]$ if $\gamma \in \Gamma_0$. There is a unique c.s.s. structure in $\overline{W}(\Gamma)$, easily written explicitly, which turns p into a map of $\mathfrak{M}^v$. It then turns out that $W(\Gamma) = \overline{W}(\Gamma) \times {}_\xi\Gamma$ where $\xi : \overline{W}(\Gamma) \longrightarrow \Gamma$ is given by

$$\xi[\gamma_0, \ldots, \gamma_i, \ldots, \gamma_{q-1}] = \gamma_{q-1}.$$

It is not hard to prove (by writing a homotopy) that $W(\Gamma)$ has all homotopy groups trivial; and the principal twisted Cartesian product $(W(\Gamma), \overline{W}(\Gamma), \Gamma, \xi, \Gamma) = T(\Gamma)$, say, exhibits $\overline{W}(\Gamma)$ as a classifying space for Γ. It is easily seen that the construction $T(\Gamma)$ is "functorial."

The property expressed by the name *classifying space* will now be made explicit.

5.5 Definition: *If $(E, B, F, \xi, \Gamma) = T$ is a twisted Cartesian product and $f : B' \longrightarrow B$ a map of $\mathfrak{M}^v$, then $(E', B', F, \xi f, \Gamma) = f^*T$ where $E' = B' \times {}_{\xi f}F$ is called the "induced twisted Cartesian product."*

With any twisted Cartesian product T (as above) we can associate a map $k_T : B \longrightarrow \overline{W}(\Gamma)$ of $\mathfrak{M}^v$ given by

$$k_T(b) = [\xi(\partial_0^{n-1}b), \ldots, \xi(b)], \qquad b \in B_n.$$

5.52 Definition: *Let $f, g: A \longrightarrow B$ be maps of $\mathfrak{M}^v_{E*}$. We say that f, g are $*$-homotopic, $f \sim_* g$, if they satisfy the conditions of Sec. 2.31 where*

$$F(t, s_0^n \text{ (base point)}) = s_0^n \text{ (base point) for } t \in I_n.$$

By $\pi_*(A, B)$, we denote the set of all $*$-homotopy classes of maps $A \longrightarrow B$.

5.53 Proposition: *If T is any principal twisted Cartesian product, then*

$$T = k_T^* T(\Gamma).$$

The assignment to any map $k : B \longrightarrow \overline{W}(\Gamma)$ of the principal twisted Cartesian product $k^*T(\Gamma)$ induces a one-to-one correspondence between $\pi_*(B, \overline{W}(\Gamma)]$ and equivalence classes—in an evident sense—of principal twisted Cartesian products with "base" B and "group" Γ.

See Barratt, Gugenheim, and Moore [1].

5.6 The functors G and W are "adjoint" in the sense of Kan [5]: If $f: K \longrightarrow \overline{W}(\Gamma)$, $v : GK \longrightarrow \Gamma$ are maps of $\mathfrak{M}^v_*$, $\mathcal{G}^v$, respectively, we define adj $f : GK \longrightarrow \Gamma$ and adj $v : K \longrightarrow \overline{W}(\Gamma)$ by $(\text{adj } f)Gk = \xi f k$, $(\text{adj } v)k = (vG(\partial_0^{n-1}k), \ldots, vGk)$ for $k \in K_{n-1}$. Then adj adj $F = F$, adj adj $v = v$, and we have a natural equivalence

5.61 $$\text{Hom}_{\mathfrak{M}^v_*}(K, \overline{W}\Gamma) = \text{Hom}_{\mathcal{G}^v}(GK, \Gamma).$$

5.7 It suggests itself to ask whether the equivalence of Sec. 5.61 passes to homotopy classes. A moment's reflection shows that we must not use the notion of homotopy appropriate to $\mathfrak{M}^v$ in $\mathcal{G}^v$; rather, we must replace it by a notion of *group-homotopy* which assures that in the "course of the homotopy" we *remain* in the category $\mathcal{G}^v$. This is done, following Kan [6], by a plausible modification of Sec. 2.3:

5.71 Definition: *Let $A, B \in \mathcal{G}^v$. The map $F: I \times A \longrightarrow B$ (of $\mathfrak{M}^v$) is called a "group-homotopy" ("loop-homotopy" in Kan [6]) if it satisfies the following condition:*

$$F(t, a)\, F(t, a') = F(t, aa')$$

for $t \in I_n$, $a, a' \in A_n$, and juxtaposition denotes the various group operations.

Two maps $f, g : A \longrightarrow B$ of $\mathcal{G}^v$ are called group-homotopic, $f \sim_g g$, if there is a group-homotopy $F : I \times A \longrightarrow B$ such that $F_0 = f$, $F_1 = g$, cf. Sec. 2.3.

Clearly $f \sim_g g$ implies $f \sim g$.

In general $\sim_g$ is not an equivalence relation for the set of maps $A \longrightarrow B$; it does become one if A satisfies the following conditions:

(i) A_n is a free group for each n with some given basis of generators.

(ii) If $\sigma \in A_n$ is one of these generators, then $s_i\sigma (0 \leq i \leq n)$ is such a generator of A_{n+1}. We call such an $A \in \mathcal{G}^v$ *strictly free*, and we denote the set of $\sim_g$ equivalence classes of maps $A \longrightarrow B$ by $\pi_g(A, B)$. For $K \in \mathfrak{M}_*^v$, GK is strictly free.

From Kan [6] we quote the following:

5.72 Proposition: Sec. 5.61 *induces an equivalence*

$$\pi_*(K, \overline{W}\Gamma) = \pi_g(GK, \Gamma) \qquad (K \in \mathfrak{M}_*^v)$$

(*cf. Sec.* 5.52.)

5.73 Proposition: *The assignment* $f \longrightarrow GF$ *sets up an equivalence*

$$\pi_*(A, B) = \pi_g(GA, GB) \qquad (A, B \in \mathfrak{M}_{E*}^v)$$

5.74 Proposition: *The assignment* $f \longrightarrow \overline{W}f$ *sets up an equivalence*

$$\pi_g(A, B) = \pi_*(\overline{W}A, \overline{W}B) \qquad (A, B \in \mathcal{G}^v)$$

provided that A *is strictly free.*

5.8 If $A \in \mathfrak{A}^v$ is a commutative group-complex, then $\overline{W}(A) \in \mathfrak{A}^v$, the multiplication being given by

$$[a_0, \ldots, a_{n-1}][a_0', \ldots, a_{n-1}'] = [a_0a_0', \ldots, a_{n-1}\, a_{n-1}'].$$

Let π be a group; we define $K(\pi, 0) \in \mathcal{G}^v$ by $(K(\pi, 0))_0 = \pi$, the higher dimensions being obtained by degeneracy operators. Clearly $\pi_0(K(\pi, 0)) = \pi$ and the higher homotopy groups are trivial. We define

$$K(\pi, 1) = \overline{W}K(\pi, 0).$$

If π is abelian, $K(\pi, 0) \in \mathfrak{A}^v$ and the operation can be iterated:

$$K(\pi, n+1) = \overline{W}K(\pi, n) \in \mathfrak{A}^v.$$

It follows easily that $\pi_n K(\pi, n) = \pi$, all other homotopy groups being trivial.

We have thus proved the existence of Eilenberg-MacLane complexes, cf. Sec. 4.2; also, $K(\pi, n) \in \mathfrak{A}^v$.

6. COMMUTATIVE GROUP COMPLEXES

If we apply the construction M, cf. Sec. 5.1, to $\mathfrak{A}_\Lambda^v$, we obtain a functor $M : \mathfrak{A}_\Lambda^v \longrightarrow d\mathfrak{A}_\Lambda$; cf. Sec. 1.4. A second functor $T : \mathfrak{A}_\Lambda^v \longrightarrow d\mathfrak{A}_\Lambda$ was defined in Sec. 1.5.

For $A \in \mathfrak{A}_\Lambda^v$, the subset DA of all degenerate elements, cf. Sec. 1.1, forms a subdifferential module $DA \subset TA \in d\mathfrak{A}_\Lambda$, as is easily verified; one has to show that $a \in DA$ implies $da \in DA$. We now define a third functor $N : \mathfrak{A}_\Lambda^v \longrightarrow d\mathfrak{A}_\Lambda$, the "normalized" functor, by $NA = TA/DA$; i.e., $(NA)_n = (TA)_n/(DA)_n$.

6.1 Lemma (Eilenberg and MacLane [1]):

$$H\, DA = 0 \quad \textit{for} \quad A \in \mathfrak{A}_\Lambda^v.$$

Proof: One proves this by first showing $H(D^{k+1}A/D^kA) = 0$ where $D^kA \subset DA$ is the subdifferential module generated by all $s_i a$ where $a \in A_n$ and $i > n - k$.

6.11 Corollary: *If $p = p(A): TA \longrightarrow NA$ denotes the natural projection, $H(p): HTA \longrightarrow HNA$ is an isomorphism.*

It is easily seen that the inclusion $j = j(A) : MA \longrightarrow TA$ is a map of $d\mathfrak{A}_\Lambda$. We now define $k = k(A): TA \longrightarrow MA$ as follows: For $a \in A_n = (TA)_n$, let

$$w_n a = s_{n-1}\, \partial_n a$$
$$w_i a = s_{i-1}\, \partial_i a - s_{i-1}\, \partial_i w_{i+1} a + w_{i+1} a \qquad (0 < i < n)$$

and $ka = a - w_1 a$. It is easily seen that k is a map of $d\mathfrak{A}_\Lambda$ and that $kj = 1$, $pjk = p$. From this we deduce

6.2 Lemma (Kan [4], Dold [1]): *$pj : MA \longrightarrow NA$ is an equivalence in $d\mathfrak{A}_\Lambda$, and the sequence*

$$0 \longrightarrow DA \longrightarrow TA \xrightarrow{k} MA \longrightarrow 0$$

is split exact in $d\mathfrak{A}_\Lambda$.

6.21 COROLLARY:

$$H(j) : HMA \longrightarrow HTA \qquad (A \in \mathfrak{A}_\Lambda^{\text{r}})$$

is an isomorphism.

6.22 COROLLARY:

$$\pi_n(A) = H_n(MA) = H_n(TA) \qquad (A \in \mathfrak{A}^{\text{r}} = \mathfrak{A}_Z^{\text{r}}).$$

Proof: Due to the naturality of the constructions, we see that $p: T \longrightarrow N$, $j: M \longrightarrow T$, and $k: T \longrightarrow M$ are transformations of functors.

The functor M has an interesting "inverse" $\overline{M}: d\mathfrak{A}_\Lambda \longrightarrow \mathfrak{A}_\Lambda^{\text{r}}$; cf. Dold [1] and Kan [4]; in the latter, $\overline{M}$ appears as a special case of a more general construction.

Let $X \in d\mathfrak{A}_\Lambda$. Then $(\overline{M}X)_n$ is the Λ-module of all maps of $d\mathfrak{A}_\Lambda$

$$f: M\Lambda\Delta^n \longrightarrow X.$$

See Sec. 1.2 for the definition of Λ, Sec. 2.1 for that of Δ^n.

$\partial_i f$ and $s_i f$ are defined as the compositions

$$M\Lambda\Delta^{n-1} \xrightarrow{M\Lambda\epsilon^i} M\Lambda\Delta^n \xrightarrow{f} X$$
$$M\Lambda\Delta^{n+1} \xrightarrow{M\Lambda\eta^i} M\Lambda\Delta^n \xrightarrow{f} X,$$

respectively. If $\phi: X \longrightarrow Y$ is a map of $d\mathfrak{A}_\Lambda$, $\overline{M}\phi: \overline{M}X \longrightarrow \overline{M}Y$ is defined by $(\overline{M}\phi)f = \phi f$.

6.3 PROPOSITION (Dold [1], Kan [4]): *The functors* $M: \mathfrak{A}_\Lambda^{\text{r}} \longrightarrow d\mathfrak{A}_\Lambda$, $\overline{M}: d\mathfrak{A}_\Lambda \longrightarrow \mathfrak{A}_\Lambda^{\text{r}}$ *are equivalences of categories and "inverses" of each other. In other words, the compositions* $M\overline{M}$, $\overline{M}M$ *are naturally equivalent to the identity functors on* $d\mathfrak{A}_\Lambda$, $\mathfrak{A}_\Lambda^{\text{r}}$, *respectively.*

Proof: Observe, cf., Sec. 6.2, that $M\Lambda\Delta^n$ is freely generated by kt where t runs through the set of nondegenerate elements of Δ^n. Therefore $f \in (\overline{M}X)_n$ is uniquely determined if we know the elements fkt. Moreover, $f \in (M\overline{M}X)_n$ implies that $\partial_i f = 0$ if $i > 0$; whence $f\epsilon^i = 0$, $i > 0$, from which we easily deduce $fkt = 0$ unless $t = \delta^n$ or $\partial_0 \delta^n$; and $f(k\, \partial_0\, \delta^n) = df(k\, \delta^n)$. Hence the assignment

$$f \longrightarrow fk\, \delta^n \qquad (f \in (M\overline{M}X)_n)$$

sets up an isomorphism $M\overline{M}X \longrightarrow X$.

To deal, similarly, with $\overline{M}M$ we need

6.31 LEMMA: *Let $A, B \in \mathcal{A}_\Lambda^v$. Any map $f: MA \longrightarrow MB$ of $d\mathcal{A}_\Lambda$ has a unique extension $\bar{f}: A \longrightarrow B$ in $\mathcal{A}_\Lambda^v$.*

Proof: $(MA)_0 = A_0$ and hence $\bar{f}_0 = f_0$. Suppose we have found $\bar{f}_q$ for $q < n$, $n \geq 1$. We determine $\bar{f}_n$ by a second induction; suppose $\bar{f}_n$ is known for a such that $\partial_i a = 0$ for $i \geq k$ $(k \geq 1)$. Now, let $\partial_i a = 0$ for $i > k$. We observe

$$a = a' + s_{k-1}\,\partial_k a \quad \text{where} \quad a' = a - s_{k-1}\,\partial_k a.$$

It is easily seen that $\partial_i a' = 0$ for $i \geq k$. Hence, if a suitable $\bar{f}_n$ exists at all, it must be defined by

$$\bar{f}_n a = \bar{f}_n a' + s_{k-1}\bar{f}_{n-1}\,\partial_k a$$

and direct verification proves that this will, indeed, satisfy $\partial_i f_n = f_{n-1}\,\partial_i$, $s_i f_{n-1} = f_n s_i$.

We can now complete the proof of Sec. 6.3. Let $A \in \mathcal{A}_\Lambda^v$. An element of $(\overline{M}MA)_n$ is a map $f: M\Lambda\Delta^n \longrightarrow MA$ of $d\mathcal{A}_\Lambda$; this can be extended to a unique map $\bar{f}: \Lambda\Delta^n \longrightarrow A$ of $\mathcal{A}_\Lambda^v$; and the assignment

$$f \longrightarrow \bar{f}\,\delta^n \in A$$

sets up an isomorphism $\overline{M}MA \longrightarrow A$.

6.32 REMARK: *In view of Sec. 6.2 Sec. 6.3 could equally well be formulated in terms of N, $\overline{N}$ where $\overline{N}$ is related to N as $\overline{M}$ is to M.*

6.33 COROLLARY (J. C. Moore): *Let $A, B \in \mathcal{A}^v$ and $\pi_n(A) \approx \pi_n(B)$ for all $n \geq 0$. Then A, B are of the same homotopy type.*

Proof: Since we can find a freely generated $X \in d\mathcal{A}$ such that $H_n(X) = \pi_n(A) = \pi_n(B)$ for all n, let $f: X \longrightarrow MA$, $g: X \longrightarrow MB$ be chain maps realizing this isomorphism; then $\overline{M}f$, $\overline{M}g$ are homotopy equivalences by Secs. 6.22 and 2.44.

One way of expressing this result is to say that the Postnikov system, cf. Sec. 4, of a commutative group-complex is "trivial."

6.4 Once again there arises the question whether the equivalence of Sec. 6.3 preserves homotopies. The appropriate notion of homotopy in $d\mathcal{A}_\Lambda$ is the classical one of chain-homotopy; i.e., f, $g: X \longrightarrow Y$ of $d\mathcal{A}_\Lambda$ are chain-homotopic if there is a sequence of Λ-homomorphisms $D = D_n: X_n \longrightarrow Y_{n+1}$ $(n \geq 0)$ such that

$$f - g = d\,D + D\,d.$$

It is best, for our purposes, to relate this to the idea of the *tensor product* of two objects of $d\mathfrak{A}_\Lambda$:

6.41 DEFINITION: *If* $X, Y \in d\mathfrak{A}_\Lambda$, *we define* $X \otimes Y \in d\mathfrak{A}_\Lambda$ *by* $(X \otimes Y)_n = \oplus_{p+q} = n\, X_p \otimes Y_q$.
Maps $f: X \longrightarrow X'$, $g: Y \longrightarrow Y'$ *of* $d\mathfrak{A}_\Lambda$ *define a map* $f \otimes g: X \otimes Y \longrightarrow X' \otimes Y'$.

Now, we can see that $f, g: X \longrightarrow Y$ are chain-homotopic if and only if there is a map

$$F: N\Lambda I \otimes X \longrightarrow Y$$

such that $F(0 \otimes x) = fx$, $F(1 \otimes x) = gx$, cf., Sec. 2.3 for the notation. F and D are related by the formula $Dx = F(\delta^1 \otimes x)$.

6.42 DEFINITION: *If* $A, B \in \mathfrak{A}_\Lambda^v$, *we define* $A \otimes B \in \mathfrak{A}_\Lambda^v$ *by* $(A \otimes B)_n = A_n \otimes B_n$, $\partial_i(a \otimes b) = (\partial_i a \otimes \partial_i b)$, $s_i(a \otimes b) = (s_i a \otimes s_i b)$.

6.43 PROPOSITION (Eilenberg and Zilber): *For* $A, B \in \mathfrak{A}_\Lambda^v$, *there exist maps of* $d\mathfrak{A}_\Lambda$

$$k : N(A \otimes B) \longrightarrow N(A) \otimes N(B)$$
$$k' : N(A) \otimes N(B) \longrightarrow N(A \otimes B)$$

such that

(i) $kk' = \text{identity}$
$k'k - \text{id} = d\,D + D\,d$ (*cf. Sec.* 6.4)

(ii) k, k' *and* D *are natural.*

For a proof, see Eilenberg and Zilber [2] or Eilenberg and MacLane [2].

6.431 COROLLARY: *Let* $A, B \in \mathfrak{A}^v$, *and* $\pi_i(A) = 0$, $i \leq p$; $\pi_i(B) = 0$, $i \leq q$. *Then* $\pi_i(A \otimes B) = 0$ *for* $i \leq p + q$.

6.44 The appropriate notion of homotopy in $\mathfrak{A}_\Lambda^v$ is that analogous to Sec. 5.71, which it reduces to when $\Lambda = Z$. Thus, the definition is exactly Sec. 5.71, except that we now have the condition

$$\lambda F(t, a) + \mu F(t, b) = F(t, \lambda a + \mu a')$$

for $t \in I_n$, $a, a' \in A_n$, $\lambda, \mu \in \Lambda$.

In this case, we say that F_0, F_1 are *group-homotopic*, and we write $F_0 \sim_\Lambda F_1$.

Since ΛI is freely generated by I, it is easily seen that a *group-homotopy* $F: I \times A \longrightarrow B$ induces a map $F': \Lambda I < A \longrightarrow B$ of $\mathfrak{A}_\Lambda^v$, and vice versa.

Using Sec. 6.43, we easily prove

6.45 PROPOSITION: *Maps f, g of $\mathfrak{A}_\Lambda^v$ are group-homotopic if and only if $N(f)$, $N(g)$ of $d\mathfrak{A}_\Lambda$ are chain-homotopic (cf. Sec. 6.4).*

6.451 COROLLARY: *Let $A, B \in \mathfrak{A}^v = \mathfrak{A}_Z^v$ be free; i.e., A_n, B_n are free for $n \geq 0$; and let $\pi_i(A) = \pi_i(B)$ for $i \geq 0$. Then there are maps $v: A \longrightarrow B$, $v': B \longrightarrow A$ such that $vv' \sim_Z \mathrm{id}$, $v'v \sim_Z \mathrm{id}$.*

This follows from Sec. 6.32 and the fact that in this case the isomorphism can be realized by a map $N(A) \longrightarrow N(B)$ of $d\mathfrak{A}_z$.

6.5 The preceding results can be applied to prolonged functors; cf. Kan [7], Dold and Puppe [1].

6.51 DEFINITION: *Let $\mathfrak{C}$, $\mathfrak{D}$ be categories and $T: \mathfrak{C} \longrightarrow \mathfrak{D}$ a covariant functor; we define the prolonged functor $T^v: \mathfrak{C}^v \longrightarrow \mathfrak{D}^v$—cf. Sec. 1.1—by $T^vK = TK$ and for a map $f: K \longrightarrow L$, $T^v(f)(TK_n) = T(f_n)$. It is usually convenient, with a slight abuse of notation, to write $T^v = T$.*

6.52 LEMMA: *Let $T: \mathfrak{G} \longrightarrow \mathfrak{A}_\Lambda$ ($T: \mathfrak{A}_\Lambda \longrightarrow \mathfrak{A}_\Lambda$) be a covariant functor. If f, g are maps of $\mathfrak{G}^v(\mathfrak{A}_\Lambda)$ such that $f \sim_g g$ ($f \sim_\Lambda g$), then $Tf \sim_\Lambda Tg$.*

6.53 PROPOSITION: *Let $T: \mathfrak{A} \longrightarrow \mathfrak{A}$ be a covariant functor. If $A, B \in \mathfrak{A}$ are free and $\pi_n A = \pi_n B$ for all $n \geq 0$, then TA, TB have the same homotopy type.*

This follows from Secs. 6.451 and 6.52.

For an example of Sec. 6.53, let Γ be a subgroup of the symmetric group S_n. Then Γ operates on $\otimes_n K$ and M^n (where $K \in \mathfrak{A}^v$, $M \in \mathfrak{M}^v$), the n-fold tensor and Cartesian products, respectively. We can thus form the identification objects $\otimes_n K/\Gamma \in \mathfrak{A}^v$, $M^n/\Gamma \in \mathfrak{M}^v$. The functor $K \longrightarrow \otimes_n K/\Gamma$ is one to which Sec. 6.53 can be applied. Putting $K = ZM$ and noting

$$\pi_n(K) = H_n(M, Z), \qquad \pi_n\left(\frac{\otimes_n K}{\Gamma}\right) = H_n\left(\frac{M_n}{\Gamma}, Z\right),$$

we obtain

6.54 COROLLARY (Dold [1]): *The homology groups of* M^n/Γ *depend on the homology groups of* M *and on* Γ *only.*

For more explicit results, see A. Dold [1].

6.6 We end this chapter by applying Sec. 6.22 to infinite symmetric products; for details, see Puppe [1], [2].

Let $A \in \mathfrak{M}^v$ and let $* \in A_0$. Let $P^nA = A^n/S_n$, i.e., the n-fold Cartesian product modulo the operation of the symmetric group, cf. Sec. 6.53. By identifying $(a_1, \ldots, a_n)$ $(a_1 \in A_p)$ with $(s_0^p*, a_1, \ldots, a_n)$, we embed P^nA in $P^{n+1}A$ and can form $PA = \bigcup_{n=1}^{\infty} P^nA$, the infinite symmetric product.

Similarly, if X is a topological space and $* \in X$ a chosen point, we can define the infinite symmetric product PX.

6.61 LEMMA: *If* $A \in \mathfrak{M}^v$ *is countable (as a set), then* $P(|A|) = |PA|$ [Puppe [1], p. 403, (11)].

Now, let $(*) \in A$ be the subcomplex generated by $*$, and let

$$\overline{Z}(A) = \frac{ZA}{Z(*)}$$

$\overline{Z}^+(A)$ = the elements of $\overline{Z}(A)$ whose coefficients are nonnegative integers.

An element of $(\overline{Z}^+(A))_n$ is given by knowing for each $a \in A_n$ a nonnegative integer, all but a finite number of these being zero. Hence $\overline{Z}^+(A) = P(A)$.

6.62 LEMMA (Puppe [1]): *Let* $K \in \mathfrak{A}^v$ *and* $L \subset K$ *be a monoid subcomplex which generates* K *and is connected (i.e.,* $|L|$ *is connected). Then* $|L|$ *is a deformation retract of* $|K|$.

In particular, if A is connected, $|PA| = |\overline{Z}^+A|$ is a deformation retract of $|\overline{Z}A|$.

Hence $\pi_n(PA) = \pi_n(\overline{Z}A) = \pi_n(ZA) = H_n(A, Z)$ by Sec. 6.22. Using Sec. 6.61, we find

6.63 PROPOSITION (Dold and Thom): *Let* $A \in \mathfrak{M}^v$ *be connected and countable. Then*

$$\pi_n(P|A|) = H_n(|A|; Z).$$

To apply this result to a topological space X, it is sufficient for $S(X)$ to have a countable deformation retract.

7. RELATIONS BETWEEN HOMOLOGY AND HOMOTOPY

The homology groups—at least of finite polyhedra—are finitely computable. Thus, it is desirable to set up relations between homology and homotopy; the most important of these is the theorem of Hurewicz, which in the semisimplicial context can be considerably generalized.

The theory of the present chapter is due to D. M. Kan [2] and E. B. Curtis [1], [2].

By $A : \mathcal{G} \longrightarrow \mathcal{A}$, we denote the "abelianization" functor $AG = G/[G, G]$.

Let $K \in \mathfrak{M}_*^v$ (cf. the paragraph following Sec. 5.2) and let $T'ZK$ be defined by introducing the relations $s_0 k = 0$ in TZK, cf. Secs. 1.2 and 1.5. It is easily verified that the map $k \longrightarrow Gk$, cf. Sec. 5.4, induces an isomorphism

$$\alpha' : (T'ZK)_n \longrightarrow (TAGK)_{n-1} \qquad (n > 0)$$

which commutes with the differentials; it is also easy to show that the natural map $TZK \longrightarrow T'ZK$ induces isomorphisms in homology; this is analogous to Sec. 6.11. We thus obtain a natural isomorphism

$$\alpha_n : H_n TZK \longrightarrow H_{n-1}TAGK \qquad (n > 0).$$

Using Sec. 6.22 and the notation of Sec. 1.5, we thus have

7.1 Proposition: *There are natural isomorphisms*

$$\alpha_n : H_n(K) \longrightarrow \pi_{n-1}(AGK) \qquad (n > 0).$$

We compare this with the statement (Secs. 5.3 and 5.4) $\pi_n(K) = \pi_{n-1}(GK)$. The natural map $k : G \longrightarrow AG = G/[G, G]$ induces a homeomorphism

$$k_{n-1} : H_{n-1}(MGK) \longrightarrow H_{n-1}(MAGK);$$

i.e., $\pi_{n-1}GK = \pi_n K \longrightarrow \pi_{n-1}(AGK)$. Putting $\mathcal{H}_n = \alpha_n^{-1} k_{n-1}$, we thus have a natural homeomorphism

$$\mathcal{H}_n : \pi_n(K) \longrightarrow H_n(K) \qquad (n > 0)$$

which can be verified—by following the definitions back to the pseudogeometric theory—to agree with the classical Hurewicz homeomorphism.

The advantage of the present definition is that the properties of $\mathcal{H}_n$ are those of k_{n-1}—which can be investigated, owing to its definition, by purely group-theoretic means. In particular, the following was proved by Kan [2]:

7.2 PROPOSITION: *Let* $F \in \mathcal{G}^v$ *be free; i.e.,* F_n *is a free group for all* n*; and let* $k : F \longrightarrow AF$ *be the natural map.*

$$k_0 : H_0(MF) \longrightarrow H_0(MAF)$$

is onto and has kernel $[H_0(MF), H_0(MF)]$.

If $H_i : (MF) = 0$, $0 \leq i < n$, *then*

$$k_n : H_n(MF) \longrightarrow H_n(MAF)$$

is an isomorphism.

Observing that, for $K \in \mathfrak{M}_*^v$, $GK = F$ satisfies the conditions of Sec. 7.2, the classical Hurewicz theorem follows at once.

The condition "F is free" in Sec. 7.2 is essential, as Kan showed by an example.

We now generalize Sec. 7.1; we begin with some group-theoretical facts. We define a family of functors $\Gamma_r: \mathcal{G} \longrightarrow \mathcal{G}$ $(r \geq 1)$ (lower central series) by

$$\Gamma_1 G = G$$

$$\Gamma_{r+1} G = [\Gamma_r G, G],$$

the subgroup generated by elements of the form $[x, y] = x^{-1}y^{-1}xy$, where $x \in \Gamma_r G$, $y \in G$. It is easily seen that $\Gamma_r G$ is normal in G and that $\Gamma_{r+1} G \subset \Gamma_r G$.

Next we define the functors $A^r: \mathcal{G} \longrightarrow \mathcal{A}$ $(r \geq 1)$ by

$$A^r G = \frac{\Gamma_r G}{\Gamma_{r+1} G}$$

so that $A^1 = A$ in our previous notation. A theorem of E. Witt shows that, for G free, $A^r G$ depends on $AG = A^1 G$ only; to explain this theorem, we introduce

7.3 Definition: *A "Lie ring" L is an additively written abelian group, i.e., object of* $\mathfrak{A}$, *together with a binary operation* $[\ ,\ ]$ *(the Lie-product) such that, for* $x, y, z \in L$,

(i) $[x + y, z] = [x, z] + [y, z]$,
$\quad [x, y + z] = [x, y] + [x, z]$.

(ii) $[x, x] = 0$.

(iii) $[[x, y], z] + [[y, z], x] + [[z, x], y] = 0$.

From Eqs. (i) *and* (ii), *we easily deduce*

(iv) $[x, y] + [y, x] = 0$.

A map of Lie rings $f : L \longrightarrow K$ is a map of $\mathfrak{A}$ such that $f[x, y] = [fx, fy]$.

Now, let $M \in \mathfrak{A}$. We define the free nonassociative algebra $Q^\infty(M)$ by $Q^\infty(M) = \oplus_{r \geq 1} Q^r(M)$, where $Q^1(M) = M$ and $Q^r(M) = \oplus_{p+q=r} Q^p(M) \otimes Q^q(M)$.

If we introduce into this the relation $x \otimes x$ and $(x \otimes y) \otimes z + (y \otimes z) \otimes x + (z \otimes x) \otimes y$, we obtain a Lie ring $L^\infty(M) = \oplus_{r \geq 1} L^r(M)$. This so-called *free* Lie ring has the following universal property:

7.4 Lemma: *Let L be any Lie ring and* $f : M \longrightarrow L$ *be any map of* $\mathfrak{A}$. *There is a unique map of Lie rings* $f^\infty : L^\infty(M) \longrightarrow L$ *such that* $f^\infty \mid L^1(M) = f$.

Note: $L^1(M) = M$.

We now return to the constructions Γ_r, A^r. Let $x, y, z \in G \in \mathcal{G}$ and let us write

$$x^y = y^{-1}, x, y, \qquad [x, y, z] = [[x, y], z].$$

The following identities can be verified, cf. Hall [2]:

$$[xy, z] = [x, z][x, z, y][y, z]$$
$$[x, yz] = [x, z][x, y][x, y, z]$$
$$[x, y^{-1}, z]^y [y, z^{-1}, x]^z [z, x^{-1}, y]^x = 1$$
$$[x, y, z][y, z, x][z, x, y] =$$
$$[[x, y], [x, z]] \{[[x, y][y, z]^x][[y, z]^x [z, x]^y][[z, x]^y [z, x]]\}^{[x,z]}.$$

From these one can deduce that if $x \in \Gamma_r G$, $y \in \Gamma_s G$, then $[x, y] \in \Gamma_{r+s} G$ and that $[x, y]$ induces in

$$A^\infty(G) = \oplus_{r=1}^{\infty} A^r(G)$$

the structure of a Lie ring. From Sec. 7.4 we thus find a map of Lie rings

$$u(G) = u\colon L^\infty(AG) \longrightarrow A^\infty(G)$$

which maps $L^r(AG) \longrightarrow A^r(G)$ and is defined by $u \mid L^1(AG) =$ the identity on AG.

7.5. Proposition (E. Witt [1]; cf. Hall [2]): *If F is a free group, then $u(F)$ is an isomorphism.*

Now, all the functors we have introduced may be prolonged, cf. Sec. 6.5. We obtain the following

7.6 Proposition (E. Curtis [1]): *If $K \in \mathfrak{M}_*^v$, then $A^rGK(r \geq 1)$ is determined by AGK; the relationship is functorial: $A^rGK = L^r(AGK)$.*

7.61 Corollary: *The homotopy type of $A^rGK(r \geq 1)$ is determined by the homology groups $H_n(K)$ $(n \geq 1)$.*

Generalizing group-theoretical methods of M. Hall [1], the main idea of which is the construction of a basis for $L^\infty(M)$, see Sec. 8. E. Curtis has proved

7.7 Proposition: *Let $F \in \mathcal{G}^v$ be free and n-connected, $n \geq 0$; let $\{a\}$ denote the least integer $\geq a$.*

(i) *A^rF is $\{n + \log_2 r\}$-connected* (E. Curtis [1]).

(ii) *Γ_rF is $\{n + \log_2 r\}$-connected* (E. Curtis [2]).

Of course, statement (i) is an immediate consequence of statement (ii); but statement (ii) is apparently much deeper and harder to prove; the methods used, however, are similar.

As an immediate consequence of statement (ii) and the fibration $\Gamma_rF \longrightarrow F \longrightarrow F/\Gamma_rG$, we obtain the following generalization of the Hurewicz theorem—to which it reduces for $r = 2$:

7.71 Corollary: *With the assumptions of Sec. 7.7, the quotient morphism*

$$F \longrightarrow \frac{F}{\Gamma_rF}$$

induces isomorphisms in dimensions $\leq \{n + \log_2 r\}$.

An important application of these propositions is to the homotopy exact couple, cf. Massey [1], associated with the filtration

$$G = \Gamma_1 \supset \Gamma_2 \supset \cdots \supset \Gamma_r \supset \Gamma_{r+1} \supset \cdots,$$

with an associated spectral sequence which begins with

$$E^2_{p,q} = \pi_q(A^pG).$$

A part of this exact couple is exhibited below:

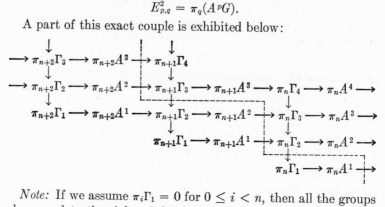

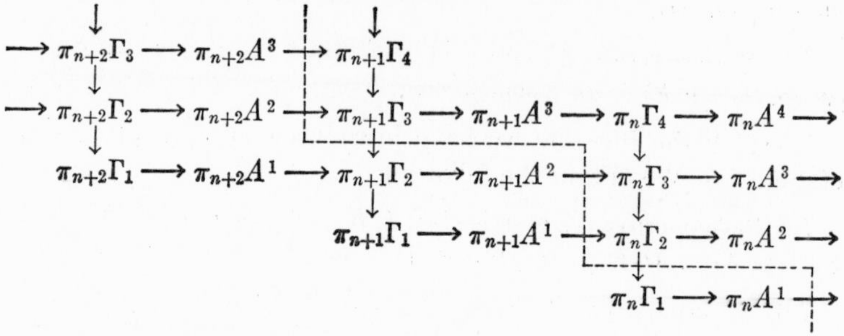

Note: If we assume $\pi_i\Gamma_1 = 0$ for $0 \leq i < n$, then all the groups above and to the right of the dotted line are zero, by Sec. 7.7(i) and (ii), provided G is free.

An immediate consequence of Sec. 7.7(ii) is that if F is free, for sufficiently large r, $\pi_n(\Gamma_r)$ is trivial. Hence

7.8 Proposition (E. Curtis [2]): *If $F \in \mathcal{G}^v$ is free and n-connected, $n \geq 0$, then there is a spectral sequence with $E^2_{p,q} = \pi_q(A^pF)$ which converges to the graded group associated with a filtration of $\pi_q(F)$.*

In particular, this proposition is applicable to the case $F = GK$ where $K \in \mathfrak{M}^v_*$ is n-connected, $n \geq 1$.

Since, cf. Sec. 7.61, the groups $\pi_n(A^rGK)$ are functions of the homology groups only, these propositions promise to lead toward effective methods of computing homotopy groups. In particular, Curtis [2] has used the spectral sequence to give a new proof of the theorem of E. H. Brown: The homotopy groups of a simply connected finite polyhedron are finitely computable.

The simplest case arises for $K = S^{n+1}$, $n > 0$, an $(n+1)$-sphere. By Sec. 7.1, we have

$$\pi_i(AGS^{n+1}) = H_{i+1}S^{n+1}$$

so that AGS^{n+1} is an Eilenberg-MacLane space $K(Z, n)$, cf. Sec. 5.8.

J. W. Schlesinger [1] has recently proved

7.9 PROPOSITION: *Let p be an odd prime.*

$$\begin{aligned} \pi_{n+1}L^pK(Z, n) &= Z_p \quad \text{if} \quad k \equiv -1 \bmod 2(p-1) \\ & \qquad\quad \text{and} \quad 0 \leq k < n(p-1) \\ &= 0 \quad \text{otherwise.} \end{aligned}$$

Thus, using Sec. 7.8, we find the well-known result on the first nonzero p-primary component of $\pi_i(S^{n+1})$.

In all these investigations the theory of symmetric products, cf. Dold and Puppe [1], plays a considerable part.

8. A THEOREM OF HILTON AND MILNOR

We shall apply Sec. 7.8 to prove the main theorem of Milnor [2]; this application is suggested in Curtis [1]; see Hall [2] for the group-theoretical material.

We begin by explaining a few facts about the Hall basis for $L^\infty(M)$.

Let M be freely generated by $l_1, l_2, \ldots, l_k$. Then the free nonassociative algebra $Q^\infty(M)$ has as an additive basis products of l_i's—each determined by the sequence of factors as well as, due to the nonassociativity, the "bracketing." Terms with r factors are said to be of weight r, and they generate $Q^r(M)$.

If we pass from $Q^\infty(M)$ to $L^\infty(M)$, these monomials are no longer independent. The Hall-basis is a selection among these monomials of certain "basic types" so that the basic types of weight r form a basis for $L^r(M)$.

The basic types are ordered, beginning with $l_1 < l_2 < \cdots < l_k$—these are the basic types of weight 1—and then in such a way that, for $r < s$,

$$\text{any type of weight } r < \text{any type of weight } s.$$

We need not describe the ordering of the basic types of a given weight.

Now, let $K \in \mathfrak{M}^v_*$; let us denote by $*$ the base point and all its degeneracies. By $FK \in \mathcal{G}^v$, we denote the free group-complex obtained by letting $(FK)_n$ be the free group generated by elements

Fk, one for each $k \in K_n$, with the relation $F* = 1$; $\partial_i Fk = F\,\partial_i k$, $s_i Fk = F s_i k$.

If one gives a suitable definition for the "suspension" of K—the pseudogeometric theory suggests one—and then applies the functor G, one obtains FK, which therefore has the homotopy type of the loop-space of the suspension of K; cf. Milnor [2].

Let $K, L \in \mathfrak{M}_*^v$. By $K \vee L$, we denote the union with base points identified; and by $K \wedge L = K \times L/K \vee L \in \mathfrak{M}_*^v$, the complex obtained from the Cartesian product by the identifications

$$(k, *) = (*, l) = * \quad \text{for} \quad k \in K, l \in L.$$

$K \wedge L$ is often denoted by $K \# L$ and called the *smash* (*product*) of K and L.

Now, let $K_1, K_2, \ldots, K_k \in \mathfrak{M}_*^v$; and let b be a basic type of weight r. By regarding $\wedge$ as a *multiplication sign*— we can define a repeated smash product K_b; thus, for instance, if $b = ((l_1 l_2) l_3)$, then $K_b = (K_1 \wedge K_2) \wedge K_3$.

It is easily seen that $F(K \vee L) = FK * FL$, where $*$ denotes the free product of two groups.

We now define a map of

$$F(K \wedge L) \longrightarrow F(K \vee L) = FK * FL$$

by $F(k, l) = [Fk, Fl]$; this is legitimate because the commutator equals 1 if $k = *$ or $l = *$.

Continuing by an evident induction, we obtain for each basic type b a map

$$j_b : FK_b \longrightarrow F(K_1 \vee \cdots \vee K_k).$$

Now, let ΠFK_b denote the weak Cartesian product over all basic types, taken in their order; thus an n-simplex $z \in \Pi FK_b$ assigns to each basic type b an n-simplex $z_b \in FK_b$ so that $z_b = *$ for all but a finite number of b's.

Then we can define the map

$$j : \Pi FK_b \longrightarrow F(K_1 \vee \cdots \vee K_k)$$

by $jz = \Pi j_b z_b$, the product being taken in the order of the basic types.

8.1 Proposition: *j is a homotopy equivalence.*

Proof: Let $\Lambda_r \subset \Pi FK_b$ be the subcomplex for which $z_b = *$ when weight $b < r$. Then

$$\Pi FK_b = \Lambda_1 \supset \Lambda_2 \supset \cdots \supset \Lambda_r \supset \Lambda_{r+1} \supset \cdots.$$
$$F = F(K_1 \vee \cdots \vee K_k) = FK_1 * \cdots * FK_k$$

is filtered by $\Gamma_1 \supset \Gamma_2 \supset \cdots$ as in Section 7.

It is clear from the construction of the map j and that of $u(G)$ (preceding Sec. 7.5) that $j\Lambda_r \subset \Gamma_r$. Hence j induces a map of the associated homotopy exact couples, which begin with

$$\Pi_q\left(\frac{\Lambda_p}{\Lambda_{p+1}}\right) \quad \text{and} \quad \Pi_q\left(\frac{\Gamma_p}{\Gamma_{q+1}}\right)$$

at level E^2. It is clear that Λ_p/Λ_{p+1} is the product of the K_b's for weight $b = p$; since the basic types of weight p are a basis for $L^pAF = \Gamma_p/\Gamma_{p+1}$, Sec. 7.5, it follows that $E^2(j)$ is an isomorphism.

Since the connectivity of $\Lambda_r \longrightarrow \infty$ as $r \longrightarrow \infty$, the first spectral sequence converges to the graded group associated with a filtration of $\pi_q(\Pi FK_b)$; and the theorem follows from a standard spectral sequence argument.

The most important case of Sec. 8.1 arises when $K_i = S^{n_i}$, a sphere. Note that $S^n \wedge S^m = S^{n+m}$, so the K_b are all spheres; and we obtain the theorem of Hilton [1].

BIBLIOGRAPHY

Note: The following list of references is far from complete. I have merely tried to attribute the main theorems to their authors and to indicate where the omitted proofs can be found.

There are in existence a variety of mimeographed expositions—by Cartan, Kan, MacLane, Moore—but wherever possible, I have tried to refer to published sources.

Barratt, M. G., V. K. A. M. Gugenheim, and J. C. Moore.
[1] "On semisimplicial fibre bundles," *Amer. J. Math.*, **81** (1959), 639–57.

Curtis, E. B.
[1] "Lower central series of semisimplicial complexes," *Topology*, **2** (1963), 159–71.
[2] Some Relations between Homotopy and Homology (to be published).

Dold, A.

[1] "Homology of symmetric products and other functors of complexes," *Ann. Math.*, **68** (1958), 54–80.

Dold, A., and D. Puppe.

[1] "Homologie Nicht-Additiver Funktoren," *Ann. L'Inst. Fourier*, **XI**, (1961), 201–312.

Eilenberg, S., and S. MacLane.

[1] "On the groups $H(\pi, n)$," I, *Ann. Math.*, **58** (1953), 55–106.

[2] "On the groups $H(\pi, n)$," II, *Ann. Math.*, **60** (1954), 49–139.

Eilenberg, S., and J. A. Zilber.

[1] "Semisimplicial complexes and singular homology," *Ann. Math.*, **51** (1950), 499–513.

[2] "On products of complexes," *Am. Jour. Math.*, **75** (1953), 200–204.

Gugenheim, V. K. A. M.

[1] "On supercomplexes," *Trans. Amer. Math. Soc.*, **85** (1957), 35–51.

[2] "On a theorem of E. H. Brown," *Illinois Jour. Math.*, **4** (1960), 292–311.

Hall, M.

[1] "A basis for free Lie rings and higher commutators in free groups," *Proc. Am. Math. Soc.*, **1** (1950), 575–81.

[2] *The Theory of Groups*. New York: The Macmillan Co., 1959.

Heller, Alex

[1] "Homotopy resolutions of semisimplicial complexes," *Trans. Am. Math. Soc.*, **80** (1955), 299–344.

Hilton, P. J.

[1] "On the homotopy groups of the union of spheres," *Jour. Lond. Math. Soc.*, **30** (1959), 154–72.

Kan, D. M.

[1] "A combinatorial definition of homotopy groups," *Ann. Math.*, **67** (1957), 282–312.

[2] "The Hurewicz Theorem," *Proc. Intern. Sym. Alg. Top. Appl.*, Mexico (1956).

[3] "On c.s.s. complexes," *Am. Jour. Math.*, **79** (1957), 449–76.

[4] "Functors involving c.s.s. complexes," *Trans. Am. Math. Soc.*, **87** (1958), 330–46.

[5] "Adjoint functors," *Trans. Am. Math. Soc.*, **87** (1958), 294–329.

[6] "On homotopy theory and c.s.s. groups," *Ann. Math.*, **68** (1958), 38–53.

[7] "On the homotopy relation for c.s.s. maps," *Bol. Soc. Math. Mexicana*, (1957), 75–81.

MacLane, S.

[1] "Constructions simpliciales acycliques," *Coll. Henri Poincaré*, Paris, 1954.

Massey, W. S.

[1] "Exact couples in algebraic topology," I and II, *Ann. Math.*, **56** (1952), 363–96.

Milnor, J. W.

[1] "The geometric realisation of a semi-simplicial complex," *Ann. Math.*, **65** (1957), 357–62.

[2] *The Construction FK*, Mimeographed notes, Princeton 1957.

Moore, J. C.

[1] "Semisimplicial complexes and Postnikov systems," *Sym. Int. Top. Alg.*, Mexico (1958), 232–47.

[2] *Algebraic Homotopy Theory*, Mimeographed notes, Princeton 1957.

[3] "Homotopie des complexes monoidaux I, II," *Séminaire H. Cartan*, 7, *Exp.*, **18**, **19** (1954155).

Postnikov, M. M.

[1] *Dokl. Akad. Nauk. SSSR* (1951) *Tom* 76, 3, 359–62; *Tom* 76, 6, 789–91; *Tom* 79, 4, 573–76.

Puppe, Dieter

[1] "Homotopie und Homologie in Abelschen Gruppen und Monoidkomplexen, I and II," *Math. Zeit.*, **68** (1958), 367–421.

[2] "A theorem on semisimplicial monoid complexes," *Ann. Math.*, **70** (1959), 379–94.

Schlesinger, J. W.

[1] The Semisimplicial Free Lie Ring (to be published).

Witt, E.

[1] "Treue Darstellung Liescher Ringe," *Jour. Reine Angew. Math.*, **177** (1937), 152–60.

Shih-Weishuh.

[1] "Homologie des Espaces Fibrés," *Publ. Math.*, **13**, *Inst. de Hautes Etudes*, Paris (1962).

THE FUNCTORS OF ALGEBRAIC TOPOLOGY

Eldon Dyer

A very effective means of attacking many problems of a topological or geometrical nature is to describe algebraic invariants reflecting, in part, the structures of interest and to analyze these invariants. This is the method of algebraic topology. In the past 3 decades a great variety of such invariants has been discovered, studied, and applied with remarkable successes.

The object of this article is to present a unified development of many of these invariants. While this affords an efficient presentation, it appears somewhat artificial and unmotivated. Actually, there is no loss of effective computability, and many relations are clarified. Also, the way of looking at the invariants presented here has had a number of successes recently toward finding important new invariants.

The discussion is necessarily abbreviated, oversimplified, and in some places vague. It is hoped that adequate references are given for those who may wish to go into these matters more deeply.

HOMOTOPY

Section A. Let (C, c_0) and (X, x_0) be pairs consisting of topological spaces and points of them, $c_0 \in C$ and $x_0 \in X$. Two ("pointed") mappings

$$f\colon (C, c_0) \longrightarrow (X, x_0) \quad \text{and} \quad g\colon (C, c_0) \longrightarrow (X, x_0)$$

$[f(c_0) = x_0$ and $g(c_0) = x_0]$ are *homotopic* if there is a mapping

$$H\colon C \times I \longrightarrow X,$$

where $I = [0, 1]$, such that

$$H(c, 0) = f(c) \quad \text{for all} \quad c \in C,$$

$$H(c, 1) = g(c) \quad \text{for all} \quad c \in C,$$

and

$$H(c_0, t) = x_0 \quad \text{for all} \quad t \in I.$$

Homotopy is an equivalence relation. The collection of equivalence classes so defined is denoted

$$[(C, c_0), (X, x_0)].$$

This is a "pointed" set; i.e., it has a distinguished object—the equivalence class of pointed maps homotopic to the mapping which sends all C to the point x_0.

Consider mappings

$$(A, a_0) \xrightarrow{\alpha} (B, b_0), \qquad (B, b_0) \xrightarrow{\beta} (C, c_0)$$

$$(X, x_0) \xrightarrow{g} (Y, y_0), \qquad (Y, y_0) \xrightarrow{h} (Z, z_0).$$

For an element f in a class in $[(C, c_0), (X, x_0)]$, the composite $g \circ f$ determines a class in $[(C, c_0), (Y, y_0)]$, which is independent of the choice of representative f in its class. We denote this class by $g_*(\{f\})$. The composite $f \circ \beta$ similarly determines a class $\beta^*(\{f\}) \in [(B, b_0), (X, x_0)]$. Each of the morphisms

$$g_*\colon [(C, c_0), (X, x_0)] \longrightarrow [(C, c_0), (Y, y_0)]$$

and

$$\beta^*\colon [(C, c_0), (X, x_0)] \longrightarrow [(B, b_0), (X, x_0)]$$

carries distinguished object into distinguished object. Furthermore,

$$(h \circ g)_* = h_* \circ g_* \quad \text{and} \quad (\beta \circ \alpha)^* = \alpha^* \circ \beta^*.$$

The identity maps $\mathrm{Id}_C: C \longrightarrow C$ and $\mathrm{Id}_X: X \longrightarrow X$ induce the identity morphism; i.e.,

$$(\mathrm{Id}_X)_* = \mathrm{Id}_{[(C,c_0),(X,x_0)]} = (\mathrm{Id}_C)^*.$$

Section B. Suppose it is true that $[(C, c_0), (X, x_0)]$ has a group structure which is natural with respect to maps $\beta: (B, b_0) \longrightarrow (C, c_0)$; i.e., for every two spaces (B, b_0) and (C, c_0) and map $\beta: (B, b_0) \longrightarrow (C, c_0)$,

$$[(C, c_0), (X, x_0)] \quad \text{and} \quad [(B, b_0), (X, x_0)]$$

are groups and β^* is a homomorphism, (X, x_0) being fixed throughout.

Let $p_1: X \times X \longrightarrow X$ and $p_2: X \times X \longrightarrow X$ be the projections onto the two factors: $p_1(x, y) = x$ and $p_2(x, y) = y$; and let μ be an element of the class $\{p_1\} \cdot \{p_2\} \in [(X \times X, x_0 \times x_0), (X, x_0)]$ determined by the group structure. Then for $f: (C, c_0) \longrightarrow (X, x_0)$ and $g: (C, c_0) \longrightarrow (X, x_0)$, the composition

$$C \xrightarrow{\Delta} C \times C \xrightarrow{f \times g} X \times X \xrightarrow{\mu} X$$

is an element of the class $\{f\} \cdot \{g\} \in [(C, c_0), (X, x_0)]$, where Δ is the diagonal mapping $\Delta(c) = (c, c)$.

Let $1_X: X \longrightarrow x_0$ and $\nu \in \{\mathrm{Id}_X\}^{-1} \in [(X, x_0), (X, x_0)]$. It can be shown that

(i) $\{\mu(x, x_0)\} = \{\mathrm{Id}_X\} = \{\mu(x_0, x)\}$.
(ii) $\{\mu(x, \nu(x))\} = \{1_X\} = \{\mu(\nu(x), x)\}$.
(iii) $\{\mu(x, \mu(y, z))\} = \{\mu(\mu(x, y), z)\}$.

Thinking of μ as a multiplication on X, x_0 as the identity element of X, and ν as an inverse operation, we see that conditions (i), (ii), and (iii) are precisely those asserting that X is a topological group, except the usual assertions of equality are replaced by assertions of equality "up to a homotopy." A space X so equipped is called an H-space, in honor of H. Hopf.

Thus, under the assumption that $[(\ ,\ ), (X, x_0)]$ has a natural group structure, we see that (X, x_0) is an H-space and that this H-space structure on X determines the group operations in $[(C, c_0), (X, x_0)]$ for every (C, c_0) [8].

Let $X \vee Y$ be the subspace of $X \times Y$ consisting of all pairs (x, y_0) and (x_0, y). The condition (i) can be stated equivalently: the diagram

$$\begin{array}{ccc} X \times X & \xrightarrow{\mu} & X \\ \uparrow{\scriptstyle \subset} & \nearrow{\scriptstyle \Delta'} & \\ X \vee X & & \end{array}$$

is homotopy commutative, where Δ' is the folding map $\Delta'(x, x_0) = x = \Delta'(x_0, x)$.

Dually, suppose there are maps

$$\mu' \colon C \longrightarrow C \vee C \quad \text{and} \quad \nu \colon C \longrightarrow C$$

such that

(i) The diagram

$$\begin{array}{ccc} C & \xrightarrow{\Delta} & C \times C \\ & \searrow{\scriptstyle \mu'} & \uparrow{\scriptstyle \subset} \\ & & C \vee C \end{array}$$

homotopy commutes.

(ii) each of the compositions

$$C \xrightarrow{\mu'} C \vee C \xrightarrow{\mathrm{Id}_C \vee \nu} C \vee C \xrightarrow{\Delta'} C$$

and

$$C \xrightarrow{\mu'} C \vee C \xrightarrow{\nu \vee \mathrm{Id}_C} C \vee C \xrightarrow{\Delta'} C$$

is homotopic to the trivial map $1_C \colon C \longrightarrow c_0$

(iii)

$$\begin{array}{ccc} C & \xrightarrow{\mu'} & C \vee C \\ \downarrow{\scriptstyle \mu'} & & \downarrow{\scriptstyle \mathrm{Id}_C \vee \mu'} \\ C \vee C & \xrightarrow{\mu' \vee \mathrm{Id}_C} & C \vee C \vee C \end{array}$$

homotopy commutes. Then C is said to be a co-H-space.

We have the dual proposition that $[(C, c_0), (\ \ ,\ \ )]$ has a natural group structure if and only if (C, c_0) is a co-H-space. The group structure is given by the composition

$$C \xrightarrow{\mu'} C \vee C \xrightarrow{f \vee g} X \vee X \xrightarrow{\Delta'} X.$$

Finally, one can show that if (C, c_0) is a co-H-space and (X, x_0) is an H-space, then the two group structures on $[(C, c_0), (X, x_0)]$ coincide and are abelian.

Section C. An important class of H-spaces is that of *loop-spaces.* For a space (X, x_0), let $\Omega(X, x_0)$ be the space of maps α of I into X with $\alpha(0) = \alpha(1) = x_0$, topologized with the compact open topology. For α and β in $\Omega(X, x_0)$, we define

$$\mu(\alpha, \beta)(t) = \begin{cases} \alpha(2t) & 0 \leqq t \leqq \frac{1}{2} \\ \beta(2t - 1) & \frac{1}{2} \leqq t \leqq 1. \end{cases}$$

Then

$$\nu: \Omega(X, x_0) \longrightarrow \Omega(X, x_0)$$

is defined by $\nu(\alpha)(t) = \alpha(1 - t)$. The identity element is $e_{x_0}: I \longrightarrow x_0$. The maps μ, ν, e_{x_0} give $\Omega(X, x_0)$ an H-space structure.

To describe an important class of co-H-spaces, we first define the *smash product* $X \wedge Y$ to be the quotient space of $X \times Y$ with $X \vee Y$ identified to a point. If N is a co-H-space with co-product μ', $C \wedge N$ has a co-H-space structure given by the composition

$$C \wedge N \xrightarrow{\mathrm{Id}_C \wedge \mu'} C \wedge (N \vee N) \longrightarrow (C \wedge N) \vee (C \wedge N),$$

where the last map is a canonically defined homeomorphism.

The unit circle $S^1 = \{z \in C \mid |z| = 1\}$ with $z = 1$ as base point has co-product

$$\mu': S^1 \longrightarrow S^1 \vee S^1$$

given by

$$\mu'(e^{i\theta}) = \begin{cases} e_1^{2i\theta} & 0 \leqq \theta \leqq \Pi \\ e_2^{2i\theta} & \Pi \leqq \theta \leqq 2\Pi. \end{cases}$$

The map defined by $e^{i\theta} \longrightarrow e^{-i\theta}$ is a co-inverse.

The *reduced suspension* ΣC is defined to be $C \wedge S^1$, and it is thus a co-H-space.

We note also that there is a one-to-one correspondence between pointed maps

$$C \wedge S^1 \xrightarrow{f} X \quad \text{and} \quad C \xrightarrow{\chi(f)} \Omega X$$

defined by $\chi(f)(c)(t) = f(c \wedge t)$. And this correspondence preserves homotopies. Finally, a direct computation shows that

$$\chi\colon [C \wedge S^1, X] \longrightarrow [C, \Omega X]$$

is an isomorphism.

Section D. For pointed spaces (C, c_0) and (X, x_0) we define

$$\Pi_n^{(C,c_0)}(X, x_0) \equiv [\Sigma^p C, \Omega^q X],$$

where $p + q = n$, $\Sigma^p C = (\Sigma^{p-1}C) \wedge S^1$, and $\Omega^q X = \Omega(\Omega^{q-1}X)$. The isomorphism above shows this definition is independent of choice of p and q, so long as $p + q = n$.

Combining previous assertions, we have

$\Pi_0^{(C,c_0)}(X, x_0)$ is a set with distinguished object,

$\Pi_1^{(C,c_0)}(X, x_0)$ is a group,

and

$\Pi_i^{(C,c_0)}(X, x_0)$, $i \geqq 2$, is an abelian group.

Also, for (C, c_0) the assignment $\Pi_i^{(C,c_0)}(\ ,\ )$ is a covariant functor, and for (X, x_0) the assignment $\Pi_i^{(\ ,\ )}(X, x_0)$ is a contravariant functor.

For $(C, c_0) = (S^0, +1)$, where S^0 is the 0-sphere of two points $+1$ and -1 in the complex line,

$$\Pi_i^{(S^0,+1)}(X, x_0) \equiv \Pi_i(X, x_0)$$

are the *homotopy groups* of (X, x_0).

Section E. It is something of an understatement to say that in general homotopy groups are not easy to compute.

Let us compute $\Pi_1(S^1, s_0)$. Note that since S^1 is an H-space, it is abelian.

For $\mathbf{R}$ the real line, define $p\colon \mathbf{R} \longrightarrow S^1$ by $p(x) = e^{2\Pi ix}$. One can prove that if $\omega\colon I \longrightarrow S^1$ and $x_0 \in \mathbf{R}$ such that $p(x_0) = \omega(0)$, then there is a unique path $\tau\colon I \longrightarrow \mathbf{R}$ such that $\tau(0) = x_0$ and $p \circ \tau = \omega$. This generalizes slightly to the following:

Suppose

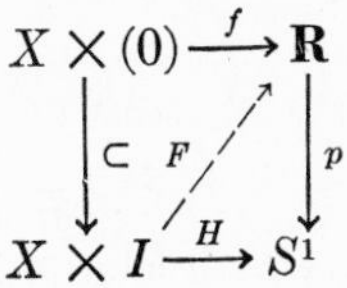

is a commutative diagram. Then there exists uniquely a map $F: X \times I \longrightarrow \mathbf{R}$ such that F extends f and $p \circ F = H$.

Since $\Pi_1(S^1, s_0) \cong \Pi_0(\Omega(S^1, s_0), e_{s_0})$, the path components of $\Omega(S^1, s_0)$ are in one-to-one correspondence with $\Pi_1(S^1, s_0)$, where the group operation is given by adding loops by loop composition. A loop $f \in \Omega(S^1, s_0)$ lifts uniquely to a path $\tilde{f}: I \longrightarrow \mathbf{R}$ such that $\tilde{f}(0) = 0$. Then $\tilde{f}(1) \in Z$, the additive group of integers. Loops f and g have $\tilde{f}(1) = \tilde{g}(1)$ if and only if they lie in the same path component of $\Omega(S^1, s_0)$. Furthermore, $(f + g)^{\sim}(1) = \tilde{f}(1) + \tilde{g}(1)$. Thus, the operation $\tilde{f}(1)$ defines a monomorphism

$$\Pi_1(S^1, s_0) \longrightarrow Z.$$

Also, $\tilde{Id}(1) = 1$. Thus, it is an isomorphism.

We shall return to further computations of homotopy groups.

Section F. Generalizing the situation of the preceding paragraph, we say that a map $p: X \longrightarrow B$ is a *fiber map* if it has the covering homotopy property; i.e., if for every pair of maps $H: A \times I \longrightarrow B$ and $g: A \times (1) \longrightarrow X$, such that $p \circ g(a, 1) = H(a, 1)$, there is a map $G: A \times I \longrightarrow X$ which extends g and for which $p \circ G = H$.

$$\begin{array}{ccc} A \times (1) & \xrightarrow{g} & X \\ \downarrow \subset & \overset{G}{\nearrow} & \downarrow p \\ A \times I & \xrightarrow{H} & B. \end{array}$$

$F = p^{-1}(b_0)$ is the *fiber*, X is the *total space*, and B the *base space*. The triple (X, B, p) is called a *fibration* [11].

If $b_1 \in B$ lies in the path component of b_0, then $p^{-1}(b_1)$ is of the same *homotopy type* as F. This means there are maps $\alpha: F \longrightarrow p^{-1}(b_1)$ and $\beta: p^{-1}(b_1) \longrightarrow F$ such that $\alpha \circ \beta$ and $\beta \circ \alpha$ are homotopic to the identity maps in $p^{-1}(b_1)$ and F, respectively.

Two important sources of fiber maps are

(1) Locally trivial maps $p: X \longrightarrow B$ for B paracompact (p is locally trivial if for each point b of B there is a neighborhood U of b such that $p|p^{-1}(u)$ is a projection map of a Cartesian product).

(2) For A and B subspaces of X and $E(X; A, B)$, the space of paths $\omega: I \longrightarrow X$ such that $\omega(0) \in A$ and $\omega(1) \in B$, the map

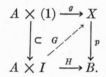

$$p\colon E(X\colon A, B) \longrightarrow A \times B,$$

defined by $p(\omega) = (\omega(0), \omega(1))$, is a fiber map.

Also, compositions of fiber maps are fiber maps. Thus, for example,

$$E(X; A, B) \longrightarrow A,$$

defined by composing p with the projection map $A \times B \longrightarrow A$, is a fiber map.

Consider

$$\begin{array}{ccc} \Omega B \times (1) & \xrightarrow{g} & X \\ \downarrow \subset & & \downarrow p \\ \Omega B \times I & \xrightarrow{H} & B \end{array}$$

where $H(\omega, t) = \omega(t)$ and $g(\omega, 1) = x_0 \in F = p^{-1}(b_0)$. The lifting $G\colon \Omega B \times I \longrightarrow X$ when restricted to $\Omega B \times (0)$ is a mapping

$$\lambda\colon \Omega B \longrightarrow F.$$

This defines inductively a sequence

$$\cdots \longrightarrow \Omega^2 X \longrightarrow \Omega^2 B \xrightarrow{\Omega\lambda} \Omega F \xrightarrow{\Omega i} \Omega X \xrightarrow{\Omega p} \Omega B \xrightarrow{\lambda} F \xrightarrow{i} X \xrightarrow{p} B$$

of spaces and maps. It is an exact sequence in the sense that for every pointed space (C, c_0), the sequence

$$\cdots \longrightarrow [C, \Omega^2 B] \longrightarrow [C, \Omega F] \longrightarrow [C, \Omega X] \longrightarrow [C, \Omega B] \longrightarrow [C, F] \longrightarrow [C, X] \longrightarrow [C, B]$$

or, equivalently,

$$\cdots \longrightarrow \Pi_2^C(B) \longrightarrow \Pi_1^C(F) \longrightarrow \Pi_1^C(X) \longrightarrow \Pi_1^C(B) \longrightarrow \Pi_0^C(F) \longrightarrow \Pi_0^C(X) \longrightarrow \Pi_0^C(B)$$

is an exact sequence of sets with distinguished object—the image of each map is precisely the set of elements which the next map carries into the distinguished element [8].

For $(C, c_0) = (S^0, +1)$, this is the exact homotopy sequence of a fibration.

Section G. For $x_0 \in A \subset X$, $E(X; A, X) \longrightarrow X$ is a fibration with fiber $E(X; A, x_0)$. The total space has the homotopy type of A. The exact homotopy sequence is

$$\cdots \longrightarrow \Pi_2(X, x_0) \longrightarrow \Pi_1(E(X; A, x_0), *) \longrightarrow \Pi_1(A, x_0) \longrightarrow$$
$$\Pi_1(X, x_0) \longrightarrow \Pi_0(E(X, A, x_0), *) \longrightarrow \Pi_0(A, x_0) \longrightarrow \Pi_0(X, x_0).$$

We define the *relative homotopy groups*

$$\Pi_{i+1}(X, A, x_0) \equiv \Pi_i(E(X; A, x_0), *), \qquad i \geqq 0.$$

The exact sequence above is then the relative homotopy sequence

$$\cdots \longrightarrow \Pi_2(X, x_0) \longrightarrow \Pi_2(X, A, x_0) \longrightarrow \Pi_1(A, x_0) \longrightarrow$$
$$\Pi_1(X, x_0) \longrightarrow \Pi_1(X, A, x_0) \longrightarrow \Pi_0(A, x_0) \longrightarrow \Pi_0(X, x_0).$$

Similarly, we define triad groups

$$\Pi_n(X; A, B, x_0) \equiv \Pi_{n-1}(E(X; B, x_0), E(A; A \cap B, x_0)), \qquad n \geqq 2.$$

Inductively, one can define the $(k + 1)$-ad homotopy groups

$$\Pi_n^{(k+1)}(X; A_1, \ldots, A_k, x_0) \equiv \Pi_{n-1}^{(k)}(E(X; A_k, x_0);$$
$$E(A_1; A_1 \cap A_k, x_0), \ldots, E(A_{k-1}; A_{k-1} \cap A_k, x_0)),$$

for $n \geqq k$, and prove

I. If σ is a permutation on $(1, \ldots, k)$, then

$$\Pi_n^{(k+1)}(X; A_1, \ldots, A_k, x_0) \cong \Pi_n^{(k+1)}(X; A_{\sigma(1)}, \ldots, A_{\sigma(k)}, x_0).$$

II. If $A_k \subset A_i$ for some i, $1 \leqq i \leqq k - 1$, then

$$\Pi_n^{(k+1)}(X; A_1, \ldots, A_k, x_0) \cong \Pi_n^{(k)}(X; A_1, \ldots, A_{k-1}, x_0).$$

III. There is a natural exact triangle

$$\begin{array}{ccc} & \Pi_*^{(k+1)}(X; A_1, \ldots, A_k, *) & \\ \nearrow & & \searrow \text{degree } -1 \\ \Pi_*^{(k)}(X; A_2, \ldots, A_k, *) & \longleftarrow & \Pi_*^{(k)}(A_1; A_1 \cap A_2, \ldots, A_1 \cap A_k, *). \end{array}$$

Section H. In a dual manner one defines cofiber maps and shows that the sequence

$$A \xrightarrow{\subset} X \longrightarrow X \cup TA \longrightarrow \hat{\Sigma} A \longrightarrow \hat{\Sigma} X \longrightarrow \hat{\Sigma}(X \cup TA) \longrightarrow \cdots$$

is coexact. $X \cup TA$ denotes the union of X and the join of a point with A; $\hat{\Sigma}$ denotes the nonreduced suspension. The map

$$X \cup TA \longrightarrow \hat{\Sigma} A$$

is defined by identifying X to a point. Coexact means that the sequence obtained on mapping from these spaces to a fixed space is an exact sequence of sets with distinguished object.

Section I. In making some constructions later, it will be convenient to replace the spaces, pairs, and triads under consideration by simpler ones. These are the CW-complexes of J. H. C. Whitehead.

A *complex* is a Hausdorff space K which is the union of an increasing sequence $K^0 \subset K^1 \subset K^2 \subset \cdots$ of *skeleta* wherein for each i, $K^{(i+1)}$ is obtained from $K^{(i)}$ by attaching cells $\{e_\lambda^{i+1}\}$ by maps

$$f_\lambda: S^i \longrightarrow K^{(i)}.$$

The complex is *closure finite* if each of the attaching maps f_λ has $\operatorname{Im}(f_\lambda)$ contained in a finite subcomplex of K. A closure finite complex has the *weak topology* if a subset L is closed if and only if its intersection with each finite subcomplex is compact. A closure finite complex with the weak topology is a CW-complex [19].

If $y_0 \in D \subset Y$ is a pair of spaces, there is a relative CW-complex (Y', D), Y'/D is a CW-complex, and a map $Y' \longrightarrow Y$ such that it is the identity on D and induces isomorphisms of relative homotopy groups. Further, if $\Pi_i(Y, D) = 0$ for $i \leqq n$, the first cells in Y' can be taken in dimension $n + 1$. Such a relative CW-complex can be formed inductively by attaching $(n + 1)$-cells to D by maps $(e^{n+1}, S^n) \longrightarrow (Y, D)$ generating $\Pi_{n+1}(Y, D, *)$ restricted to S^n. The space so formed maps into (Y, D) inducing an epimorphism on Π_{n+1}. By attaching $(n + 2)$-cells, the kernel of this epimorphism can be killed. This yields

$$(Y^{(n+1)}, D) \xrightarrow{f_{n+1}} (Y, D)$$

with $\Pi_i(f_{n+1})$ and isomorphism for $i \leqq n + 1$. This process can be continued. Since the resultant homomorphisms in relative homotopy are isomorphisms, the absolute groups $\Pi_i(Y') \longrightarrow \Pi_i(Y)$ also map isomorphically; this is seen using the relative homotopy sequences and the five lemmas. Thus, if $D = y_0$, we have a CW-complex and map

$$Y' \longrightarrow Y$$

inducing isomorphisms of homotopy. If we first find a CW-substitute

$$D' \xrightarrow{g} D$$

for D and then a relative CW-substitute for $(Y \cup C(g), D')$, where $Y \cup C(g)$ is the union of Y with the mapping cylinder of g, we obtain a pair of CW-complexes (Y', D') and a map $(Y', D') \longrightarrow (Y, D)$ inducing isomorphisms on absolute and relative homotopy groups.

HOMOLOGY AND COHOMOLOGY

Section J. A triad $(X; A, B, x_0)$ is a *good* triad if $x_0 \in A \cap B$ and $X = (\text{interior } A) \cup (\text{interior } B)$ or if it can be mapped into such a triad by a map inducing isomorphisms on $\Pi_*(X, A)$, $\Pi_*(X, B)$, $\Pi_*(A, A \cap B)$, $\Pi_*(B, A \cap B)$, and $\Pi_*(A \cap B)$. For example, if A and B are closed in X and $A \cap B = C$ has a neighborhood N in A such that there is a deformation of N into C carrying C into C throughout the deformation, then letting $X' = X$, $A' = A$, and $B' = B \cup N$, the inclusion map

$$(X; A, B) \longrightarrow (X'; A', B')$$

has the necessary properties.

PROPOSITION: *If $(X; A, B, x_0)$ is a good triad and*

$$f\colon (X'; A', B', x_0) \longrightarrow (X; A, B, x_0)$$

is a map of triads such that $\Pi_*(f|A')$, $\Pi_*(f|B')$, and $\Pi_*(f|C')$ are isomorphisms, then $\Pi_*(f)$ is an isomorphism of triad homotopy groups.

We can assume $X = \text{int } A \cup \text{int } B$; and attaching X' to X by the mapping cylinder of f and identifying $X; A, B$ with their correspondents in that mapping cylinder, we can assume f is an inclusion map of triads.

An element of $\Pi_n(X; A, B, x_0)$ is a homotopy class of maps

$$f\colon (D^n; D_+^{n+1}, D_-^{n-1}, *) \longrightarrow (X; A, B, x_0),$$

where $D^n = \{x \in \mathbf{R}^n | \ \|x\| \leqq 1\}$, $D_+^{n-1} = \{x \in D^n | \ \|x\| = 1$ and $x_n \geqq 0\}$, and $D_-^{n-1} = \{x \in D^n | \ \|x\| = 1$ and $x_n \leqq 0\}$. We shall compress f into $(X'; A', B', x_0)$ by triangulating D^n so finely that it is the union of simplicial complexes P and Q with $f(P) \subset A$ and $f(Q) \subset B$. Compress f on $P \cap Q$ by induction on skeleta into C'.

Then, leaving this fixed, compress P into A' and Q into B'. Similar constructions on $D^n \times I$ allow a homotopy in $(X; A, B)$ to be compressed into $(X'; A', B')$.

As an application of this proposition, we see that we can replace a good triad by a CW-triad. Replace (A, C) and (B, C) by CW-pairs

$$(A', C') \longrightarrow (A, C)$$

$$(B', C') \longrightarrow (B, C)$$

with maps inducing isomorphisms on relative and absolute homotopy. Letting $X' = A' \cup B'$, we see that by the proposition above

$$(X'; A', B') \longrightarrow (X; A, B)$$

induces isomorphisms of triad homotopy groups.

Consider the triad sequence

$$\longrightarrow \Pi_{n+1}(X; A, B) \longrightarrow \Pi_n(A, A \cap B) \xrightarrow{i_*} \Pi_n(X, B) \longrightarrow \Pi_n(X; A, B) \longrightarrow \cdots.$$

The map $(A, A \cap B) \longrightarrow (X, B)$ is a relative homeomorphism and one might expect i_* to be an isomorphism. Such a property, when valid, is called *excision*. Nonvanishing of triad groups is a measure of lack of excision. A characteristic property of homology and cohomology theories is that excision holds for them in most cases of interest.

As we step toward describing such theories, we now state the crucial result on triad homotopy groups regarding excision.

TRIAD CONNECTIVITY THEOREM: *If $(X; A, B, x_0)$ is a good triad and*

$$\Pi_i(A, A \cap B, x_0) = 0 \quad \textit{for} \quad i \leqq n$$

and

$$\Pi_i(B, A \cap B, x_0) = 0 \quad \textit{for} \quad i \leqq m,$$

then

$$\Pi_i(X; A, B, x_0) = 0 \quad \textit{for} \quad i \leqq m + n.$$

Proof: The proof of this theorem will be only very briefly sketched here. Replace $(X; A, B, x_0)$ by a CW-triad. By an inductive argument on cells, one sees it suffices to prove the result where

$$A = C \cup e^{n+1} \quad \text{and} \quad B = C \cup e^{m+1}.$$

The result in this case is established by a general position argument on a locally simplicial approximation. Details for an argument similar to the latter are in [18]. Two quick consequences of this are given.

THEOREM: *Suppose* $\Pi_i(X, A) = 0$ *for* $i \leqq n$ *and* $\Pi_i(A) = 0$ *for* $i < k$, *then*

$$\Pi_i(X, A) \longrightarrow \Pi_i(X \cup TA, TA) \xleftarrow{\cong} \Pi(X \cup TA)$$

is an isomorphism for $i < n + k$ *and is onto for* $i = n + k$.

This follows from the triad exact sequence of the good triad $(X \cup TA; X, TA)$.

Let $E: \Pi_q(A) \longrightarrow \Pi_{q+1}(\hat{\Sigma}A)$ be the composition

$$\Pi_q(A) \xleftarrow{\cong} \Pi_{q+1}(TA, A) \longrightarrow \Pi_{q+1}(TA \cup T_1A, T_1A) \xleftarrow{\cong} \Pi_{q+1}(\hat{\Sigma}A),$$

where T_1A is a second cone over A.

COROLLARY: *If* $\Pi_i(A) = 0$ *for* $i < k$, *then*

$$E: \Pi_q(A) \longrightarrow \Pi_{q+1}(\hat{\Sigma}A)$$

is an isomorphism for $q < 2k - 1$ *and is onto for* $q = 2k - 1$. *In particular, this is true for* $A = S^k (\hat{\Sigma}A = S^{k+1})$.

Section K. In this section we shall construct some spaces with preassigned homotopy. First we need the

THEOREM: $E: \Pi_n(S^n) \longrightarrow \Pi_{n+1}(S^{n+1})$ *is an isomorphism for* $n \geqq 1$. (*Recall that* $\Pi_1(S^1) \cong \mathbf{Z}$.)

We know already this is true for $n < 2n - 1$, i.e., for $1 < n$, and we know E is onto for $n = 1$. If we can show that $\Pi_2(S^2) \cong \mathbf{Z}$, we are done.

The technique for doing this involves the very important Hopf maps. The space whose points are the complex lines through (0, 0) in $\mathbf{C}^2$, with suitable topology, is homeomorphic to S^2. The space of vectors in $\mathbf{C}^2$ of unit norm is homeomorphic to S^3; and the map $S^3 \longrightarrow S^2$, defined by taking each vector of unit norm into that complex line through (0, 0) containing it, is locally trivial. This map is thus a fiber map; it has fiber S^1. Since $\Pi_1(S^3) = \Pi_2(S^3) = 0$, the homotopy sequence of the fibration

$$\cdots \longrightarrow \Pi_2(S^3) \longrightarrow \Pi_2(S^2) \longrightarrow \Pi_1(S^1) \longrightarrow \Pi_1(S^3) \longrightarrow \cdots$$

shows that $\Pi_2(S^2) \cong \Pi_1(S^1) \cong \mathbf{Z}$.

Similar constructions can be made using the quaternions and Cayley numbers [15].

Let Π be an abelian group and n a positive integer. We shall construct a CW-complex $K(\Pi, n)$ such that

$$\Pi_i(K(\Pi, n)) \cong \begin{cases} 0 & i \neq n \\ \Pi & i = n. \end{cases}$$

Let $\{g_\alpha\}$ be a family of generators of Π. Let

$$K^{(n)} = \bigvee_\alpha S^n_\alpha.$$

Let $\{r_\beta\}$ generate the relations defining Π and let

$$f_\beta \colon S^n \longrightarrow K^{(n)}$$

have r_β as its homotopy class in $\Pi_n(K^{(n)})$. Attach $(n+1)$-cells by the maps f_β to form $K^{(n+1)}$. Then

$$\begin{aligned} \Pi_i(K^{(n+1)}) &= 0 \quad \text{for} \quad i < n \\ &\cong \Pi \quad \text{for} \quad i = n. \end{aligned}$$

Attach $(n+2)$-cells to $K^{(n+1)}$ by maps generating $\Pi_{n+1}(K^{(n+1)})$ to form $K^{(n+2)}$. Then

$$\begin{aligned} \Pi_i(K^{(n+1)}) &= 0 \quad \text{for} \quad i < n,\ i = n+1 \\ &\cong \Pi \quad \text{for} \quad i = n. \end{aligned}$$

Continue in this fashion to form $K(\Pi, n)$.

Let G and H be abelian groups, $f \colon G \longrightarrow H$ a homomorphism, X a space with

$$\Pi_i(X) \cong \begin{cases} 0 & i \neq n \\ H & i = n, \end{cases}$$

and $Y = K(G, n)$, as above. Then there is a map

$$\bar{f} \colon Y \longrightarrow X$$

such that $\Pi_n(\bar{f}) = f$, and any two such maps are homotopic. This is seen by mapping the S_α^n into X so as to lie in the class of $f(g_\alpha)$. This defines a map of $\bigvee_\alpha S_\alpha^n$ into X which extends on $K^{(n+1)}$ since the compositions with the f_β are null-homotopic. As all the higher homotopy of X is trivial, the map so defined on $K^{(n+1)}$ can be extended inductively on skeleta to a map $\bar{f}$. The assertion of homotopy is similarly established.

One can show in a similar way that if $g: (X, x_0) \longrightarrow (Y, y_0)$ is a map of spaces with base point inducing isomorphisms of homotopy, (B, b_0) is a CW-complex and $f: (B, b_0) \longrightarrow (Y, y_0)$, then there is a map $h: (B, b_0) \longrightarrow (X, x_0)$ such that $g \circ h \simeq f$ and any two such maps are homotopic.

It follows from this, for example, that if (X, x_0) is a space and $(X_1, *)$ and $(X_2, *)$ are CW-complexes and $f_1: (X_1, *) \longrightarrow (X, x_0)$ and $f_2: (X_2, *) \longrightarrow (X, x_0)$ are maps inducing isomorphisms of homotopy, then there are maps $i_1: (X_1, *) \longrightarrow (X_2, *)$ and $i_2: (X_2, *) \longrightarrow (X_1, *)$ such that $f_2 \circ i_1 \simeq f_1$ and $f_1 \circ i_2 \simeq f_2$; they are uniquely determined up to homotopy by these conditions and $i_2 \circ i_1 \simeq \mathrm{Id}_{X_1}$ and $i_1 \circ i_2 \simeq \mathrm{Id}_{X_2}$. Thus, we can speak of the CW-substitute of space, for it is uniquely determined up to a uniquely defined homotopy equivalence. One can proceed similarly for pairs, maps, triads, etc.

Section L. Each of the spaces $K(\Pi, n)$ is defined with a particular isomorphism of $\Pi_n(K(\Pi, n))$ with the group Π. The homotopy sequence of the fibration $\Omega K(\Pi, n+1) \longrightarrow E(K(\Pi, n+1); K(\Pi, n+1), *) \longrightarrow K(\Pi, n+1)$ defines an isomorphism $\Pi_{n+1}(K(\Pi, n+1)) \cong \Pi_n(\Omega K(\Pi, n+1))$, and all other homotopy groups of $\Omega K(\Pi, n+1)$ are zero. This isomorphism of $\Pi_n(\Omega K(\Pi, n+1))$ with Π and results of the previous section imply there is a map

$$K(\Pi, n) \longrightarrow \Omega K(\Pi, n+1)$$

which is well-defined, up to a homotopy, inducing isomorphisms on Π_n. The adjoint is a map

$$\epsilon_n: K(\Pi, n) \wedge S^1 \longrightarrow K(\Pi, n+1).$$

The sequence of CW-complexes $K(\Pi, n)$ and maps ϵ_n is an example of a *spectrum*, the spectrum $K(\Pi)$. In general, a *spectrum*, $\mathfrak{A}$, is a sequence $\{A_n, \epsilon_n\}$ of CW-complexes with base point and maps

$$\epsilon_n: A_n \wedge S^1 \longrightarrow A_{n+1}.$$

Another spectrum is the sphere spectrum $\mathcal{S}$ of spheres S^n and maps

$$S^n \wedge S^1 \longrightarrow S^{n+1}.$$

For a spectrum $\mathcal{A}$, we define

$$\Pi_n(\mathcal{A}) = \xrightarrow{\lim} \{\Pi_{n+i}(A_i, *), \lambda_i\},$$

where

$$\lambda_i: \Pi_{n+i}(A_i, *) \longrightarrow \Pi_{n+i+1}(A_{i+1}, *)$$

is the composition

$$\Pi_{n+i}(A_i, *) \xrightarrow{E} \Pi_{n+i+1}(\hat{\Sigma}A, *) \xrightarrow{\cong} \Pi_{n+i+1}(A_i \wedge S^1, *) \xrightarrow{\epsilon_i} \Pi_{n+i+1}(A_{i+1}, *).$$

For a CW-complex $(X, *)$, we define the *reduced homology of* X *with coefficients in the spectrum* $\mathcal{A}$ as follows:

Let $(X', *) \longrightarrow (X, *)$ be a CW-substitute for $(X, *)$. Then

$$\tilde{H}_n(X; \mathcal{A}) \equiv \Pi_n(X' \wedge \mathcal{A}).$$

The uniqueness theorems of the previous section show these groups are well-defined and have the following properties: corresponding to each mapping $f: (X, *) \longrightarrow (Y, *)$, there is a homomorphism

$$\tilde{H}_n(f): \tilde{H}_n(X; \mathcal{A}) \longrightarrow \tilde{H}_n(Y; \mathcal{A})$$

such that

(1) If $(X, *) \xrightarrow{f} (Y, *) \xrightarrow{g} (Z, *)$, then
$$\tilde{H}_n(g \circ f) = \tilde{H}_n(g) \circ \tilde{H}_n(f).$$

(2) $\tilde{H}_n(\mathrm{Id}_X) = \mathrm{Id}_{\tilde{H}_n}(X)$.

(3) If $f, g: (X, *) \longrightarrow (Y, *)$ are homotopic, then
$$\tilde{H}_n(f) = \tilde{H}_n(g).$$

Slightly more difficult to verify is that there is an isomorphism

$$\sigma_*: \tilde{H}_n(X; \mathcal{A}) \longrightarrow \tilde{H}_{n+1}(\hat{\Sigma}X; \mathcal{A}).$$

This isomorphism is defined, using CW-substitutes, by the homomorphism

$$\Pi_{n+i}(X' \wedge A_i) \xrightarrow{\Sigma *} \Pi_{n+i+1}(X' \wedge A_i \wedge S^1) \xrightarrow{(-1)^i T_*} \Pi_{n+i+1}(X' \wedge S^1 \wedge A_i),$$

where $T: X' \wedge A_i \wedge S^1 \longrightarrow X' \wedge S^1 \wedge A_i$ interchanges the last two factors.

For a pair (X, A), we define

$$H_n(X; A; \mathcal{A}) = \tilde{H}_n(X \cup TA; \mathcal{A}).$$

Let $X^+ = X \cup (+)$, where $+$ is a point disjoint from X. Define

$$H_n(X, \phi; \mathcal{A}) = \tilde{H}_n(X^+; \mathcal{A}).$$

Also, define

$$\partial: H_{n+1}(X, A; \mathcal{A}) \longrightarrow H_n(A, \phi; \mathcal{A})$$

to be the composition

$$\tilde{H}_{n+1}(X \cup TA; \mathcal{A}) \longrightarrow \tilde{H}_{n+1}(T_1X \cup TA; \mathcal{A}) \xrightarrow{\cong} \tilde{H}_{n+1}(\Sigma A; \mathcal{A}) \xrightarrow{\sigma_*^{-1}} \tilde{H}_n(A; \mathcal{A}) \longrightarrow \tilde{H}_n(A^+; \mathcal{A}).$$

THEOREM: *$H_n(\ ,\ ; \mathcal{A})$ is a covariant functor from pairs of topological spaces to abelian groups; $\partial: H_{n+1}(X, A; \mathcal{A}) \longrightarrow H_n(A, \phi, \mathcal{A})$ is a natural transformation. Also,*

(1) *If $f \cong g: (X, A) \longrightarrow (Y, B)$, then $H_n(f) = H_n(g)$ for all n.*

(2) *The sequence*

$$\cdots \longrightarrow H_{n+1}(X, A; \mathcal{A}) \xrightarrow{\partial} H_n(A, \phi; \mathcal{A}) \longrightarrow H_n(X, \phi; \mathcal{A}) \longrightarrow H_n(X, A; \mathcal{A}) \longrightarrow \cdots$$

is exact.

(3) *If U is an open set in X and $\overline{U} \subset$ interior A, then*

$$H_n(X - U, A - U; \mathcal{A}) \longrightarrow H_n(X, A; \mathcal{A})$$

is an isomorphism for all n.

We have verified the assertion in statement (1). Statement (2) follows essentially from the homotopy sequence of a pair. Statement (3) follows by making suitable CW-substitutions and applying the proposition of Sec. I [17].

The statement of Theorem (1) is essentially the statement of the Eilenberg-Steenrod axioms for singular homology [9] except the following condition was omitted:

$$H_i(\text{point}, \phi; \mathcal{A}) = 0 \qquad i \neq 0.$$

This condition is indeed false when one uses certain spectra as coefficients, e.g., $\mathcal{S}$. However, for the spectrum $K(\Pi)$ it is easy to show that

$$\Pi_i(K(\Pi)) \cong \begin{cases} 0 & i \neq 0 \\ \Pi & i = 0. \end{cases}$$

Thus,

$$H_i(\text{point}, \phi; K(\Pi)) \cong \begin{cases} 0 & i \neq 0 \\ \Pi & i = 0, \end{cases}$$

and the spectrum $K(\Pi)$ thus yields ordinary singular homology. Instead of writing $H_*(\ \ ; K(\Pi))$, we shall write $H_*(\ \ ; \Pi)$. The other homology theorems are labeled extraordinary. We shall give examples of other interesting spectra later. The homology theory with coefficients $\mathcal{S}$ is of course *stable homotopy.*

Section M. In this section we wish to compare homotopy with $H_*(\ \ ; \mathbf{Z})$. To this end, we note that if

$$f: A \longrightarrow X$$

is a mapping with $\Pi_i(f)$ an isomorphism for $i \leqq n$ and an epimorphism for $i = n + 1$, and K is a CW-complex with $\Pi_i(K) = 0$ for $i \leqq m - 1$, then

$$f \wedge \mathrm{Id}_K : A \overset{\omega}{\wedge} K \longrightarrow X \overset{\omega}{\wedge} K$$

induces isomorphisms in homotopy in dimensions $i \leqq m + n$ and an epimorphism in dimension $m + n + 1$. In this statement the notation $A \overset{\omega}{\wedge} K$ denotes $A \times K \cup T(A \vee K)$. For A and K CW-complexes, $A \overset{\omega}{\wedge} K$ has the same homotopy type as $A \wedge K$. The statement is proved by replacing $f: A \longrightarrow X$ by a CW-pair $i: A' \longrightarrow X'$, with i an inclusion map. The first cell of X' not in A' is of dimension $n + 2$. Then the first cell of $X' \wedge K$ not in $A' \wedge K$ is dimension $m + n + 2$, and the conclusion follows.

Consider the composition

$$\Pi_i(X) \longrightarrow \tilde{H}_i(X; \mathcal{S}) \longrightarrow \tilde{H}_i(X; \mathbf{Z}),$$

where the latter homeomorphism is induced by the map of spectra $\mathcal{S} \longrightarrow K(\mathbf{Z})$ defined by maps $S^n \longrightarrow K(\mathbf{Z}, n)$ in the class of $1 \in \mathbf{Z} \cong \Pi_n(K(\mathbf{Z}, n))$. If $\Pi_i(X) = 0$ for $i \leqq m - 1$, then since

$\tilde{H}_i(X; \mathbb{S})$ is just the stable homotopy of X and $\Pi_i(X) \longrightarrow \tilde{H}_i(X; \mathbb{S})$ is the projection into $\xrightarrow{\lim} \Pi_{i+n}(X \wedge S^n)$, the map

$$\Pi_i(X) \longrightarrow \tilde{H}_i(X; \mathbb{S})$$

is an isomorphism for $i \leqq 2m - 2$ and is onto for $i = 2m - 1$. Since $\Pi_i(S^n) \longrightarrow \Pi_i(K(\mathbf{Z}, n))$ is an isomorphism for $i \leqq n$ and is onto for $i = n + 1$,

$$\Pi_{i+n}(X \wedge S^n) \longrightarrow \Pi_{i+n}(X \wedge K(\mathbf{Z}, n))$$

is $\cong$ for $i < m + 1$ and is onto for $i = m + 1$. (We may as well assume X is CW and use $\wedge$.) We have then the theorem of Hurewicz:

If X is $(m - 1)$-connected, then

for $m = 1$, $\Pi_1(X) \longrightarrow \tilde{H}_1(X; \mathbf{Z})$ is onto, and
for $m > 1$, $\Pi_i(X) \longrightarrow \tilde{H}_i(X; \mathbf{Z})$ is an isomorphism
for $i \leqq m$ and is onto for $i = m + 1$.

In the relative case, we have

if A is $(k - 1)$-connected, $k \geqq 1$, and (X, A) is n-connected, then

if $k = 1$, $H_i(X, A; \mathbf{Z}) = 0$ for $i \leqq n$, and
if $k \geqq 2$, $\Pi_i(X, A) \longrightarrow H_i(X, A; \mathbf{Z})$ is an isomorphism
for $i \leqq n + 1$ and is onto for $i = n + 2$.

This follows from the Hurewicz theorem since $\Pi_i(X, A) \longrightarrow \Pi_i(X \cup TA, *)$ is an isomorphism for $i < n + k$ and is onto for $i = n + k$. Then $\Pi_i(X \cup TA) \longrightarrow \tilde{H}_i(X \cup TA; \mathbf{Z}) \cong H_i(X, A; \mathbf{Z})$ is an isomorphism for $i \leqq n + 1$ and is onto for $i = n + 2$.

A fruitful consequence of this relative Hurewicz theorem is the

Theorem (Whitehead, J. H. C.): *Suppose X and Y are 0-connected spaces and $f\colon X \longrightarrow Y$. Then*

(1) *If $\Pi_i(f)$ is $\cong$ for $i \leqq n - 1$ and is onto for $i = n$, then $H_i(f; \mathbf{Z})$ is $\cong$ for $i \leqq n - 1$ and is onto for $i = n$.*

(2) *If X and Y are 1-connected and $H_i(f; \mathbf{Z})$ is $\cong$ for $i \leqq n - 1$ and is onto for $i = n$, then $\Pi_i(f)$ is $\cong$ for $i \leqq n - 1$ and is onto for $i = n$.*

Let C_f denote the mapping cylinder of f. In case (1), $\Pi_i(C_f, X) = 0$ for $i \leqq n$ and, applying the relative Hurewicz theorem for $k = 1$, we have $H_i(C_f, X; \mathbf{Z}) = 0$ for $i \leqq n$. The conclusion follows. In case (2), C_f is 1-connected and X is $(2-1)$-connected. Thus, $\Pi_i(C_f, X)$ and $H_i(C_f, X)$ first fail to vanish in the same dimension. Consequently, (C_f, X) is n-connected and the conclusion follows.

Section N. For a space (X, x_0), we define *reduced cohomology with coefficients in* $\mathfrak{A}$ as follows:

$$\tilde{H}^n(X; \mathfrak{A}) = \xrightarrow{\lim} \{[X \wedge S^i, A_{n+i}], \mu_{n+i}\},$$

where μ_{n+i} is the composition

$$[X \wedge S^i, A_{n+i}] \xrightarrow{\Sigma_*} [X \wedge S^i \wedge S^1, A_{n+i} \wedge S^1] \xrightarrow{\epsilon_{i*}} [X \wedge S^{i+1}, A_{n+i+1}].$$

Define

$$\sigma^*: \tilde{H}^n(X; \mathfrak{A}) \longrightarrow \tilde{H}^{n+1}(X \wedge S^1; \mathfrak{A})$$

to be the $\xrightarrow{\lim}$ of

$$\sigma_i: [X \wedge S^{i+1}, A_{n+i+1}] \longrightarrow [X \wedge S^1 \wedge S^i, A_{n+1+i}]$$

the identity map. Then σ^* is clearly an isomorphism.

We proceed much as with homology, defining

$$H^n(X, A; \mathfrak{A}) = \tilde{H}^n(X \cup TA; \mathfrak{A}),$$

$$H^n(X, \phi; \mathfrak{A}) = \tilde{H}^n(X^+; \mathfrak{A}),$$

and

$$\delta: H^n(A, \phi; \mathfrak{A}) \longrightarrow H^{n+1}(X, A; \mathfrak{A})$$

to be the composition

$$\tilde{H}^n(A^+; \mathfrak{A}) \longrightarrow \tilde{H}^n(A; \mathfrak{A}) \longrightarrow \tilde{H}^{n+1}(A \wedge S^1; \mathfrak{A}) \longrightarrow \tilde{H}^{n+1}(X \cup TA; \mathfrak{A}).$$

(We should be using ΣA instead of $A \wedge S^1$; this involves certain technical changes we shall not go into.)

A mapping $\beta: (X, A) \longrightarrow (Y, B)$ induces

$$\beta^*: [(Y \cup TB) \wedge S^{n+i}, A_i] \longrightarrow [(X \cup TA) \wedge S^{n+i}, A_i]$$

as discussed in Sec. A; and thus, it induces homomorphisms

$$\beta^*: H^n(Y, B; \mathfrak{A}) \longrightarrow H^n(X, A; \mathfrak{A}).$$

In this way we obtain a family of *contravariant* functors from the category of pairs of topological spaces and continuous mappings to the category of abelian groups and homomorphisms, and a natural connecting homomorphism δ. This *cohomology theory* with coefficients in the spectrum $\mathfrak{A}$ has essentially the same properties as those asserted in Sec. K for homology, differing principally because it is contravariant.

Cohomology theories frequently have a richer algebraic structure than their companion homology theories, namely—a ring structure. Let us first illustrate this by considering the case for $K(\Pi)$ spectra.

Let F, G, and H be abelian groups and $h\colon F \otimes G \longrightarrow H$ be a homomorphism. One can show that $\Pi_{p+q}(K(F, p) \wedge K(G, q))$ is isomorphic to $F \otimes G$ and there is a well-defined map, up to homotopy,

$$h_{p,q}\colon K(F, p) \wedge K(G, q) \longrightarrow K(H, p + q)$$

inducing the homomorphism h in homotopy in dimension $p + q$. The diagram

$$\begin{array}{ccc} & K(F,p)\wedge S^1 \wedge K(G,q) \longrightarrow K(F,p+1)\wedge K(G,q) & \\ \nearrow & & \searrow{\scriptstyle (-1)^q\cdot h_{p+1,q}} \\ K(F,p)\wedge K(G,q)\wedge S^1 \to & K(H,p+q)\wedge S^1 & \to K(H,p+q+1) \\ \searrow & & \nearrow{\scriptstyle h_{p,q+1}} \\ & K(F,p)\wedge K(G,q+1) & \end{array}$$

is homotopy commutative.

Let $\alpha_p \in [X \wedge S^p, K(F, n + p)]$ and $\beta_q \in [Y \wedge S^q, K(G, m + q)]$ be representatives of classes $\mathfrak{A} \in \tilde{H}^n(X; F)$ and $\beta \in \tilde{H}^m(Y; G)$. Then

$$\alpha_p \wedge \beta_q \in [X \wedge Y \wedge S^p \wedge S^q, K(F, n + p) \wedge K(G, m + q)]$$

and

$$(-1)^{pm}(h_{p,q})_* (\alpha_p \wedge \beta_q) \in [X \wedge Y \wedge S^{p+q}, K(H, m + n + p + q)].$$

Furthermore, the latter classes commute with the respective μ's and thus define a class

$$\alpha \times \beta \in \tilde{H}^{n+m}(X \wedge Y; H).$$

Since $X^+ \wedge Y^+ = (X \times Y)^+$, for $\alpha \in H^n(X, \phi; F)$ and $\beta \in H^m(Y, \phi; G)$,

$$\tilde{\alpha} \times \tilde{\beta} \in \tilde{H}^{n+m}(X^+ \wedge Y^+; H)$$

determines a class

$$\alpha \times \beta \in H^{n+m}(X \times Y, \phi; H).$$

For $X = Y$, the diagonal map $\Delta: X \longrightarrow X \times X$ induces a homomorphism carrying $\alpha \times \beta$ into a class

$$\alpha \cup \beta = \Delta^*(\alpha \times \beta) \in H^{n+m}(X, \phi; H).$$

In particular, for $R = F = G = H$, a ring, and $R \otimes R \longrightarrow R$, the homomorphism defining the ring structure of R, for

$$\alpha \in H^n(X, \phi; R) \quad \text{and} \quad \beta \in H^n(X, \phi; R),$$

$$\alpha \cup \beta \in H^{n+m}(X, \phi; R).$$

For R a commutative ring with unit, this "cup product" defines a "graded" commutative ring structure on

$$H^*(X, \phi; R);$$

i.e., $\alpha \cup \beta = (-1)^{mn}\beta \cup \alpha$.

For a pairing $\mathcal{A} \wedge \mathcal{B} \longrightarrow \mathcal{C}$ of spectra having the properties assumed of the maps $h_{p,q}$, pairings

$$H^n(X, \phi; \mathcal{A}) \otimes H^m(Y, \phi; \mathcal{B}) \longrightarrow H^{n+m}(X \times Y, \phi; \mathcal{C})$$

and

$$H^n(X, \phi; \mathcal{A}) \otimes H^m(X, \phi; \mathcal{B}) \longrightarrow H^{n+m}(X, \phi; \mathcal{C})$$

are similarly defined [17]. In case the pairing is of the form

$$\mathcal{A} \wedge \mathcal{B} \longrightarrow \mathcal{B},$$

we say $\mathcal{B}$ is a *left $\mathcal{A}$-spectrum,* and for $\mathcal{B} = \mathcal{A}$, that $\mathcal{A}$ is a *ring spectrum.* Such spectra define *multiplicative cohomology theories.*

FURTHER PROPERTIES OF HOMOLOGY AND COHOMOLOGY

Section O. We have constructed and described axioms (not to be herein demonstrated) for homology and cohomology theories. We have also indicated further structures on cohomology. This is all uninteresting if we cannot compute the groups or rings in question, or at least relate them to something else we can compute.

For the case of coefficients in spectra $K(\Pi)$ and for CW-complexes of which we have a good knowledge of the attaching maps, we can compute these groups through an inductive process using excision. Thus, it may be shown that

$$H_i(X^{(n)}, X^{(n-1)}; \Pi) \cong \begin{cases} 0 & i \neq n \\ \text{direct sum of copies of } \Pi & i = n. \end{cases}$$

The homomorphism d_n, equal to the composition,

$$H_n(X^{(n)}, X^{(n-1)}; \Pi) \xrightarrow{\partial} H_{n-1}(X^{(n-1)}, \phi; \Pi) \longrightarrow H_{n-1}(X^{(n-1)}, X^{(n-2)}; \Pi),$$

has the property that $d_n \circ d_{n+1} = 0$ and

$$H_n(X, \phi; \Pi) \cong \frac{\operatorname{Ker} d_n}{\operatorname{Im} d_{n+1}}.$$

In the case of simplicial complexes, for example, there are simple formulas for computing the homomorphisms d_n, see [9].

If the coefficients are some other spectrum $\mathfrak{A}$ or if the space is somewhat more complicated, as in the instance of the total space X of a fiber map $p: X \longrightarrow B$, an extension of this method is used for many computations. This extension involves the use of exact couples and spectral sequences. We shall say very little of the method here; excellent references are [7], [10], [11], and [13].

An exact couple is a triangle of groups and homomorphisms

$$\begin{array}{ccc} A & \xrightarrow{f} & A \\ {\scriptstyle h}\nwarrow & & \swarrow{\scriptstyle g} \\ & C & \end{array}$$

which is exact. Associated with this exact couple is another exact couple

$$\begin{array}{ccc} A^{(1)} & \xrightarrow{f^{(1)}} & A^{(1)} \\ {\scriptstyle h^{(1)}}\nwarrow & & \swarrow{\scriptstyle g^{(1)}} \\ & C^{(1)}, & \end{array}$$

the first derived couple, defined as follows:

$$A^{(1)} = \operatorname{Im} f,$$

$$C^{(1)} = \frac{\operatorname{Ker} d}{\operatorname{Im} d}, \quad \text{where} \quad d = g \circ h,$$

$$f^{(1)} = f|A^{(1)},$$

$$g^{(1)}(f(a)) = \{g(a)\} \in C^{(1)},$$

and

$$h^{(1)}\{z\} = h(z).$$

One can then form the sequence $\{C^{(n)}, d^{(n)}\}$, from the sequence of iterated derived exact couples, with $d^{(n)} = g^{(n)} \circ h^{(n)}$ and

$$C^{(n+1)} = \frac{\operatorname{Ker} d^{(n)}}{\operatorname{Im} d^{(n)}}.$$

Such a sequence is called a *spectral sequence*. It can have a great deal more structure. For example, if X is a CW-complex and $\mathcal{A}$ is a spectrum, let

$$A = \bigoplus_{p,q} H_{p+q}(X^{(p)}, \phi; \mathcal{A})$$

and

$$C = \bigoplus_{p,q} H_{p+q}(X^{(p)}, X^{(p-1)}; \mathcal{A}).$$

The analogy of the formation of this exact couple with the simpler computational scheme indicated above is clear. In this case, the first derived couple of the exact couple will have terms in $C^{(1)}$ with two gradings; it will be called the E^2-term of the spectral sequence. It can be shown that in this case

$$E^2_{p,q} = H_p(X, \phi; \Pi_q(\mathcal{A})).$$

The homomorphism $d^{(1)}$ will break into components labeled $d^2_{p,q}$ which map as follows:

$$d^2_{p,q}\colon E^2_{p,q} \longrightarrow E^2_{p-2,q+1}.$$

The later derived $E^r_{p,q}$ have d's mapping according to the rule

$$d^r_{p,q}\colon E^r_{p,q} \longrightarrow E^r_{p-r,q+r-1}.$$

In each case $\operatorname{Im} d^r_{p+r,q-r+1} \subset \operatorname{Ker} d^r_{p,q}$ and the quotient is isomorphic to $E^{r+1}_{p,q}$. For a fixed (p, q) these groups, in good cases, eventually stabilize to groups $E^\infty_{p,q} \cong \operatorname{Im} (H_{p+q}(X^{(p)}, \phi; \mathcal{A}) \longrightarrow$

$H_{p+q}(X, \phi; \mathfrak{A}))$ modulo Im $(H_{p+q}(X^{(p-1)}, \phi; \mathfrak{A}) \longrightarrow H_{p+q}(X, \phi; \mathfrak{A}))$. This *filtration* of the groups $H_{p+q}(X, \phi; \mathfrak{A})$ in fortunate cases leads to their determination; in less fortunate cases it may still determine enough of their properties to play a crucial role in answering some geometric problem.

In the case of a fiber map $p: X \longrightarrow B$, with fiber F and with base a CW-complex, a similarly formed exact couple leads to a spectral sequence:

$$A = \bigoplus_{p,q} H_{p+q}(p^{-1}(B^{(p)}), \phi; \mathfrak{A})$$

$$C = \bigoplus_{p,q} H_{p+q}(p^{-1}(B^{(p)}), p^{-1}(B^{(p-1)}); \mathfrak{A}).$$

For this couple it can be shown that

$$E^2_{p,q} \cong H_p(B, \phi; H_q(F, \phi; \mathfrak{A}))$$

and $E^\infty_{p,q}$ is associated with a filtration of the group $H_{p+q}(X, \phi; \mathfrak{A})$.

Very similar constructions can be made for cohomology. As might be expected, when the cohomology theory under consideration has a multiplicative structure, the spectral sequences reflect this structure with pairings

$$E_r^{p,q} \otimes E_r^{p',q'} \longrightarrow E_r^{p+p',q+q'}$$

and differentials $d_r^{p,q}$ which respect these products [11].

Section P. Some cohomology theories have another useful structural property—cohomology operations. These can be described more generally as follows:

Let $\theta: \mathfrak{A} \longrightarrow \mathfrak{B}$ be a map of spectra ($\theta_n: A_n \longrightarrow B_n$ and $\epsilon_n \circ (\theta_n \wedge \mathrm{Id}_{S^1}) \simeq \theta_{n+1} \circ \epsilon_n$). There is induced a *natural transformation* of cohomology theories

$$\theta_*: H^*(\quad,\quad; \mathfrak{A}) \longrightarrow H^*(\quad,\quad; \mathfrak{B});$$

i.e., θ_* preserves grading, is additive, commutes with homomorphisms induced by mappings, and commutes with the coboundary homomorphism δ. Let $\mathfrak{A}^{(i)}$ be the spectrum $\mathfrak{A}$ reindexed by $A^i_n = A_{n+i}$. For $\theta: \mathfrak{A} \longrightarrow \mathfrak{A}^{(i)}$, we say θ_* is a cohomology operation in the cohomology theory with coefficients in the spectrum $\mathfrak{A}$.

Consider the situation for $\mathcal{K}(\mathbf{Z}_p)$. Since

$$[X \wedge S^n \wedge S^1, K(\mathbf{Z}_p, n+1+i)] \cong [X \wedge S^n, \Omega K(\mathbf{Z}_p, n+1+i)] \cong [X \wedge S^n, K(\mathbf{Z}_p, n+i)],$$

it might be suspected that the homomorphism

$$[X \wedge S^n, K(\mathbf{Z}_p, n+i)] \longrightarrow \tilde{H}^i(X; \mathbf{Z}_p)$$

is an isomorphism (see Sec. L). This is true; in particular it is true for $n = 0$. Then a cohomology operation in the cohomology theory $H^*(\ , \ ; \mathbf{Z}_p)$ is given by a sequence of cohomology classes

$$u_n^i \in \tilde{H}^{n+i}(K(\mathbf{Z}_p, n); \mathbf{Z}_p)$$

related by the condition that

$$\epsilon_n^*(u_{n+1}^i) = \Sigma^*(u_n^i),$$

where

$$\tilde{H}^{n+i}(K(\mathbf{Z}_p, n); \mathbf{Z}_p) \xrightarrow{\Sigma^*} \tilde{H}^{n+i+1}(K(\mathbf{Z}_p, n) \wedge S^1; \mathbf{Z}_p) \xleftarrow{\epsilon_n^*} \tilde{H}^{n+i+1}(K(\mathbf{Z}_p, n+1); \mathbf{Z}_p).$$

By nontrivial computations on the spectral sequences of the fibrations

$$\Omega K(\mathbf{Z}_p, n+1) \longrightarrow E(K(\mathbf{Z}_p, n+1); K(\mathbf{Z}_p, n+1), *) \longrightarrow K(\mathbf{Z}_p, n+1)$$

it is possible to determine all such sequences, using a theorem of Kudo [12]. The sequences are generated by a family

$$P^i: \mathcal{K}(\mathbf{Z}_p) \longrightarrow \mathcal{K}(\mathbf{Z}_p)^{2i(p-1)},$$

together with a map

$$\delta_p: \mathcal{K}(\mathbf{Z}_p) \longrightarrow \mathcal{K}(\mathbf{Z}_p)^1.$$

These are, respectively, the *Steenrod Operations* and the *Bockstein Operation*. They have a number of special properties making them calculable for many spaces and enriching the cohomology structure in a very significant way [16].

We shall give another example of cohomology operations in the next section.

Section Q. In this final section we give a very abbreviated description of two more important classes of spectra. These are the spectra leading to cobordism theory and to the theory of stable vector bundles. There are several of each of these theories using various families of Lie groups. For simplicity we discuss only the unitary theories here.

Let $\mathbf{C}^n$ denote the complex n-dimensional vector space equipped with a positive definite Hermitian inner product. The unitary group $U(n)$ is the topological group of linear transformations preserving this inner product. An orthogonal decomposition

$$\mathbf{C}^m \oplus \mathbf{C}^n = \mathbf{C}^{m+n}$$

of $\mathbf{C}^{m+n}$ defines a homomorphism

$$U(m) \times U(n) \longrightarrow U(m+n).$$

For n fixed,

$$\underset{m}{\xrightarrow{\lim}} \frac{U(m+n)}{U(m) \times U(n)} \equiv B_{U(n)}$$

and if

$$E_{U(n)} \equiv \xrightarrow{\lim} \frac{U(m+n)}{U(m)},$$

there is a fibration

$$U(n) \longrightarrow E_{U(n)} \xrightarrow{\pi_n} B_{U(n)}.$$

The group $U(n)$ "acts" on $E_{U(n)}$ in the sense that each $\alpha \in U(n)$ determines a homeomorphism

$$\alpha\colon E_{U(n)} \longrightarrow E_{U(n)},$$

with $1 = \mathrm{Id}_{E_{U(n)}}$ and $(\alpha\beta)(x) = \alpha(\beta(x))$. Since $U(n)$ also acts on $\mathbf{C}^n$, we can form the identification space $X_n = \mathbf{C}^n \times_{U(n)} E_{U(n)}$, identifying pairs $(\vec{v}\alpha, x)$ and $(\vec{v}, \alpha x)$, and define a map $p_n\colon X_n \longrightarrow B_{U(n)}$ by $p_n(\vec{v}\alpha, x) = \pi_n(x)$. The map p_n is a fiber map with fiber $\mathbf{C}^n$. The fiber space $\mathbf{C}^n \longrightarrow X_n \xrightarrow{p_n} B_{U(n)}$ is said to be the *universal complex n-plane bundle*, λ_n [15]. If $f\colon A \longrightarrow B_{U(n)}$, the subspace $\{(a, x) \in A \times X_n | f(a) = p_n(x)\}$ is the total space of a fiber space with base A and fiber $\mathbf{C}^n$, the *induced fiber space of the map* f, $f^*(\lambda_n)$. The map of this total space to A is defined by mapping the point (a, x) to the point $a \in A$.

The inner products on the fibers $\mathbf{C}^n$ of the universal bundle vary continuously over points of $B_{U(n)}$. Thus, the subspace of those vectors of fibers of this bundle of length greater than or equal to 1 is a closed subspace of X_n. Identifying it to a point, we obtain the *Thom space* $T(\lambda_n)$. Similarly we could define the Thom space of $f^*(\lambda_n)$ and there is an obvious map $T(f^*(\lambda_n)) \longrightarrow T(\lambda_n)$. In particular, an inclusion $U(n-1) \longrightarrow U(n)$ induces a map $B_{U(n-1)} \xrightarrow{h_n} B_{U(n)}$. It is not difficult to show that $T(h_n^*(\lambda_n))$ and $T(\lambda_{n-1}) \wedge S^2$ are homeomorphic; thus, the inclusion $U(n-1) \longrightarrow U(n)$ induces a map

$$T(\lambda_{n-1}) \wedge S^2 \longrightarrow T(\lambda_n).$$

We define a spectrum $\mathfrak{MU}$ as follows

$$MU_i = \begin{cases} pt & i \leqq 1 \\ T(\lambda_n) & i = 2n,\ n \geqq 1 \\ T(\lambda_n) \wedge S^1 & i = 2n+1. \end{cases}$$

The maps $\epsilon_i\colon MU_i \wedge S^1 \longrightarrow MU_{i+1}$ are defined using the above maps $T(\lambda_{n-1}) \wedge S^2 \longrightarrow T(\lambda_n)$.

The homology and cohomology theories with coefficients in $\mathfrak{MU}$ are the *complex bordism* and *cobordism theories* [3] and [14]. There are various other such theories using $O(n)$, $SO(n)$, $SU(n)$, $SP(n)$, Spin (n) instead of $U(n)$. These theories have been very useful in studying differentiable manifolds and have been used in the study of elliptic differential operators [5].

Since the inclusions $U(n-1) \longrightarrow U(n)$ determine inclusions $B_{U(n-1)} \longrightarrow B_{U(n)}$, we can define the direct limit $B_U = \xrightarrow{\lim} B_{U(n)}$. This is the universal base space for stable complex vector bundles. We shall define a map

$$b\colon B_U \times \mathbf{Z} \longrightarrow \Omega U,$$

which by a theorem of Bott's is a homotopy equivalence [6]. We shall then use this map to define the unitary spectrum $\mathfrak{U}$.

For $\mathbf{C}^{m+n} = \mathbf{C}^m \oplus \mathbf{C}^n$, let $x \in \mathbf{C}^{m+n}$ have components denoted by $x_1 \in \mathbf{C}^m$ and $x_2 \in \mathbf{C}^n$, $x = x_1 + x_2$. For $\theta \in \mathbf{R}$, let $\phi_{m,n}(\theta)(x) = x_1 e^{i\theta} + x_2 e^{-i\theta}$. For $A \in U(m+n)$, let $\tilde{b}_{m,n}(A)$ be the loop in $U(m+n)$, in fact it is in $SU(m+n)$, defined by the commutator

$$\tilde{b}_{m,n}(A)(\theta) = [\phi_{m,n}(\theta), A], \qquad 0 \leqq \theta \leqq \Pi.$$

For $A \in U(m) \times U(n)$, $\tilde{b}_{m,n}(A)$ is the trivial loop. Thus, $\tilde{b}_{m,n}$ induces

$$b_{m,n}\colon \frac{U(m+n)}{U(m) \times U(n)} \longrightarrow \Omega U(m+n).$$

The inclusion $\mathbf{C}^m \oplus \mathbf{C}^n \longrightarrow \mathbf{C}^{m'} \oplus \mathbf{C}^{n'}$, $m \leqq m'$ and $n \leqq n'$, induces maps

$$\frac{U(m+n)}{U(m) \times U(n)} \longrightarrow \frac{U(m'+n')}{U(m') \times U(n')}$$

and

$$\Omega U(m+n) \longrightarrow \Omega U(m'+n')$$

which commute with $b_{m,n}$ and $b_{m',n'}$. Thus, a map

$$b'\colon B_U \longrightarrow \Omega U$$

is defined in the limit. The space ΩU has $\Pi_0 \cong \mathbf{Z}$; and B_U, being connected, is mapped into the connected component corresponding to $0 \in \mathbf{Z}$. We can extend b' in an obvious way to a map

$$b\colon B_U \times \mathbf{Z} \longrightarrow \Omega U.$$

The unitary spectrum $\mathfrak{U}$ is defined by

$$U_{(i)} = \begin{cases} B_U \times \mathbf{Z} & \text{for} \quad i = 2n \\ U & \text{for} \quad i = 2n+1. \end{cases}$$

The map $(B_U \times \mathbf{Z}) \wedge S^1 \longrightarrow U$ is the adjoint of the map b and $U \wedge S^1 \longrightarrow B_U \times \mathbf{Z}$ is the adjoint of the homotopy equivalence $U \longrightarrow \Omega(B_U \times \mathbf{Z})$. Tensor products of vector spaces $\mathbf{C}^n \otimes \mathbf{C}^m \cong \mathbf{C}^{nm}$ induces a mapping

$$B_{U(n)} \times B_{U(m)} \longrightarrow B_{U(nm)}$$

which can be used in the limit to give $\mathfrak{U}$ the structure of a ring spectrum [4].

The operation of kth exterior product on $\mathbf{C}^n$ determines a homomorphism

$$\wedge_k^n\colon U(n) \longrightarrow U\left(\binom{n}{k}\right).$$

Let p_n^r denote the polynomial in n variables such that

$$p_n^r(\sigma_1^n, \ldots, \sigma_r^n) = (x_1)^r + \cdots + (x_n)^r,$$

where σ_i^n is the ith elementary symmetric function in $x_1, \ldots, x_n$. The combination

$$p_n^r(\wedge_1^n, \ldots, \wedge_r^n)$$

determines a homomorphism $U(n) \longrightarrow U$. These commute with inclusions $U(n) \longrightarrow U(n+1)$ and define a map

$$\psi^k\colon B_U \longrightarrow B_U[1].$$

These maps thus define (nonstable) cohomology operations for this cohomology theory. These are the operations used by Adams with great success in solving the vector field problem for spheres [1] and in gaining vital new information on homotopy structures [2].

BIBLIOGRAPHY

1. Adams, J. F., "Vector fields on spheres," *Ann. Math.*, **75** (1962).
2. ———, "On the groups $J(X)$—I," *Topology*, **2** (1963), 181–95.
3. Atiyah, M. F., "Bordism and cobordism," *Proc. Camb. Phil. Soc.*, **57** (1961), 200–208.
4. ———, and F. Hirzebruch, "Vector bundles and homogeneous spaces," *Proc. Symp. Pure Math., AMS.*, **III**, Differential Geometry, 1961, 7–38.
5. ———, and I. M. Singer, "The index of elliptic operators on compact manifolds," *Bull. Am. Math. Soc.*, **69** (1963), 422–33.
6. Bott, R., "The stable homotopy of the classical groups," *Ann. Math.*, **70** (1959), 313–37.
7. Bourgin, D. G., *Modern Algebraic Topology*. New York: Macmillan, 1965.
8. Eckmann, B., and P. J. Hilton, "Homotopy groups of maps and exact sequences," *Comm. Math. Helv.*, **34** (1960), 271–304.
9. Eilenberg, S., and N. E. Steenrod, *Foundations of Algebraic Topology*. Princeton, N.J.: Princeton University Press, 1952.
10. Hilton, P. J., and S. Wylie, *Homology Theory*. Cambridge: Cambridge University Press, 1960.
11. Hu, S. T., *Homotopy Theory*. New York: Pure and Applied Math., Vol. VIII, Academic Press, New York-London, 1959.

12. Kudo, T., "A transgression theorem," *Mem. Fac. Sci.*, Kyûsyû Univ., Ser. A, **9** (1956), 79–81.

13. Massey, W. S., "Exact couples in algebraic topology," *Ann. Math.*, **56** (1952), 363–96, **57** (1953), 248–86.

14. Milnor, J., "On the cobordism ring Ω^* and a complex analogue," *Am. Jour. Math.*, **82** (1960), 505–21.

15. Steenrod, N. E., *Topology of Fibre Bundles*. Princeton, N.J.: Princeton University Press, 1951.

16. ———, *Cohomology Operations*. *Ibid.*, 1962.

17. Whitehead, G. W., "Generalized homology theories," *Trans. Am. Math. Soc.*, **102** (1962), 227–83.

18. Whitehead, J. H. C., "Note on suspension," *Quart. Jour. Math.*, **1** (1950), 9–22.

19. ———, "Combinatorial homotopy I," *Bull. Am. Math. Soc.*, **55** (1949), 213–45.

ON THE GEOMETRY OF DIFFERENTIABLE MANIFOLDS

Valentin Poénaru

1. INTRODUCTION

Roughly speaking, a differentiable manifold is a space on which differentiable calculus makes sense. In recent years, these kinds of spaces have become one of the main objects of study for the topologist; there is a twofold reason for this: on one hand they appear naturally in a great variety of mathematical problems; on the other hand a differentiable manifold is quite a rich and complex structure which generates a very nice piece of mathematics.

Our object here will be to give some basic ideas on the geometrical problems connected with differentiable manifolds. More precisely, we shall deal with embeddings (when can a differentiable manifold be embedded in Euclidean space?), cobordism (when is a differentiable manifold the "boundary" of another?), and handle-bodies (which is a method of studying the problem: when are two differentiable manifolds "differentiably," or "topologically" equivalent?).

2. SOME BASIC DEFINITIONS IN DIFFERENTIABLE MANIFOLDS

A *topological n-manifold* is a Hausdorff space such that every point has a neighborhood homeomorphic to the Euclidean space E_n. We shall consider only manifolds with countable basis.

A *differentiable structure* on a topological n-manifold M is a collection of pairs (U_i, h_i) consisting of an open subset $U_i \subset E_n$ and a homeomorphism $h_i\colon U_i \longrightarrow M$ such that

(a) $M = \bigcup h_i(U_i)$.

(b) For every pair i, j, the map

$$h_j^{-1}h_i\colon h_i^{-1}(h_i(U_i) \cap h_j(U_j)) \longrightarrow h_i^{-1}(h_i(U_i) \cap h_j(U_j))$$

is a C^∞ homeomorphism.

A pair (U_i, h_i) is called *coordinate neighborhood.*

A topological manifold M, together with a differentiable structure $\mathcal{O} = \{(U_i, h_i)\}$, is called a *differentiable manifold.* In fact we have to consider the following equivalence relation: two differentiable structures, $\mathcal{O} = \{(U_i, h_i)\}$ and $\mathcal{O}' = \{(V_j, g_j)\}$ on M, are *equivalent,* by definition, if $\mathcal{O} \cup \mathcal{O}'$ is a differentiable structure. In what follows, we shall never distinguish between two equivalent differentiable structures. In 1956, J. Milnor proved the very remarkable fact that two differentiable structures on the same topological manifold M are *not* necessarily equivalent [4]. More exactly, he produced an "exotic" differentiable structure on the 7-sphere S_7 which is not diffeomorphic (see p. 167) to the usual one.

Let us consider now two differentiable manifolds M, with the structure $\mathcal{O} = \{(U_i, h_i)\}$, and N, with the structure $\mathcal{O}' = \{(V_j, g_j)\}$. A continuous map $\phi\colon M \longrightarrow N$ will be called *differentiable* if, for every i and j, the map

$$g_j^{-1}\phi h_i\colon h_i^{-1}(h_i(U_i) \cap \phi^{-1}g_j(V_j)) \longrightarrow V_j$$

is differentiable. It is easy to prove that the definition is not changed if we replace $\mathcal{O}$ and $\mathcal{O}'$ by equivalent structures. A differential isomorphism is called a *diffeomorphism* (i.e., a homeomorphism which is differentiable together with its inverse).

In particular if we consider $N = R$, the real line [with its "usual" differentiable structure $\mathcal{O} = (R, \text{identity})$], we find the *differentiable* (C^∞) *functions* on M. If M is a topological manifold, we can consider the algebra (over the real numbers) $\mathcal{C}(M)$ of all the continuous, real-valued functions over M. A differentiable structure $\mathcal{O}$ on M determines a subalgebra $\mathcal{C}^\infty_{\mathcal{O}}(M)$ of the differentiable functions, with respect to $\mathcal{O}$. It is easy to prove that $\mathcal{O}$ and $\mathcal{O}'$ are equivalent if and only if $\mathcal{C}^\infty_{\mathcal{O}}(M) = \mathcal{C}^\infty_{\mathcal{O}'}(M)$.

It is very useful to define a slightly general class of spaces, the *manifolds with boundary.*

The definitions will run on the same lines as before, but we shall allow the space to have neighborhoods homeomorphic to $E_n^+ = \{x^1 \geq 0\}$. It is easy to extend the definition of differentiable structure to this case. Differentiable maps can be defined exactly as before. The points corresponding to $x^1 = 0$ form obviously a (differentiable) manifold of dimension $(n - 1)$ which is called the *boundary.* The manifolds defined at the beginning are *the manifolds with boundary, whose boundary is* $\varnothing$. From now on, by *manifold* we shall understand a differentiable manifold with boundary. A *closed manifold* will be a compact manifold whose boundary is 0.

3. REVIEW OF VECTOR BUNDLE THEORY

In this section we shall recall a number of basic definitions and facts on vector bundles. More details and proofs can be found in Milnor's notes [3] or in Steenrod's book [8].

An *n-dimensional vector bundle* ξ is a triple (π, E, B), where E and B are topological (Hausdorff) spaces; and $\pi: E \longrightarrow B$ is a continuous surjective map such that, for every $b \in B$, $\pi^{-1}(b) = F_b$ is the Euclidean n-space E_n, *together with* the following structure:

(a) On each *fiber* F_b a structure of n-dimensional vector space, over R, is defined, and the operations $F_b \times F_b \longrightarrow F_b$, $R \times F_b \longrightarrow F_b$ (vector addition and scalar multiplication) are continuous in E.

(b) We can consider, for every Hausdorff space X, the *trivial* vector bundle $(\pi', X \times E_n, X)$ where $\pi'\colon X \times E_n \longrightarrow X$ is the natural projection, and the vector-space operations on $\pi'(x) = x \times E_n$ are the usual vector-space operations on E_n [so every point in E is a collection $(x; x_1, \ldots, x_n)x_i \in R$ and

$$(x; x_1, \ldots, x_n) + (x; y_1, \ldots, y_n) = (x; x_1 + y_1, \ldots, x_n + y_n)$$
$$\lambda \in R, \lambda(x; x_1, \ldots, x_n) = (x; \lambda x_1, \ldots, \lambda x_n)].$$

For every $p \in B$, there exists a neighborhood U such that $(\pi|\pi^{-1}(U), \pi^{-1}(U), U)$ together with our vector-space operations on $\pi^{-1}(b)$ for various $b \in U$ is isomorphic to the *trivial* vector bundle $(\pi', U \times E_n, U)$. A vector bundle will be called differentiable if E, B are a differentiable manifold, π is differentiable, and the isomorphism of $\pi^{-1}(U)$ with $U \times E_n$ is differentiable.

A continuous map $f\colon B \longrightarrow E$ such that $\pi \circ f =$ identity is called a *cross section.* A cross section is obviously an injection. The continuous cross sections of ξ form a *module* $S(\xi)$ over the ring of continuous functions on B, $\mathcal{C}(B)$. The O-element of this module is the *O-cross section* which associates to every $b \in B$, $O_b \in E_b$ (the O in the vector space E_b). [The fact that this map is continuous follows easily from condition (b).] It is not difficult to prove (at least if B is *reasonable*) that ξ is trivial if and only if $S(\xi)$ is free over $\mathcal{C}(B)$. [In general, $S(\xi)$ is just an arbitrary projective module over $\mathcal{C}(B)$.]

All the maps of spaces considered from now on will be continuous.

A *bundle map* $\psi\colon \xi \longrightarrow \xi'$, where $\xi = (\pi, E, B)$, $\xi' = (\pi', E', B')$ are two vector bundles, is by definition a commutative diagram:

$$\begin{array}{ccc} E & \xrightarrow{F} & E' \\ {\scriptstyle \pi}\downarrow & & \downarrow{\scriptstyle \pi'} \\ B & \xrightarrow{f} & B' \end{array}$$

such that, for every $b \in B$, $F|\pi^{-1}(b)$ is a *linear isomorphism:* $\pi^{-1}(b) \longrightarrow (\pi')^{-1}(f(b))$.

If f is a homeomorphism, ψ will be called a *(bundle) isomorphism.* We shall not distinguish, in the following, between two isomorphic bundles.

Let us consider now a bundle $\xi' = (\pi', E', B')$, a space B, and a continuous map $f\colon B \longrightarrow B'$. It can be proved that there is a *unique* bundle $f^{-1}(\xi') = \xi = (\pi, E, B)$, for which a bundle map

$$\begin{array}{ccc} E & \xrightarrow{F} & E' \\ {\scriptstyle \pi}\downarrow & & \downarrow{\scriptstyle \pi'} \\ B & \xrightarrow{f} & B' \end{array}$$

exists (the *induced* bundle). If f and g are homotopic maps $B \longrightarrow B'$, $f^{-1}(\xi) = g^{-1}(\xi)$. (This is a consequence of the so-called *Covering homotopy theorem* for bundle maps.)

If $\xi = (\pi, E, B)$, $\xi' = (\pi', E', B')$ are two bundles, we can define the *product-bundle*

$$\xi \times \xi' = (\pi \times \pi', E \times E', B \times B').$$

If $\xi = (\pi, E, B)$, $\eta = (\pi', E', B)$ are two bundles over the same space B, and $\Delta\colon B \longrightarrow B \times B$ is the diagonal map $b \longrightarrow (b; b)$, then we can define the *Whitney sum* $\xi \oplus \eta$ as the vector bundle over B:

$$\xi \oplus \eta = \Delta^{-1}(\xi \times \eta).$$

Let us go back to differentiable manifolds. Let M be an n-dimensional differentiable manifold, and $p \in M$. Let us consider the set of differentiable functions defined on open neighborhoods of p in M. Two such functions $f\colon U \longrightarrow R$, $g\colon V \longrightarrow R$ will be considered equivalent if there exists an open neighborhood of p, $W \subset U \cap V$ such that $f|W = g|W$. This is obviously an equivalence relation, and the equivalence classes are called the *germs* of C^∞ functions on M at p. The space of germs at p, $\mathfrak{F}_p$ forms an algebra over the real numbers R. For every germ $f \in \mathfrak{F}_p$, the value $f(p)$ is well-defined (two functions which determine the same germ at p have the same value at p—and the same partial derivatives; the converse is of course false).

A tangent vector of M at p is by definition a map $\phi\colon \mathfrak{F}_p \longrightarrow R$ such that

$$\phi(\lambda f + \mu g) = \lambda\phi(f) + \mu\phi(g) \quad \text{for} \quad \lambda, \mu \in R, \quad f, g \in \mathfrak{F}_p,$$

and

$$\phi(fg) = f(p)\phi(g) + g(p)\phi(f).$$

If we choose a coordinate system $E_n = (x_1, \ldots, x_n)$, $(0, \ldots, 0) = p$ around p, it can be proved that ϕ can be always represented uniquely in the form

$$a_1 \frac{\partial}{\partial x_1} + a_2 \frac{\partial}{\partial x_2} + \cdots a_n \frac{\partial}{\partial x_n}\bigg|_{\text{at } (x_1, \ldots, x_n) = (0, \ldots, 0)}$$

where $(a_1, \ldots, a_n) \in E_n$. Let us denote by $T(M)_p$ the set of tangent vectors of M at p. The definition shows that $T(M)_p$ is a vector space over R, and the representation given above shows that $\dim T(M)_p = n$. Let us consider now the set $T(M) = \bigcup_{p \in M} T(M)_p$ of *all* tangent vectors to M. The representation $\Sigma a_i\, (\partial/\partial x_i)$ gives a natural topology for $T(M)$ [we consider that two tangent vectors

$$a'_1 \frac{\partial}{\partial x_1} + \cdots + a'_n \frac{\partial}{\partial x_n}\bigg|_{\text{at } (x_1', \ldots, x_n')}$$

$$a''_1 \frac{\partial}{\partial x_1} + \cdots + a''_n \frac{\partial}{\partial x_n}\bigg|_{\text{at } (x_1'', \ldots, x_n'')}$$

are "close" to each other if $(x'_1, \ldots, x'_n)$, $(x''_1, \ldots, x''_n)$ and $(a'_1, \ldots, a'_n)$, $(a''_1, \ldots, a''_n)$ are "close" to each other, respectively]. By projecting every $T(M)_p$ into p, we obtain a natural projection $\pi\colon T(M) \longrightarrow M$; $(\pi, T(M), M)$ is a vector bundle of fiber $T(M)_p$, "the tangent space" $\tau(M)$ of M. $T(M)$ in fact is a differentiable manifold [the differentiable structure is defined by considering the $2n$-dimensional, "coordinate neighborhoods" $(x_1, \ldots, x_n, a_1, \ldots, a_n)$]. Here π and the O-cross section $i\colon M \longrightarrow T(M)$, which associates to every $p \in M$ the O-tangent vector at p, are differentiable. More exactly $\tau(M)$ is differentiable.

Intuitively, one has to view a tangent vector ϕ at p as an ("infinitesimal") arc of curve: $\Phi\colon I \longrightarrow M$, $\Phi(0) = p$. The value $\phi(f)$, where f is some function $U \longrightarrow R$ (U an open neighborhood of p), is

$$\phi(f) = \frac{\partial}{\partial t}\bigg|_{t=0} f\Phi(t).$$

Obviously everything is determined by the *germs* of f and Φ (in fact only by *their first derivatives*).

Now, if $f\colon M \longrightarrow N$ is a differentiable map of differentiable manifolds, we have a map $f_p^*: \mathfrak{F}_{f(p)}(N) \longrightarrow \mathfrak{F}_p(M)$ which is a map of R-algebras. This map is defined as follows: if $U_{f(p)}$ is an open neighborhood of $f(p)$ in M and $g: U_{f(p)} \longrightarrow R$ is a C^∞ function, f^* will map the germ of g into the germ of $g \circ f: f^{-1}(U_{f(p)}) \longrightarrow R$ (considered at p). It is easy to see that the definition makes sense. This enables us to define a linear map

$$f_*^p: T(M)_p \longrightarrow T(N)_{f(p)}$$

in the following way: if $g \in \mathfrak{F}_{f(p)}(N)$ and $\phi \in T(M)_p$, by definition,

$$(f_*^p(\phi))(g) = \phi(f_p^*(g)).$$

The intuitive sense of the definition is obvious: any small arc of curve at p in M is carried by f into a small arc of curve on N at $f(p)$.

All the maps $f_*^p: T(M_p) \longrightarrow T(N)_{f(p)}$ can be "glued" together to a differentiable map $f_*: T(M) \longrightarrow T(N)$ which makes the following diagram commutative:

$$\begin{array}{ccc} T(M) & \xrightarrow{f_*} & T(N) \\ \downarrow & & \downarrow \\ M & \xrightarrow{f} & N. \end{array}$$

The map f_*^p is very important, since it contains most of the geometry of the map f around p. More precisely, using more or less sophisticated forms of the implicit function theorem, one can prove the following facts:

If f_*^p is surjective, then there exist coordinate systems $(x_1, \ldots, x_{n+r})$ $(r \geq 0)$ and $(y_1, \ldots, y_n)$ at p and $f(p)$ such that f can be written locally as

$$y_1 = x_1,\ y_2 = x_2,\ \ldots,\ y_n = x_n.$$

If f_*^p is injective, then there exist coordinate systems $(x_1, \ldots, x_m)$, $(y_1, \ldots, y_{m+r})$ $(r \geq 0)$ at p and $f(p)$ such that f can be written locally as

$$y_1 = x_1,\ \ldots,\ y_m = x_m,\ y_{m+1} = 0,\ \ldots,\ y_{m+r} = 0.$$

(In particular, if f_*^p is bijective, f is locally, around p, a diffeomorphism.)

Now every point $p \in M$ such that $f_*^p: T(M)_p \longrightarrow T(N)_{f(p)}$ is *not* *onto* will be called a *singular point*. Let M be a differentiable manifold and $\mathfrak{O} = \{(U_i, h_i)\}$ its differentiable structure. A set $X \subset M$ is by definition of *measure* 0, if for every i, $h_i^{-1}(h_i(U_i) \cap X) \subset E_n$ has *Lebesgue measure* 0. Since differentiable maps are absolutely continuous, this definition is not changed if we take on M another differentiable structure, equivalent to $\mathfrak{O}$.

We have the following

THEOREM OF SARD: *Let $f: M \longrightarrow N$ be a differentiable map, and $S \subset M$, the singular set of f. Then $f(S) \subset N$ is a set of measure* 0.

From this we can deduce quite easily that $N - f(S)$ is dense. The theorem of Sard is quite deep, and its proof quite long (especially for dim $M >$ dim N). A good exposition can be found in [9].

We want to give only some intuitive hints about it. First of all, if we would place ourselves in a *combinatorial* context, what Sard's theorem would say is that for a *simplicial* map $\phi: K \longrightarrow K'$, $K' - \phi(\Sigma)$, where $\Sigma \subset K$ is the set of simplexes of K on which dim $\phi(\sigma) <$ dim K', is open and dense. And this is obvious.

On the other hand, it is an easy exercise in real variables to prove that if $h: R \longrightarrow R$ is a differentiable function, the set

$$h(S) = \{y | y = f(x), f'(x) = 0\}$$

has measure 0.

If dim $M \subset$ dim N, then $S = M$ and $f(M) = f(S)$ looks "like a submanifold of codimension > 0," in N, which implies that it has measure 0.

In general one will prove that $f(S)$ is "concentrated around something which looks like a submanifold of codimension > 0," and hence it has measure 0.

Let us consider now two differentiable manifolds M, N [for simplicity M is supposed closed and a differentiable *embedding* $f: M \longrightarrow N$ (we assume $f(M) \cap \text{Bd } N = \emptyset$)]. We want to define the *normal bundle* of $f(M)$ in N. In order to do this, one proceeds as follows: first one considers a *Riemannian metric* on N. This means that a nondegenerate *scalar product* (i.e., a nondegenerate, symmetric bilinear, positive map), depending differentially of p, is defined in every tangent space $T(N)_p$. A classical theorem of

Steenrod says that this can be done on every C^∞ manifold (see [8]). Then, for every point $q \in M$ we can consider the set of tangent vectors in $T(N)_{f(q)}$ *orthogonal* to $f_*^q(T(M)_q) \subset T(N)_{f(q)}$. This is a vector space of dimension $\dim N - \dim M$. These vector spaces can be easily patched together into a vector bundle of dimension $\dim N - \dim M$ and basis M, $\nu(M, f, N)$ which we call the *normal bundle* of $f(M)$ in N

$$\nu(M, f, N) = (\pi', \mathcal{W}_f, M);$$

$\nu(M, f, N)$ is a differentiable vector bundle.

Here $\nu(M, f, N)$ has the following properties:

(a) $\tau(M) \oplus \nu(M, f, N) = f^{-1}(\tau(N))$.

(b) There exists a differentiable injection: $J\colon \mathcal{W}_f \longrightarrow N$ such that the following diagram is commutative:

$$\begin{array}{ccc} \mathcal{W}_f & \xrightarrow{J} & N \\ {\scriptstyle i}\nwarrow & & \nearrow{\scriptstyle f} \\ & M & \end{array}$$

(J is, in a certain sense, unique).

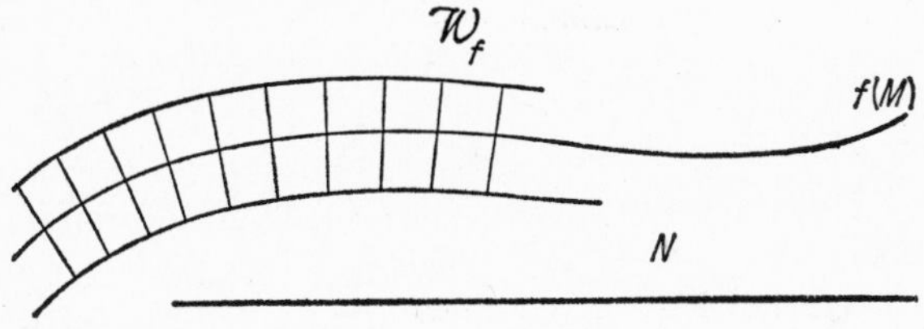

Fig. 1

Remark: *In fact $\nu(M, f, N)$ is independent of the Riemannian metric. In fact f induces a "bundle homomorphism" $\tau(M) \longrightarrow \tau(N)$, and $\nu(M, f, N)$ is the "cokernel" of this homomorphism.*

Let us define now an important manifold, the *Grassman manifold $G_{p,n}$*.

Definition: *$G_{p,n}$ is the set of all p-dimensional hyperplanes, through the origin, in E_{n+p}. $G_{p,n}$ has a natural topology which trans-*

forms it into a compact topological manifold and a natural differential structure.

In fact if we denote by $O(k)$ the orthogonal group in k-space, then it is easy to see that $G_{p,n}$ can be identified to the homogeneous space $O(n+p)/(O(n) \times O(p))$. [$O(n+p)$ operates transitively on $G_{p,n}$. These elements of $O(n+p)$ which leave $\alpha \in G_{p,n}$ invariant are direct sums of rotations in the hyperplane α and the hyperplane orthogonal to α.]

Now, there exists a vector bundle of basis $G_{p,n}$, $\xi(G_{p,n})$, defined as follows:

DEFINITION: *Let us consider the space $\hat{G}_{p,n}$ of pairs (α, β) consisting of an element $\alpha \in G_{p,n}$ and a vector β lying in the hyperplane α. $\hat{G}_{p,n}$ has a natural structure of differentiable manifold and the projection $\pi: (\alpha, \beta) \longrightarrow \alpha$ is a differentiable map. In fact $(\pi, \hat{G}_{p,n}, G_{p,n}) = \xi(G_{p,n})$ is a differentiable p-vector bundle.*

It has the following very important property:

THE CLASSIFICATION THEOREM: *The set of p-vector bundles over the* CW*-complex X, of dimension* $\dim X < n$, *is in one-to-one natural correspondence with the set of homotopy classes of maps $X \longrightarrow G_{p,n}$. More precisely, the correspondence assigns to every $f: X \longrightarrow G_{p,n}$ the bundle $f^{-1}(\xi(G_{p,n}))$ over X.*

For the proof, see [8].

In fact we can do slightly better. Let us consider the natural inclusions

$$E_1 \subset E_2 \subset E_3 \subset \cdots E_i \subset E_{i+1} \subset \cdots$$

coming from

$$(x_1) = (x_1, 0) \subset (x_1, x_2) = (x_1, x_2, 0) \subset (x_1, x_2, x_3) = \cdots.$$

This gives us natural inclusions

$$G_{p,1} \subset G_{p,2} \subset \cdots \subset G_{p,i} \subset G_{p,i+1} \subset \cdots$$

and if we denote $G_{p,i} \subset G_{p,i+1}$ by ϕ_i, it is easy to see that

$$\xi(G_{p,i}) = \phi_i^{-1}(\xi(G_{p,i+1})).$$

We can thus define the limit space

$$G_p = \lim_{n=\infty} G_{p,n}$$

and a bundle over it

$$\xi(G_p) = \lim_{n=\infty} (\xi(G_{p,n})).$$

Now, for every finite dimensional CW-complex X, the p-dimensional vector bundles over X are in one-to-one correspondence with the set of homotopy classes of maps $X \longrightarrow G_p$.

4. THOM'S TRANSVERSALITY THEOREM (For more details the reader can consult [11], [12].)

Let us consider now a manifold M, a submanifold $N \subset M$ (i.e., a differentiable injection $N \subset M$), and a third manifold P. We want to show that every differentiable map $f: P \longrightarrow M$ can be "approximated" in some appropriate topology by a map $\phi: P \longrightarrow M$ which is in "general position" with respect to N. We have first to define the terms *general position* and *approximation*.

Let us denote $\dim M = m$, $\dim N = n$, $\dim P = p$. If we were in the special case $n + p = m$, then the "natural" definition of general position would be the following:

(a) The set $P \cap f^{-1}(N)$ has only isolated points.

(b) If $f(x) \in N$, then the map

$$f_*^x: T(P)_x \longrightarrow T(M)_{f(x)}$$

is injective and $T(N)_{f(x)} \cap f_*^x(T(P)_x) = 0$.

(c) Hence if $f(x) \in N$, then

$$T(N)_{f(x)} + f_*^x(T(P)_x) = T(M)_{f(x)} \tag{1}$$

[$T(N)_{f(x)}$ and $f_*^x(T(P)_x)$ are vector subspaces of $T(M)_{f(x)}$ of dimensions n and p. We ask that together they span all $T(M)_{f(x)}$].

Actually, condition (c) is equivalent to conditions (a) plus (b). So it can be taken as the definition of general position for the case $n + p = m$.

But actually condition (c) makes sense without any dimensional restriction. If $p + n < m$, Eq. (1) will mean that $f(P) \cap N = \varnothing$. If $p + n = m$, Eq. (1) will mean, as we have seen, conditions (a)

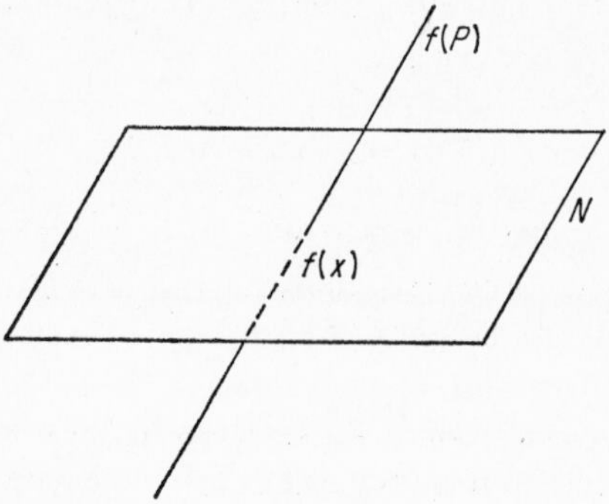

FIG. 2

plus (b). If $p + n > m$, the implicit function theorem shows the following [consequence of Eq. (1)]: There exist coordinate neighborhoods

$$V = (x_1, \ldots, x_n, y_1, \ldots, y_{m-n}) \quad \text{around} \quad (0, \ldots, 0) = f(x)$$
$$W = (z_1, \ldots, z_{p+n-m}, Y_1, \ldots, Y_{m-n}) \quad \text{around} \quad (0, \ldots 0) = x,$$

such that

$$N \cap V \text{ is } y_1 = \cdots = y_{m-n} = 0$$

and $f|W$ is $(f(W) \subset V)$ given by formulas of the following type:

$$\begin{aligned} x_1 &= f_1(z) \\ x_2 &= f_2(z) \\ &\cdots\cdots \\ x_n &= f_n(z) \\ y_1 &= Y_1 \\ y_2 &= Y_2 \\ &\cdots\cdots \\ y_{m-n} &= Y_{m-n}. \end{aligned}$$

This is a reasonably good geometrical picture of *general position*. Since we reserve in principle the term of *general position* for the case $n + p = m$, we shall call this new concept *transversality*. We sum up our information:

Let $M \supset N$ be a manifold and submanifold; $f: P \longrightarrow M$ is a differentiable map. Then f is said to be *transversal* with respect to M if for every $x \in P$ either $f(x) \notin N$ or $f(x) \in N$, and Eq. (1) holds.

Our local considerations made above imply that if f is transversal, then $f^{-1}(N)$ is a submanifold of P of dimension $p + n - m$ and its normal bundle is f^{-1} applied to the normal bundle of N in M.

Now, the topology in the space of maps, which we shall have to consider, will be the so-called C^p-topology. Two maps $f, g: P \longrightarrow M$ are "sufficiently close to each other in the C^p-topology if g, up to its derivatives of order p, differs very little from f." This definition makes sense and is very clear, if $M = E_n$ and P is compact. The reader can easily see what it means (and it makes sense only in one way) if M is general and P compact (and this will be in fact the case we shall be interested in). If P is not compact, there are several topologies which can be defined on these lines, and the reader who wishes more details can consult [12].

Let us prove now the following theorem of Thom:

THE TRANSVERSALITY THEOREM: *Let $M \supset N$ be a manifold and a submanifold. Let also P be a compact manifold,* Hom (P, M) *be the space of differentiable mappings $P \longrightarrow M$ endowed with some C^r-topology $r \geq 1$, and $T(P, M, N) \subset$* Hom (P, M) *the subset of those $f: P \longrightarrow M$ which are transversal with respect to N. $T(P, M, N)$ is open and dense in* Hom (P, M).

(Remark: If P is not compact, $T(P, M, N)$ is just dense but not necessarily open.)

Proof: For the proof we need the following lemma:

LEMMA: *Let M be a differentiable manifold and F_1, F_2 two closed subsets of M such that $F_1 \cap F_2 = \varnothing$. There exists a differentiable function f on M such that* $0 \leq f \leq 1, f|F_1 \equiv 1, f|F_2 \equiv 0$.

This is a form of the *differential partition of unity* and a proof of it can be found, for example, in [10].

Now, we go back to the proof of the transversality theorem.

The openness of $T(P, M, N)$ is very easy to prove. It follows from the fact that, in the space of $l \times k$ matrices, those matrices which are of maximum rank form an open set. Here we use, of course, the fact that our topology on the functional space is C^r, with $r \geq 1$. Otherwise the openness would be false. It is very easy to change a map in general position into a map which is not in general position, by a small deformation in the C^0-topology, but not in the C^1-topology.

We shall now prove the following:

(*) For every $x \in P$ and $f \in \text{Hom}(P, M)$, there exists a neighborhood V of x in P and a neighborhood W of f in Hom (P, M) (endowed with the C^r-topology) such that the set A of those $g \in W$ for which $g|V$ is transversal with respect to N is open and dense, in W.

Proof of (*): If $f(x) \notin N$, then the proof is immediate since we can find a neighborhood V of x and a neighborhood W of f such that if $y \in V$ and $g \in W, g(y) \notin N$.

In the general case, the openness of A is obvious, by the remark made above. The denseness is proved as follows: We consider a neighborhood E_m of $f(x)$ in M, with a Cartesian decomposition: $E_m = E_n \times E_{m-n}$ such that $E_n \times 0 = E_m \cap N$. Let us consider a closed disk $D_n \subset E_n$ and $E_n' = \text{int } D_n$. We can always assume that $f(x) = 0 \times 0$. Let us consider a disk $\overline{D}_n \subset E_n$, such that $\text{Cl}D_n \subset \text{int } \overline{D}_n$ and denote int $\overline{D}_n$ by $\overline{E}_n$. The neighborhood W will consist of those $f' : P \longrightarrow M$ such that $f'(V) \subset \overline{E}_n \times E_{m-n}$.

Let us consider now, for every $f' \in W$, the map

$$V \xrightarrow{f'} \overline{E}_n \times E_{m-n} \longrightarrow E_{m-n}.$$

It is very easy to see that $f'|V$ is transversal on N if and only if O is a regular value of V. By the theorem of Sard, there exist regular values ϵ of f' as close as we want to O. We can always find a C^∞ function $\phi : E_n \longrightarrow E_{m-n}$ such that $\phi(\overline{E}_n) = -\epsilon$, ϕ is O outside a large ball, and ϕ is very close to O in the C^r-topology we consider. We define ϕ on $E_n \times E_{m-n}$ by $\phi(x, y) = \phi(x)$. Let us represent $f'(y) \in E_n \times E_{m-n}$ by (f_1', f_2'). If we replace $f'(y)$ by $(f_1'(y), f_2'(y) + \phi(y))$, we find a map $P \longrightarrow M$ which is as close as we want to f' (which belongs anyway to W) and which belongs to A. So (*) is proved.

We pass from (*) to the proof of our theorem in the following way: We can choose a finite family $(V_1, W_1), \ldots, (V_k, W_k)$

for various x's in P and a fixed f such that (*) is fulfilled and $\bigcup V_i = P$. In $\bigcap W_i \ni f$, the set of those g which are transversal on N is dense, since the intersection of a finite number of open dense sets is dense.

5. SOME GENERALIZATIONS AND APPLICATIONS OF THOM'S TRANSVERSALITY THEOREM

Let us consider two differentiable manifolds, M and N. We shall construct (for every integer $r \geq 0$, a space is associated with M and N) the manifold of r-dimensional *jets* of M into N: $J^r(M, N)$.

Let us consider some given points $x \in M$ and $y \in N$ and the set of all differentiable mappings $f: M \longrightarrow N$ such that $f(x) = y$. We denote this set by $\mathrm{Hom}_{x,y}(M, N)$. We choose also some coordinate system $(x_1, \ldots, x_m)$ in M, around $x[(0, \ldots, 0) = x]$, and some coordinate system $(y_1, \ldots, y_n)$ in N, around $y[(0, \ldots, 0) = y]$.

On $\mathrm{Hom}_{x,y}(M, N)$ the following equivalence relation is defined: if $\phi, \psi \in \mathrm{Hom}_{x,y}(M, N)$, then ϕ and ψ are equivalent if all their partial derivatives at x, computed in the coordinate systems $(x_1, \ldots, x_m)$ and $(y_1, \ldots, y_n)$ up to order r, are the same. The equivalence classes are, by definition, the r-dimensional jets of M into N, at x, y: $j^r_{x,y}(M, N)$.

The following observations are immediate: First, this definition is independent of the choice of our coordinate systems. Second, we can replace $\mathrm{Hom}_{x,y}(M, N)$ by the functions defined only in some neighborhood of x, going into some neighborhood of y, i.e.,

$$j^r_{x,y}(M, N) = j^r_{0,0}(E_m, E_n).$$

On the other hand, $j^r_{0,0}(E_m, E_n)$ is easily seen to be a Euclidean space. We leave the computation of its dimension as a function of m, n, r as an exercise to the reader.

Now if we consider $\bigcup_{x,y} j^r_{x,y}(M, N) = J^r(M, N)$, we find a space which is easily transformed, in a natural way, into a differentiable manifold. The natural projection

$$\pi': J^r(M, N) \longrightarrow M \times N,$$

$\pi'^{-1}(x, y) = j^r_{x,y}(M, N)$, is the projection of a differentiable fiber bundle. More details can be found about jets in Ehresmann's paper [1].

Now, we shall be interested in the projection

$$\Pi: J^r(M, N) \longrightarrow M \times N \longrightarrow N$$

which is again a differentiable fiber bundle. Every differentiable map $f: M \longrightarrow N$, gives rise to a cross section $j^r f: M \longrightarrow J^r(M, N)$ [at $x \in M$, $j^r f$ is the jet determined by f at $(x, f(x))$].

The argument which was used in the last section enables us to prove the following two theorems:

THE "LOCAL" THEOREM OF THOM: *Let us consider two differentiable manifolds P, M and a submanifold $N' \subset J^r(P, M)$. P is supposed compact.*

Let us consider the space Hom (P, M) *endowed with some C^p-topology for some sufficiently large p. In* Hom (P, M) *we consider the subset A formed by those $f: P \longrightarrow M$ such that $j^r f: P \longrightarrow J^r(P, M)$ is transversal with respect to N'.*

A is open and dense in Hom (P, M).

Remark: The theorem from the preceding section is a special case of Thom's "local" theorem. With the notations from the last section, it suffices to consider $J^0(P, M) = P \times M$ and $N' = P \times N \subset P \times M$.

We have also

THOM'S THEOREM "AT THE TARGET": *Let us consider the map $f: P \longrightarrow M$ and the induced map*

$$j^r f \times j^r f: P \times P \longrightarrow J^r(P, M) \times J^r(P, M).$$

We consider some submanifold

$$N' \subset J^r(P, M) \times J^r(P, M).$$

Let us consider Hom (P, M) *endowed with some C^p-topology, for sufficiently large p.*

$A \subset$ Hom (P, M) *will denote the set of those $f: P \longrightarrow M$ such that (Δ = diagonal)*

$$j^r f \times j^r f | P \times P - \Delta: P \times P - \Delta \longrightarrow J^r(P, M) \times J^r(P, M)$$

is transversal with respect to N'.

A is open and dense in Hom (P, M).

Sometimes, in the applications, we need instead of a submanifold N', a *stratified submanifold.* We consider a differentiable manifold M and a sequence of two by two disjoint, not necessarily compact, submanifolds (without boundary) of M

$$X_k, X_{k-1}, \ldots, X_0$$

($\dim X_i > \dim X_{i-1}$) such that, for every i, $X_i \cup X_{i-1} \cup \cdots X_0$ is closed in M.

The set $X_k \cup X_{k-1} \cup \cdots X_0$ is by definition a stratified manifold. The idea is that ClX_i is a manifold "with singularities," the set of singularities being exactly $X_{i-1} \cup X_{i-2} \cup \cdots X_0$. For example, if we consider on M a smooth triangulation K and $K' \subset K$ is a subcomplex of K, K' can be considered as a stratified manifold.

If $\dim K' = k$ and K'_i is the ith-dimensional skeleton of K', we take the decomposition

$$K' - K'_{k-1}, K'_{k-1} - K'_{k-2}, \ldots, K'_0.$$

Now, if $N' \subset M$ is a stratified submanifold (in particular, a manifold, if $k = 0$) and $f: P \longrightarrow M$ is a differentiable mapping from a differentiable manifold P into M, f is said to be transversal on N' if the following condition is fulfilled,

$$f \text{ is transversal on every } X_i.$$

Now the two theorems given above can be proved without any extra difficulty for the case when N' is a stratified submanifold instead of being a usual submanifold.

Let us give some applications now.

A differentiable map $f: M \longrightarrow N$, which is such that for every $x \in M$

$$f_*^x: T(M)_x \longrightarrow T(N)_x$$

is injective, is called an *immersion.*

An immersion which is also injective is called an *embedding.* It is easy to see that locally an immersion is an embedding.

We have the following two theorems of Whitney:

THEOREM 5.1: *Let P, M be differentiable manifolds, and* $\dim M \geq 2(\dim P) + 1$. *Then, in* Hom (P, M) *(endowed with some C^p-topology . . .), the embeddings form an open dense set. In particular, any n-dimensional manifold can be embedded into E_{2m+1}.*

(Actually, by a special extra argument, E_{2m+1} can be replaced with E_{2m}.)

THEOREM 5.2: *Let P, M be differentiable manifolds, and* $\dim M \geq 2 (\dim P)$. *Then, in* Hom (P, M), *the immersions form an open dense set. In particular, any m-dimensional manifold can be embedded into* E_{2m}.

These two theorems can be deduced from Thom's theorems. We shall prove theorem 5.1.

Proof: We apply Thom's theorem at the target to $J^0(P, N) \times J^0(P, M) = (P \times M) \times (P \times M)$. $N' \subset (P \times M) \times (P \times M)$ will be the set of points of the form $(x \times y) \times (x' \times y)$ (*same* y). N' is easily seen to be a submanifold of codimension $= \dim M$. Now, a map $j: P \longrightarrow M$ is injective if and only if

$$(*) \qquad (j^r f \times j^r f(P \times P - \Delta)) \cap N' = \emptyset.$$

But, if $\dim M \geq 2 (\dim P) + 1$, then

$$\dim N' + \dim (P \times P - \Delta) < \dim (J^0(P, M) \times J^0(P, M)).$$

Hence, if $\dim M \geq 2 (\dim P) + 1$, any map $f: P \longrightarrow M$ such that

$$j^r f \times j^r f | P \times P - \Delta : P \times P - \Delta \longrightarrow J^0(P, M) \times J^0(P, M)$$

fulfills (*). We have proved hence (via Thom's theorem at the target) that the differentiable injections form an open dense set. Now, in order to ensure the injectivity condition at the level of the tangent spaces, we can produce a similar argument, using the "local" theorem and the following observation.

Let us consider in $J^1(P, M)$ the set N' of all jets such that the induced map on the tangent spaces is *not* injective. N' is easily recognized to be a stratified manifold, and a map $f: P \longrightarrow M$ is an immersion if and only if $j^1 f(P) \cap N' = \emptyset$.

Using this observation, Theorem 5.2 can be proved.

Let us consider now C^∞ functions from a manifold M into the real line R. A point $x \in M$ will be, by definition, *critical* for the function $f: M \longrightarrow R$ if all the partial derivatives of first order of f at x are 0. This definition is obviously independent of the coordinate system in which we actually compute the partial derivatives $\partial f/\partial x_1, \ldots, \partial f/\partial x_m$.

If x is critical, $f(x)$ is called a *critical level.*

Now, if x is a critical point, we choose some coordinate system $(x_1, \ldots, x_m)$ $[(0, \ldots, 0) = x]$ around it and compute the determinant $\|\partial^2 f/\partial x_k\, \partial x_j\|$. If

$$\left\|\frac{\partial^2 f}{\partial x_i\, \partial x_j}\right\| \neq 0$$

we say that x is a *nondegenerate critical point.* (The fact that $\|\partial^2 f/\partial x_i\, \partial x_j\| \neq 0$ is an invariant with respect to the choice of coordinate systems.)

A function $M \longrightarrow R$ which has only nondegenerate critical points is called a *Morse function.* We have the following theorem:

THEOREM 5.3: *Let us consider the space of functions* Hom (P, R) *with some C^p-topology (p sufficiently large). P is assumed compact.*

The Morse functions form an open dense set. In particular, a Morse function f exists on P [and if Bd $P \neq \varnothing$, we can always refine the argument such that f is constant on every component of Bd P, or even more, that for some decomposition Bd $P = P_1 \cup P_2$ (P_1 and P_2 are unions of components), $f(P_1) = m$, $f(P_2) = M (M > m)$, and $m < f(P - \text{Bd } P) < M$].

Proof: We consider the set $J^1(P, R)$ and in $J^1(P, R)$ the set N' of all jets which have *all* their (first) partial derivatives 0. N' is easily recognized to be a submanifold.

On the other hand one can prove that a function $f\colon P \longrightarrow R$ is a Morse function if and only if $j^1 f\colon P \longrightarrow J^1(P, R)$ is transversal with respect to N'. This is an exercise in linear algebra, which we leave to the reader. Thom's local theorem now gives our proof.

So far we did not say a word about the relative forms of Thom's theorem. So let us consider the manifolds with boundary P, M, N. We assume that N is a submanifold of M and Bd $N \subset$ Bd M, int $N \subset$ int M. We consider only maps $f\colon P \longrightarrow M$ such that $f^{-1}(\text{Bd } M) = \text{Bd } P$.

Moreover we consider a given map

$$\phi\colon \text{Bd } P \longrightarrow \text{Bd } M$$

which is transversal on Bd N.

$\text{Hom}_\phi(P, M)$ will denote the space (with some C^r-topology) of mappings $P \longrightarrow M$ such that the restriction to Bd P is ϕ.

We have

THE RELATIVE TRANSVERSALITY THEOREM: *In* $\text{Hom}_\phi(P, M)$ *the set of those* $f: P \longrightarrow M$ *which are transversal on* N, *is open and dense.*

6. THOM'S COBORDISM THEORY

In what follows we shall give a brief account of the geometric part of Thom's *nonoriented* cobordism theory. In a very similar manner, one can treat the geometry of oriented cobordism.

For more details, and for the algebraic part, we refer to the papers of Thom, Milnor, Wall, Averbuch, and Novicov.

In our discussion we shall consider only compact, not necessarily connected, differentiable manifolds. Two *closed* manifolds M_1, M_2 of the same dimension m will be called *cobordant* if there exists a manifold N, of dimension $m + 1$, such that $\text{Bd}\, N = M_1 + M_2$ (we denote by $+$ the disjoint union). This is easily recognized to be an equivalence relation:

M is cobordant to itself since $\text{Bd}\,(M \times 1) = M + M$; symmetry is obvious and reflexivity is shown in Fig. 3.

$$\begin{array}{l} \text{Bd}\, N_1 = M + M' \\ \text{Bd}\, N_2 = M' + M'' \\ \hline \text{Bd}\,(N_1 \cup N_2) = M + M'' \end{array}$$

(We denote by $N_1 \cup N_2$ the manifold which results by gluing N_1 and N_2 together, along M'.)

In particular, if $\text{Bd}\, N = M$, we say that M is *cobordant* (i.e., cobordant to $\varnothing$).

Let us consider the set Σ_n of all closed differentiable manifolds of dimension n (two diffeomorphic manifolds are considered identical). We add $\varnothing$ to Σ_n and consider on Σ_n the operation $+$ (disjoint union). This makes Σ_n a commutative semigroup with unit. The equivalence relation of cobordism is compatible with the oper-

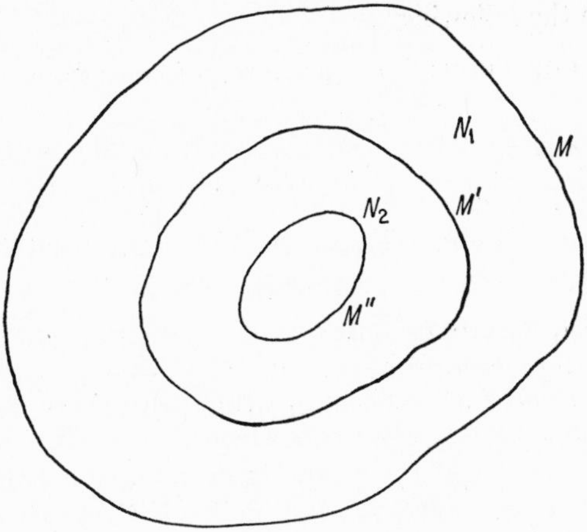

FIG. 3

ations of Σ_n (i.e., if M is cobordant to M' and N to N', then $M + N$ is cobordant to $M' + N'$).

Hence we can pass to the quotient and form a new semigroup $\mathcal{W}_n$. Actually $\mathcal{W}_n$ turns out to be a group. In fact, the 0-element of $\mathcal{W}_n$ is represented exactly by the manifolds which are cobordant. Let N be any closed manifold, and $\hat{N}$ the cobordism class of $N (N \in \Sigma_n, \hat{N} \in \mathcal{W}_n)$. Since $\text{Bd}\,(N \times I) = N + N = 2N$, we have $2\hat{N} = 0$. This proves that every $\hat{N} \in \mathcal{W}_n$ has an inverse; and since this inverse is actually $\hat{N}$ itself, every element in the group $\mathcal{W}_n$ is of order 2.

Our problem now will be the computation of $\mathcal{W}_n$.

DEFINITION: *Let ξ be the vector bundle (π, E, B). The "Thom space" of the bundle ξ, $T(\xi)$ is by definition the following space: We compactify by the point at the infinity ∞_x every fiber $\pi^{-1}(x)$ $(x \in B)$ of ξ; then we identify together all the ∞_x's. If ξ was a differentiable bundle, $T(\xi)$ is a differentiable manifold with one singular point ∞.*

If B is compact, $T(\xi)$ is the one point compactification of E.

Let us consider the Thom space $T(\xi(G_{p,n}))$ associated to the Grassmannian $G_{p,n}$ of p-planes in $(p + n)$-space, and the Thom space $T(\xi(G_p))$ of the infinite Grassmannian of p-planes.

We have the following

THEOREM OF THOM: *We have a group isomorphism*

$$\mathcal{W}_n = \pi_{n+p}(T(\xi(G_{p,m})))$$

for large m and p.

REMARK: *For large m and p (with respect to n), the groups $\pi_{n+p}(T(\xi(G_{p,m})))$ do not depend on m (they are "stable") and they can be identified with $\pi_{n+p}(T(\xi(G_p)))$.*

For large p, the groups $\pi_{n+p}(T(\xi(G_p)))$ become also stable; in fact there is a natural morphism $\pi_{n+p}(T(\xi(G_p))) \longrightarrow \pi_{n+p+1}(T(\xi(G_{p+1})))$ which becomes eventually an isomorphism.

Thom's theorem can be written

$$\mathcal{W}_n = \lim_{p=\infty} \pi_{n+p}(T(\xi(G_p))).$$

The rest of this section is devoted to the proof.

Construction of a map $\Phi: \mathcal{W}_n \longrightarrow \pi_{n+p}(T(\xi(G_{p,m})))$. Let us consider an element $\hat{N}_n \in \mathcal{W}_n$ representing a closed manifold N_n. N_n can be embedded in a sphere S_{n+p} (if p is sufficiently large). Let us consider the normal bundle $\nu(i)$ of $N_n \overset{i}{\subset} S_{n+p}$ which is a p-dimensional vector bundle over N_n. Let $N(i)$ be the total space. $N(i)$ can be considered as a submanifold $N(i) \subset S_{n+p}$ and $N_n \overset{i}{\subset} S_{n+p}$ is the composition of the 0-cross section of $N(i)$ with $N(i) \subset S_{n+p}$. Now, for large m, $\xi(G_{p,m})$ will classify bundles over N_n. Hence there will exist a map $f: N_n \longrightarrow G_{p,m}$ and a bundle map

$$\begin{array}{ccc} N(i) & \xrightarrow{F} & \hat{G}_{p,m} \\ \downarrow & & \downarrow \\ N_n & \xrightarrow[f]{} & G_{p,m}. \end{array}$$

(Now $\nu(i) = f^{-1}(\xi(G_{p,m})))$. Then f is determined uniquely, up to homotopy.

Now, $T(\xi(G_{p,m})) = \hat{G}_{p,m} \cup \infty$. Hence we can extend F to S_{n+p}, as a continuous map $\overline{F}: S_{n+p} \longrightarrow T(\xi(G_{p,m}))$ in the following way:

$$\overline{F}|N(i) = F$$
$$\overline{F}(S_{n+p} - N(i)) = \infty.$$

The continuity is obvious.

Hence, to N_n and the embedding $i: N_n \subset S_{n+p}$, we have attached a continuous map $\overline{F} = \phi(N_n, i): S_{n+p} \longrightarrow T(\xi(G_{p,m}))$. [In fact, a priori, $\overline{F}$ depends on N_n, i, f, and on the embedding $N(i) \subset S_{n+p}$; but for simplicity we write just $\phi(N_n, i)$. Anyway, $\overline{F}$ will be shown eventually (up to homotopy) to depend only on $\hat{N}_n$.]

We can always choose in S_{n+p} a base point $*$ and arrange ourselves such that $\notin N(i)$. In $T(\xi(G_{p,m}))$ the base point will be ∞: $\phi(N_n, i)(*) = \infty$ and we shall consider only based maps $S_{n+p} \longrightarrow T(\xi(G_{p,m}))$.

We shall prove that the homotopy class

$$\hat{\phi}(N_n, i) \in \pi_{n+p}(T(\xi(G_{p,m})))$$

is independent of i and of the particular choice of N_n in $\hat{N}_n$. Hence we have defined a map $\Phi: \mathfrak{W}_n \longrightarrow \pi_{n+p}(T(\xi(G_{p,m})))$ by $\Phi(\hat{N}_n) = \hat{\phi}(N_n, i)$. The independence of $\hat{\phi}(N_n, i)$ on i is easy to see, since if p is sufficiently large, any two embeddings $N_n \longrightarrow S_{n+p}$ will be isotopic (and we can also assume that the isotopy never meets $*$). It is also easy to see that $\hat{\phi}(N_n, i)$ does not depend on the particular choice of the embedding $N(i) \subset S_{n+p}$ (using for example "the uniqueness" of the tubular neighborhood).

Now if N'_n and N''_n are cobordant ($\hat{N}'_n = \hat{N}''_n$), there exists a manifold M such that $\text{Bd}\, M = N'_n \cup N''_n$. If p is large enough, we can always find an embedding $j: M \longrightarrow S_{n+p} \times I$ such that $j^{-1}(\text{Bd}\,(S_{n+p} \times I)) = \text{Bd}\, M$ and, more exactly, $j(N'_n) \subset S_{n+p} \times 0$, $j(N''_n) \subset S_{n+p} \times 1$. We consider the normal bundle of $j(M)$, $N(j) \subset S_{n+p} \times 1$. There is a bundle map

$$\begin{array}{ccc} N(j) & \xrightarrow{R} & \hat{G}_{p,m} \\ \downarrow & & \downarrow \\ M & \xrightarrow{r} & G_{p,m} \end{array}$$

and, as before, we can extend it to a map $\overline{R}: S_{n+p} \times 1 \longrightarrow T(\xi(G_{p,m}))$. Obviously $\overline{R}|S_{n+p} \times 0 = \phi(N'_n, j|N'_n)$ and $\overline{R}|S_{n+p} \times 1 = \phi(N''_n, j|N''_n)$. Hence:

$$\hat{\phi}(N'_n, j|N'_n) = \hat{\phi}(N''_n, j|N''_n).$$

(We must take care that $N(j) \cap (* \times I) = \varnothing$.)

So Φ is well-defined. It is not hard to see that it is a group-homomorphism. Exactly the same construction which was used to show that $\phi(N_n, i)$ does not depend on the cobordism class of N_n is used to show that Φ maps $O \in \mathfrak{W}_n$ into $O \in \pi_{n+p}(T(\xi(G_{p,m})))$. It is easy to check that $\Phi(a + b) = \Phi(a) + \Phi(b)$.

We have to prove now that Φ is a bijection.

Φ *is injective:* So we want to prove that if $\Phi(\hat{N}_n) = 0$, then $\hat{N}_n = 0$. Let us consider the natural inclusion $G_{p,m} \subset T(\xi(G_{p,m}))$ coming from the 0-cross section of ξ. We observe that the map $\phi(N_n, i)$ considered above can be always considered *differentiable wherever it is possible* (by taking f to be C^∞).

Then $\phi(N_n, i)$ is also obviously transversal to $G_{p,m}$. Let us assume that $\phi(N_n, i)$ can be extended to a continuous map $\psi: D_{n+p+1} \longrightarrow T(\xi(G_{p,m}))$. By an easy approximation theorem, we can assume that ψ is differentiable wherever it is possible; and by the relative transversality theorem, we can assume that it is transversal on $G_{p,m}$. Then $\psi^{-1}(G_{p,m}) \subset D_{n+p+1}$ is a manifold with boundary, whose boundary is $\operatorname{Bd} D_{n+p+1} \cap \psi^{-1}(G_{p,m}) = N_n$. Hence $\hat{N}_n = 0$.

Φ *is surjective:* Let

$$\psi: S_{n+p} \longrightarrow T(\xi(G_{p,m}))$$

be a based continuous map. We shall prove that in

$$\hat{\psi} \in \pi_{n+p}(T(\xi(G_{p,m})))$$

there exists a map $\psi': S_{n+p} \longrightarrow T(\xi(G_{p,m}))$ such that ψ' is of the form $\psi' = \phi(N_n, i)$ for some $N_n \in \hat{N}_n$ (some $\hat{N}_n$). Hence this will show that $\hat{\psi} \in \text{Image}\,\Phi$. Using the approximation and transversality theorem, we can find an approximation of ψ, ψ' which is differentiable wherever possible and transversal on $G_{p,m}$. Since approximation, if it is sufficiently close, does not change the homotopy class, $\hat{\psi} = \hat{\psi}'$. Hence $(\psi')^{-1}(G_{p,m}) \overset{i}{\subset} S_{n+p}$ is a manifold, and it is very easy to check that

$$\psi' = \phi((\psi')^{-1}(G_{p,m}), i).$$

This finishes the proof.

In fact, $\mathfrak{W}_n$ is the additive group of an algebra over Z_2. The

Z_2-multiplication is obvious and the product structure comes from the direct product of manifolds.

Using algebraic-topology techniques and the equality of the group $\mathcal{W}_n$ and $\pi_{n+p}(T(\xi(G_{p,m})))$, one can prove that $\mathcal{W}_n$ is a polynomial algebra with one generator in each dimension except those of the form $2^m - 1$. One can also formulate (and prove, using Thom's theory) the necessary and sufficient condition for a manifold N_n to be cobordant. We consider the tangent bundle $\tau(N_n)$ of N_n and the map $f: N_n \longrightarrow G_n$ such that

$$f^{-1}(\xi(G_n)) = \tau(N_n).$$

Let $H_i^*(G_n, Z_2)$ be the ith-dimensional cohomology group of G_n, with coefficients Z_2.

N_n is cobordant if and only if $f^*(H_n^*(G_n, Z_2)) \subset H_n^*(N_n, Z_2)$ is 0.

7. THE THEORY OF MORSE FUNCTIONS ON A MANIFOLD

In this section we shall review the main definitions and results of the theory of Morse functions on a *compact* manifold. More details can be found in Milnor's book [2].

First of all we have

THE LEMMA OF MORSE: *Let M be an n-dimensional manifold, $f: M \longrightarrow R$ a C^∞ function, and $x \in M$ a nondegenerate critical point of f. There exists a coordinate system $(x_1, \ldots, x_n)$ on M, around x $[(0, \ldots, 0) = x]$, such that, in the neighborhood of x, f can be written*

$$f = a - x_1^2 - x_2^2 - \cdots - x_\lambda^2 + x_{\lambda+1}^2 + \cdots x_n^2.$$

Hence f can be written as a constant term plus a nondegenerate quadratical form. Then λ, which is easily seen to be an invariant of f, at x, is called the *index* of the critical point x.

This lemma proves, incidentally, that the nondegenerate critical points are isolated.

The main problem of the theory will be the following: What is the connection between the topological structure of M and the Morse functions defined on M?

Let us denote by $\{a \le f \le b\}$ the set of points $x \in M$, such that $a \le f(x) \le b$. Similarly we define $\{f \le b\}$, $\{f = a\}$, $\{a < f < b\}$ a.s.o.

If a is not a critical level, then $\{f = a\}$ is a manifold of codimension 1. If the boundary of M is nonvoid, we shall assume that f is constant on every connected component of Bd M. (Of course we consider only functions with nondegenerate critical points, unless the contrary is explicitly stated.)

If a and b are both noncritical, $\{a \le f \le b\}$ is a manifold with boundary, and Bd $\{a \le f \le b\} = \{f = a\} \cup \{f = b\}$.

We need some definitions:

Let us consider a manifold with nonvoid boundary M_n (dim $M_n = n$) and the n-dimensional disk D_n which we factor $D_n = D_\lambda \times D_{n-\lambda}$. $S_{n-1} = \text{Bd}\, D_n$ can be expressed as follows:

$$\begin{aligned}\text{Bd}\, D_n = \text{Bd}\,(D_\lambda \times D_{n-\lambda}) &= \text{Bd}\, D_\lambda \times D_{n-\lambda} + D_\lambda \times \text{Bd}\, D_{n-\lambda} \\ &= S_{\lambda-1} \times D_{n-\lambda} + D_\lambda \times S_{n-\lambda-1}.\end{aligned}$$

$S_{\lambda-1} \times D_{n-\lambda}$ and $D_\lambda \times S_{n-\lambda-1}$ are compact bounded manifolds, having the same boundary $S_{\lambda-1} \times S_{n-\lambda-1}$. By gluing together the boundaries of $S_{\lambda-1} \times D_{n-\lambda}$ and $D_\lambda \times S_{n-\lambda-1}$ we find S_{n-1}. The reader can obtain a very good picture of what happens by considering the decomposition $S_3 = S_1 \times D_2 + D_2 \times S_1$. We find S_3 by considering two full tori $S_1 \times D_2 = T'$ and $S_1 \times D_2 = T''$. We consider a diffeomorphism Bd $T' \longrightarrow$ Bd T'' which identifies the meridians of T_1' with the parallels of T'' and conversely. [If we write Bd $(S_1 \times D_2) = S_1 \times S_1 = \text{Bd}\,(D_2 \times S_1)$, the first S_1 in $S_1 \times S_1$ will be meridian in $S_1 \times D_2$ and parallel in $D_2 \times S_1$ and the second S_1 (in $S_1 \times S_1$) will be parallel in $S_1 \times D_2$ and meridian in $D_2 \times S_1$.] (See Fig. 4.)

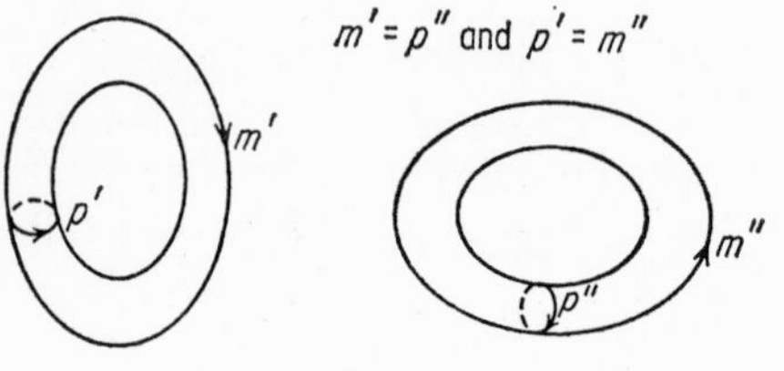

FIG. 4

$$m' = p''$$
$$p' = m''$$

Let us consider now a differentiable embedding $f: S_{\lambda-1} \times D_{n-\lambda} \longrightarrow \text{Bd}\, M_n$ and the quotient space $X = (M_n \cup (D_\lambda \times D_{n-\lambda}))/\Phi$, where every $x \in S_{\lambda-1} \times D_{n-\lambda}$ is identified with $f(x) \in \text{Bd}\, M_n$. X is obviously a manifold with boundary (topologically) and if we "smoothen its angles," it has a natural differentiable structure. (See Fig. 5.)

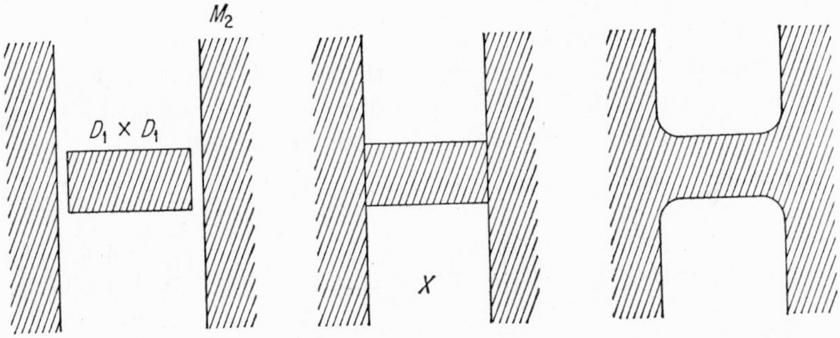

FIG. 5. Smoothing angles.

There are standard techniques for this smoothing procedure but we shall not go into their description here. X, together with its "natural" differentiable structure (induced by M_n), will be denoted by $\chi(M_n; f; \lambda)$. We shall say that we go from M_n to $\chi(M_n; f; \lambda)$ by adding a *handle of index* λ. (The terminology will be justified later.) The following elementary and easy lemma will be crucial:

LEMMA: *If f, f': $S_{\lambda-1} \times D_n \longrightarrow \text{Bd}\, M_n$ are isotopic embeddings (i.e., they can be connected by a continuous arc in the space of embeddings $S_{\lambda-1} \times D_n \longrightarrow \text{Bd}\, M_n$), then $\chi(M_n; f, \lambda)$ and $\chi(M_n; f', \lambda)$ are diffeomorphic.*

Sometimes it will be convenient to consider k copies of D_n,

$$D_n^1 = D_\lambda^1 \times D_{n-\lambda}^1, \qquad D_n^2 = D_\lambda^2 \times D_{n-\lambda}^2, \ldots, D_n^k = D_\lambda^k \times D_{n-\lambda}^k,$$

and differentiable injections,

$$f^i: S_{\lambda-1}^i \times D_{n-\lambda}^i \longrightarrow \text{Bd}\, M_n,$$

such that Image $f^i \cap$ Image $f^j = \varnothing$. We can then add simultaneously our k handles (D_n^i, f^i), $i = 1, \ldots, k$, and the result will be denoted by

$$\chi(M_n; f^1, \ldots, f^k; \lambda).$$

Another operation which we shall have to consider is the following: We take a *closed* $(n-1)$-dimensional manifold M'_{n-1} and an embedding $S_{\lambda-1} \times D_{n-\lambda} \overset{1}{\subset} M'_{n-1}$. When we write $S_{n-1} = S_{\lambda-1} \times D_{n-\lambda} + D_\lambda \times S_{n-\lambda-1}$, a natural identification

$$\text{Bd}\,(S_{\lambda-1} \times D_{n-\lambda}) = S_{\lambda-1} \times S_{n-\lambda-1} \xrightarrow{j} S_{\lambda-1} \times S_{n-\lambda-1} = \text{Bd}\,(D_\lambda \times S_{n-\lambda-1})$$

is defined. Let us consider

$$\text{Bd}\,(M'_{n-1} - \text{int}\,(S_{\lambda-1} \times D_{n-\lambda})) = S_{\lambda-1} \times S_{n-\lambda-1}$$

and its natural identification j with $S_{\lambda-1} \times S_{n-\lambda-1} = \text{Bd}\,(D_\lambda \times S_{n-\lambda-1})$. By gluing together $M'_{n-1} - \text{int}\,(S_{\lambda-1} \times D_{n-\lambda})$ and $D_\lambda \times S_{n-\lambda-1}$ (via j), we obtain a new manifold which we denote by $\mu(M'_{n-1}; i; \lambda)$. We say that we go from M'_{n-1} to $\mu(M'_{n-1}; i; \lambda)$ by a *Morse surgery of index* λ. In order to find an intuitive picture, one can consider a full torus T' embedded in a 3-manifold M_3. One can perform a surgery of index 2 by taking out the interior of T' and gluing instead another full torus, which will reverse the roles of meridians and parallels.

The connection between handle-adding and surgery can be expressed as follows:

$$\text{Bd}\,(\chi(M_n; f; \lambda)) = \mu(\text{Bd}\, M_n; f; \lambda).$$

Now, if we come back to handle-adding, there is a natural inclusion

$$M_n \subset \chi(M_n; f; \lambda)$$

and obviously

$$H_*(\chi(M_n; f; \lambda), M_n) = H_*(D_\lambda, S_{\lambda-1}).$$

This follows immediately from the observation that $\chi(M_n; f; \lambda)$ has the homotopy type of M_n to which a λ-dimensional disk is glued, along its boundary, by a map homotopic to f.

With these definitions we can go back now to the theory of Morse functions. We consider, as in the beginning of this section, a manifold M (compact) and a Morse function f on M. We want to compare $\{f \leq a\}$ and $\{f \leq b\}$ for a pair of numbers $a < b$ (a and b are not critical levels). Since we can filtrate the space M with help of the $\{f \leq a\}$, for variable a, this will be very valuable information for the structure of M. We have two cases:

THEOREM 7.1: *If* $[a, b]$ *does not contain any critical level, then*

$$\{f \leq a\} = \{f \leq b\} \qquad (\textit{diffeomorphically}).$$

THEOREM 7.2: *If* $[a, b]$ *contains exactly one critical level* $c: a < c < b$ *and* c *corresponds to* c_0 *critical point of index* 0; c_1 *critical points of index* 1; . . . , c_i *critical points of index* i; . . . , c_n *critical points of index* n; *then* $\{f \leq b\}$ *is diffeomorphic to* $\{f \leq a\}$ *to which we have added (on the component* $\{f = a\}$ *of the boundary)*

c_0 *handles of index* 0

c_1 *handles of index* 1

. . . .

c_i *handles of index* i

. . . .

c_n *handles of index* n.

The first theorem is the "easy" part, and it is proved by considering the orbits of the differential equation

$$\frac{dx}{dt} = \operatorname{grad} f$$

on M, running from $\{f = a\}$ to $\{f = b\}$.

The second theorem is relatively harder. Using the Morse lemma, its proof is reduced to the following consideration: One starts with the function $f = -x_1^2 - x_2^2 - \cdots - x_\lambda^2 + x_{\lambda+1}^2 + \cdots + x_n^2$, defined on E_n, and considers a small positive number $\epsilon > 0$. One has to prove that $\{f \leq \epsilon\}$ is diffeomorphic to $\{f \leq -\epsilon\}$ with one handle of index λ added. The reader can obtain a good intuitive picture of what happens, by analyzing the example

$$f = -x^2 - y^2 + z^2.$$

Figure 6 shows what happens for $f = -x^2 + y^2$.

In fact, theorem 7.2 has an inverse, which can be proved by a similar argument.

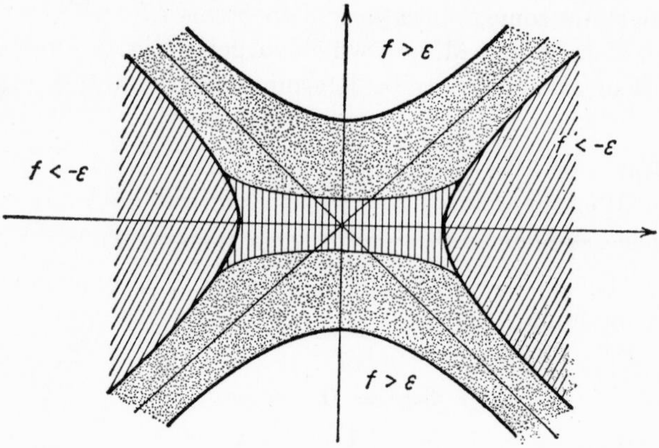

Fig. 6

Theorem 7.3: *Let M_n be an n-dimensional manifold on which a Morse function f is defined. Let us assume that f reaches its maximum on the component Q of* Bd M_n *(f is as usual supposed to be constant on any component of* Bd M_n*). Let us consider h handles of index λ, added to M_n on Q:*

$$N_n = \chi(M_n; f_1, \ldots, f_h; \lambda).$$

There exists a Morse function φ defined on N_n such that φ coincides with f outside some small tubular neighborhood of Q, and φ has exactly h new critical points, all of index λ and with the same value.

We illustrate this theorem with an example, in Fig. 7. We start with D_2 on which a function with one minimum (index *O*) is considered (the level lines of our functions are drawn). We add a handle of index 1 and a singularity of index 1 in the same time.

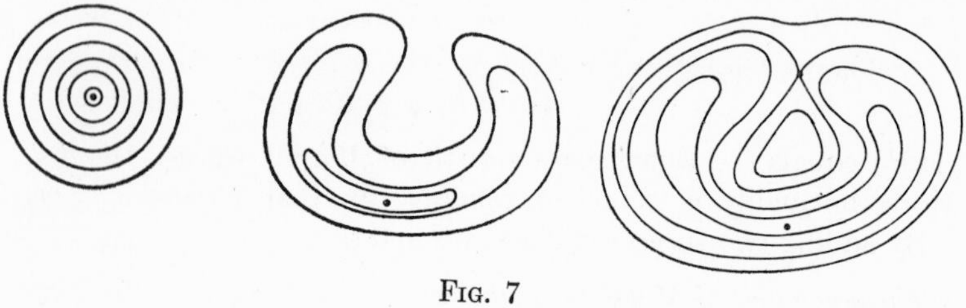

Fig. 7

We give now some applications of theorems 7.1 and 7.2. First a theorem of Reeb and Milnor, which suggests how the topological structure of a manifold can be determined by the Morse functions on it:

THEOREM OF REEB-MILNOR: *Let M_n be a closed manifold on which a Morse function f with exactly 2 critical points is defined. M_n is homeomorphic to S_n.*

Proof: Let x, y be the two points. One has to be a maximum, the other a minimum. Let $f(x) = 0$, $f(y) = 1$. By theorems 7.1 and 7.2,

$$\begin{aligned} \{f \leq \tfrac{1}{4}\} &= D_n \\ \{\tfrac{1}{4} \leq f \leq \tfrac{3}{4}\} &= S_{n-1} \times I \\ \{f \geq \tfrac{3}{4}\} &= D_n. \end{aligned}$$

This gives our theorem.

The next theorem (the Morse inequalities) shows a connection between the homological properties of a closed manifold and the Morse functions which we can define on it. There is a lower bound for the "amount of singularity" of f, depending on $H_*(M)$.

We consider some field F, $H_*(M, F)$ and

$$R_\lambda(M) = \dim H_\lambda(M, F).$$

We denote by C_λ the number of critical points of index λ of some given Morse function f on M. We have then

The first set of Morse inequalities:

$$\begin{aligned} C_0 &\geq R_0 \\ C_1 - C_0 &\geq R_1 - R_0 \\ C_2 - C_1 + C_0 &\geq R_2 - R_1 + R_0 \\ &\cdots\cdots\cdots\cdots \end{aligned}$$

$$C_n - C_{n-1} + C_{n+2} + \cdots \pm C_0 = R_n - R_{n-1} + R_{n+2} \cdots \pm R_0 = \chi(M)$$

[$\chi(M)$ equals the Euler characteristic of M]. As we see, the last Morse inequality is in fact an *equality*. We shall discuss it later.

By adding two successive lines, we find

The second set of Morse inequalities:

$$C_0 \geq R_0$$
$$C_1 \geq R_1$$
$$C_2 \geq R_2$$
$$\cdot \quad \cdot \quad \cdot \quad \cdot$$
$$C_n \geq R_n.$$

The Morse inequalities are simple and easy consequences of theorems 7.1 and 7.2. In fact, if we combine our homotopy interpretation of handle-adding with theorems 7.1 and 7.2, we see the following: If a Morse function f is defined on M, then M has the homotopy type of a CW-complex with C_λ-cells of dimension λ. This strongly suggests an analogy between a Morse function on M and a cell decomposition on M. In fact, a Morse function f represents *simultaneously* a cell decomposition, and its dual $(n - f)$.

Let us note some interesting things about the last Morse *equality*.

If we consider a Morse function f on M and the vector field grad f on M, then the singularities of grad f are exactly the critical points of f. If x is a critical point of index λ, then the index of grad f at x is $(-1)^\lambda$. (The index of a vector field at a singular point x is the "winding number" of the vector field at x or, more exactly, the degree of the map $S_{n-1} \longrightarrow S_{n-1}$ induced by the vector field around x.) If ν is a vector field on M, let us denote by $N(\nu)$ the "sum of the indexes of its singular points" (see Steenrod's book [8]). The last Morse equality shows that

$$N(\operatorname{grad} f) = \chi(M).$$

On the other hand, it is easy to show that any two vector fields on M have the same $N(\ldots)$ (see [8]), and that the singularity can be always concentrated to a point. We have proved hence that

THEOREM OF STIEFEL: *A nonsingular vector field can be defined on M if and only if $\chi(M) = 0$.*

Now, the last Morse equality admits also the following generalization:

Let M_n be a compact C^∞-manifold such that $\operatorname{Bd} M_n = M'_{n-1} + M''_{n-1}(M'_{n-1} \cap M''_{n-1} = \varnothing)$. *Let f be a Morse function defined on M_n with its minimum m on M'_{n-1} and maximum M on M''_{n-1}. Let us assume that C_λ is the number of critical points of index λ, of f. Then*

$$\chi(M_n) = \Sigma(-1)^\lambda C_\lambda + \chi(M_1).$$

We shall use this theorem in the last section.

8. COBORDISM AND MORSE THEORY

The connection between Morse theory and cobordism can be summarized in the following theorem due to A. H. Wallace and J. Milnor.

THEOREM: *Let M'_n, M''_n be two closed n-dimensional manifolds. The necessary and sufficient condition for M'_n and M''_n to be cobordant is that one can be derived from the other by a finite number of Morse surgeries.*

Proof: The proof will be an easy consequence of the preceding considerations. Let us suppose that M'_n, M''_n are cobordant. Then there exists an $(n + 1)$-dimensional compact manifold N_{n+1} such that $\text{Bd}\, N_{n+1} = M'_n + M''_n$. On N_{n+1} we can construct a Morse function f such that $0 \leq f(x) \leq 1, f^{-1}(0) = M'_n, f^{-1}(1) = M''_n$. We shall compare now $\{f = a\}$ and $\{f = a + \epsilon\}$ (a and $a + \epsilon$ are not critical levels). If there is no critical level between a and $a + \epsilon$, then

$$\{f = a\} = \{f = a + \epsilon\}.$$

If there is exactly one critical level between a and $a + \epsilon$, then $\{f \leq a + \epsilon\}$ is deduced from $\{f \leq a\}$ by adding handles on $\{f = a\}$. Hence $\{f = a + \epsilon\}$ is deduced from $\{f = a\}$ by Morse surgeries. By induction, $\{f = 1\} = M''_n$ is deduced from $\{f = 0\} = M'_n$ by surgeries.

Conversely, if

$$M'_n = \mu(M''_n; f; \lambda)$$

then, as we have seen,

$$\text{Bd}\,(\chi(M''_n \times I, f, \lambda)) = M'_n + M''_n$$

and this, by induction, shows that surgery implies cobordism. This finishes the proof.

There is a concept, stronger than cobordism, called *h-cobordism:*

two closed, connected and *simply connected* manifolds M'_n and M''_n are said to be *h-cobordant* if there exists a cobordism

$$\mathrm{Bd}\, N_{n+1} = M'_n + M''_n$$

such that the natural inclusions $M'_n \subset N_{n+1}$ and $M''_n \subset N_{n+1}$ are homotopy equivalences.

The following fundamental theorem of Smale relates h-cobordism and diffeomorphism:

THEOREM OF SMALE: *Let* $\mathrm{Bd}\, N_{n+1} = M'_n + M''_n$ *be an h-cobordism, and* $n \geq 5$. *Then* N_{n+1} *is diffeomorphic to* $M'_n \times I$. *Hence,* M'_n *and* M''_n *are diffeomorphic.*

In the next section we shall discuss a special case of this theorem: the generalized Poincaré conjecture in dimensions ≥ 5. The same kind of arguments can be used to prove the h-cobordism theorem. More details can be found about all these questions in Smale's original papers [5], [6].

9. SMALE'S THEORY

A homotopy sphere is a differentiable manifold M_n which has the same homotopy type as S_n. We shall prove the following theorem of Smale:

THEOREM 9.1: *The generalized Poincaré conjecture in "high dimensions": A homotopy sphere* M_n, *of dimension* $n \geq 5$, *is homeomorphic to* S_n.

Before going further, let us make some comments on this result. At the beginning of the century, H. Poincaré raised the question, Is every closed simply connected 3-manifold homeomorphic to S_3? This is the well-known *Poincaré conjecture.* In the late thirties, when homotopy theory was born, it was easily recognized that this question is equivalent to asking if every homotopy 3-sphere is S_3. Hence the natural question, *is any homotopy n-sphere* S_n*?* This was called the *generalized Poincaré conjecture.* Now, since merely topological manifolds are extremely difficult to handle, one always assumed that the homotopy n-sphere is differentiable, or piecewise-linear. In 1956, J. Milnor constructed a manifold homeomorphic, but *not* diffeomorphic, to the standard 7-sphere. This shows that we cannot ask for a differentiable homotopy n-sphere to be diffeomorphic to S_n, but merely homeomorphic. In 1960, Smale (and immediately after, Stallings and Zeeman) showed that for $n \geq 5$ the generalized Poincaré conjecture can be solved in the affirmative. The cases $n = 3, 4$ are still open.

That the generalized Poincaré conjecture is a consequence of the h-cobordism theorem can be seen as follows:

If we have a homotopy n-sphere M_n, we can consider $M'_n = M_n - \text{int}\, D_n$, where $D_n \subset M'_n$ is some differentiable embedding. By gluing together two copies of M'_n along S_{n-1} (using the *identity map*), we find a manifold $2M'_n$,† which is easily recognized to be h-cobordant to the standard sphere S_n [one has to use the observation that a simply connected manifold N_n is h-cobordant to S_n, if and only if it bounds a contractible $(n + 1)$-manifold]. Hence, by the h-cobordism theorem, $2M'_n$ is *diffeomorphic* to S_n. Using the generalized Schoenflies theorem (of Mazur and Brown), this shows that M'_n is homeomorphic to D_n; hence S_n is homeomorphic to M_n. (This works for $n \geq 5$.)

If $n \geq 6$, we can construct another argument: Consider two disjoint embeddings: $D_n \overset{i}{\subset} M_n$, $D_n \overset{j}{\subset} M_n$. $M_n - i(\text{int}\, D_n) - j(\text{int}\, D_n)$ is an h-cobordism between two copies of S_{n-1}; hence, if $n \geq 6$, it is diffeomorphic, by the h-cobordism theorem, to $S_{n-1} \times I$.

This shows the connection of the two theorems. We shall prove only the weaker one. As we noted, the methods can be applied to the general case.

So far, we have not mentioned *orientable* manifolds. Let M_n be a differentiable n-manifold and $\tau(M_n)$ its tangent bundle. By definition, M_n is orientable if the nth exterior power of $\tau(M_n)$, which is a 1-dimensional vector bundle over M_n, is trivial. (One defines easily exterior powers of vector bundles, by taking exterior powers of the fibers.)

This is easily recognized to be a homotopy property of M_n, independent of its differentiable structure. It is equivalent to the "usual" definition of orientability for combinatorial manifolds (if

† Or rather, we find $M'_n + (-M'_n)$, if we take into account the orientations.

we take a smooth triangulation for M_n). It is very easy to prove that simply connected manifolds are always orientable (since a nonorientable manifold admits a natural nontrivial two-sheeted covering). The boundary of an oriented manifold is orientable. On an orientable manifold, one can define two distinct *orientations*, each of which is characterized by a nonsingular cross section of $\Lambda^n\tau(M_n)$. [Two nonsingular cross sections $\phi, \phi': M_n \longrightarrow \Lambda^n\tau(M_n)$ will define "the same orientation" if there exists a continuous *positive* function $\psi: M_n \longrightarrow R$ such that $\phi = \psi\phi'$.]

Orientability is not disturbed by adding handles of index λ, for $\lambda \neq 1$, as one can easily see, but it might be distorted through handles of index $\lambda = 1$, as it is indicated in Fig. 8.

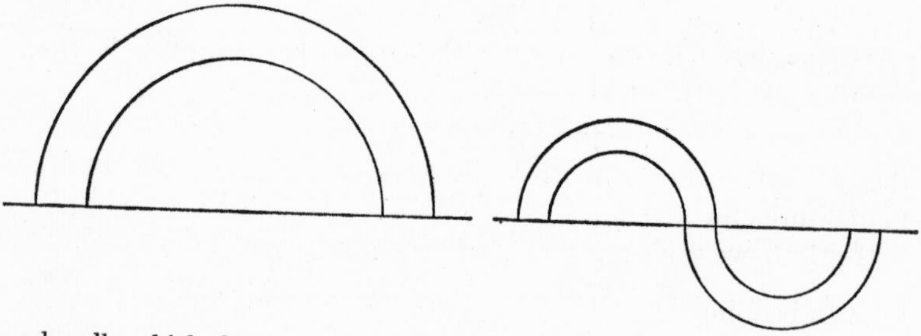

a handle which does not disturb the orientability

a handle which does.

FIG. 8

The reader can easily see how to translate the property of a 1-indexed handle which disturbs (or not) the orientability, in terms of attaching map

$$f: D_{n-1} \times S_0 \xrightarrow{\subset} \text{Bd } M_n.$$

From now on, all manifolds considered will be orientable, and all 1-handles *orientability preserving.*

Let us introduce the following notation: Let $M_n = \chi(M'_n, f, \lambda)$. As we know, f is an injection

$$f: S_{\lambda-1} \times D_n \longrightarrow \text{Bd } M'_n.$$

Let us consider in Bd ($D_\lambda \times D_{n-\lambda}$) the embedded $(n - \lambda - 1)$-dimensional sphere $O \times$ Bd $D_{n-\lambda}$, where O is the center of D_λ. This sphere does not meet $S_{\lambda-1} \times D_n$; hence we can find it again in Bd M_n (see Fig. 9). Let us denote it by $S_{n-\lambda-1}(M'_n, f, \lambda) \subset$ Bd M_n. We can

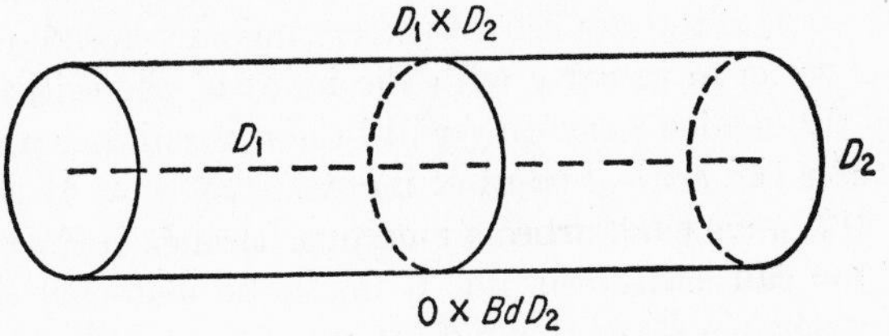

FIG. 9

now make the following crucial observation: Let us consider the following successive handle-adding:

$$M_n^2 = \chi(M_n^1; f^1, \lambda^1)$$
$$M_n^3 = \chi(M_n^2; f^2, \lambda^2).$$

Let us assume that

$$f^2(S_{\lambda^2-1} \times D_{n-\lambda^2}) \cap S_{n-\lambda^1-1}(M_n^1; f^1, \lambda^1) = \varnothing$$

[or merely

(*) $$f^2(S_{\lambda^2-1} \times 0) \cap S_{n-\lambda^1-1}(M_n^1; f^1, \lambda^1) = \varnothing$$

which is equivalent (0 the center of $D_{n-\lambda^2}$), since the result of the handle-adding is not changed by isotoping f^2].

Then M_n^3 can be obtained by adding to M_n^1 *first* a handle of index λ^2 and then a handle of index λ^1. This is an easy geometric exercise which we leave to the reader.

Now, if $\lambda^2 < \lambda^1$, then

$$(\lambda^2 - 1) + (n - \lambda^1 - 1) < n - 1;$$

hence, by transversality, we can always assume that Eq. (*) is fulfilled. Therefore,

LEMMA: *If we add to M_n first a handle of index λ^1 and then a handle of index $\lambda^2 < \lambda^1$, the result can be obtained by adding first a handle of index λ^2 and then a handle of index λ^1.*

Now, theorems 7.2 and 7.3 concerning the Morse theory showed a complete parallelism between the Morse functions and handle-adding. Hence, if we start with a Morse function on a manifold M_n, interpret it as a successive handle-adding, apply to this the precedent lemma, and then re-read the result in terms of Morse functions, we find the result that the critical values can always be rearranged so as to increase with the index of the critical point. More exactly, a nice function f will be, by definition, a function such that if x is a critical point of index λ, $f(x) = \lambda$. If Bd $M_n = M'_{n-1} + M''_{n-1}$, we shall assume moreover that $f^{-1}(-\frac{1}{2}) = M'_{n-1}$, $f^{-1}(n + \frac{1}{2}) = M''_{n-1}$. Hence:

THEOREM 9.2: *On every manifold there exists a nice function.*

Let us start now with a homotopy sphere M_n of dimension $n \geq 5$ and a nice function f defined on it. We can always assume that f has unique maximum and minimum points. If we could eliminate the other singularities, by the Reeb-Milnor theorem, M_n would be homeomorphic to S_n. That is what we shall do.

DEFINITION: *The manifold M_n, diffeomorphic to some*

$$\chi(D_n; f_1, \ldots, f_h; \lambda),$$

will be called an (n, h, λ)-handlebody.

The main tool will be the following theorem:

THE HANDLEBODY THEOREM: *Let $\lambda > 1$ and $n \geq 2\lambda + 2$. Let M be an (n, h, λ)-handlebody. Let*

$$N = \chi\,(M; f', \ldots, f^r; \lambda + 1)$$

and assume that $\pi_\lambda(N) = 0$. Then N is an $(n, r - k, \lambda + 1)$-handlebody.

Proof: We shall begin by making some simple remarks on handlebodies.

First, any (n, k, λ)-handlebody has the same homotopy type of a "*bouquet*" of k, λ-dimensional spheres: $S^1_\lambda \vee \cdots \vee S^k_\lambda$. This implies that

$$\pi_2(M) = Z + \cdots + Z \qquad (k \text{ times})$$

and $\pi_\mu(M) = 0$ if $\mu < \lambda$.

In general if we attach a λ-index handle to P, since this is homotopically equivalent to attaching a λ-dimensional disk, by a map $f: S_{\lambda-1} \longrightarrow P$ (through a map *homotopic* to the attaching map

$$S_{\lambda-1} \times 0 \subset S_{\lambda-1} \times D_{n-\lambda} \subset \text{Bd } P \subset P),$$

the effect on the homotopy groups will be the following: π_i, for $i < \lambda - 1$, is unchanged. If f is null-homotopic, $\pi_{\lambda-1}$ remains unchanged; if f is not null-homotopic, its homotopy class (and all the actions of π_1 on it) are killed in $\pi_{\lambda-1}$. The new $\pi_{\lambda-1}$ is the correspondent quotient group of the old one. Thus π_μ, $\mu > \lambda - 1$ are changed.

A simple geometric argument shows also, in the context we use, that $\pi_\lambda(\text{Bd } M) \longrightarrow \pi_\lambda(M)$ is a bijection and $\pi_i(\text{Bd } M) = 0$ for $i < \lambda$. [In particular, $\pi_1(\text{Bd } M) = 0$, so we do not use base points for the homotopy groups.]

Two spheres S_p, $S_q^*(p + q = n - 1)$ embedded in a closed $(n - 1)$-dimensional manifold will be said to *cut normally* if they are in general position (i.e., cut each other transversally) and $S_p \cap S_q^*$ consists of exactly one point.

Two systems of spheres $S_p^1, \ldots, S_p^k, \overline{S}_q^1, \ldots, \overline{S}_q^k (p + q = n - 1)$ are said to *cut normally* if

$$S_p^i \cap S_p^j = \overline{S}_q^i \cap \overline{S}_q^j = S_p^i \cap \overline{S}_q^j = \emptyset$$

for any $i \neq j$, and S_p^i, $\overline{S}_q^i$, for every i, cut normally.

It is easy to prove the following lemma:

THE HANDLE CANCELLATION LEMMA: *Let us consider*

$$M_m^2 = \chi(M_m^1; f; \mu)$$
$$M_m^3 = \chi(M_m^2; g; \mu + 1).$$

Let us assume that

$$S_{n-\mu-1}(M_m^1; f; \mu) \quad \textit{and} \quad g(S_\mu \times 0)$$

cut normally.

Then $M_m^3 = M_m^1$ diffeomorphically [i.e., the two handles cancel each other (see Fig. 10)].

Let us consider now our

$$M = \chi(D_n; g^1, \ldots, g^k, \lambda).$$

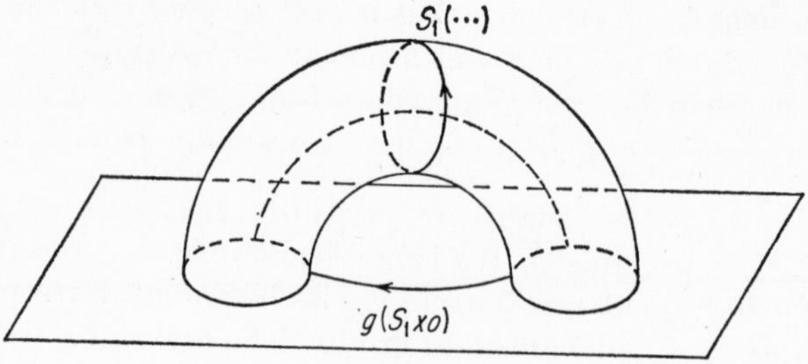

FIG. 10. Handle-cancellation.

It is easy to find a system of k-embedded λ-dimensional spheres in Bd M,

$$\phi_1(S_\lambda), \ldots, \phi_k(S_\lambda),$$

which cut normally

$$S_{n-\lambda-1}(D_n, g^1, \lambda),\ S_{n-\lambda-1}(D_n, g^2, \lambda), \ldots, S_{n-\lambda-1}(D_n, g^k, \lambda)$$

such that the homotopy classes $[\phi_1], \ldots, [\phi_k]$ form a system of generators of $\pi_\lambda(M) = \pi_\lambda(\text{Bd } M) = Z + \cdots + Z$ (k times). Let us consider now our spheres $f^1(S_\lambda \times 0) = f^1(S_\lambda), \ldots, f^r(S_\lambda)$ which represent the attaching maps of the handles added to M in order to obtain N. Let $[f^1]$ be the homotopy class of $f^1(S_\lambda)([f^1] \in \pi_\lambda(\text{Bd } M))$. Let us consider the abstract free abelian group G_r, generated by the symbols $f^1(S_\lambda) \cdots f^r(S_\lambda)$. We have a homeomorphism $\phi: G_r \longrightarrow \pi_\lambda(\text{Bd } M)$ defined by

$$\phi(f^1(S_\lambda)) = [f^1].$$

Since $\pi_\lambda(N) = 0$, ϕ *is onto.* [This would be *false* if λ were 1; then one could only deduce that the normal divisor generated by $\phi(G_r)$ was $\pi_1(\text{Bd } M)$. This obliged us to make the assumption $\lambda > 1$. It is not known whether the theorem remains true for $\lambda = 1$.]

Then, an easy group-theoretic argument shows that there is in G_r a new base $\psi^1, \ldots, \psi^r$, which can be obtained from $f'(S_\lambda), \ldots, f^r(S_\lambda)$ by a finite sequence of "elementary operations"

$$(\alpha, \beta, \ldots \longrightarrow \alpha^{-1}, \beta, \ldots ; \alpha, \beta, \ldots \longrightarrow \alpha + \beta, \beta, \ldots \text{ a.s.o.})$$

such that

$$\phi(\psi') = [\phi_1], \ldots, \phi(\psi^k) = [\phi_k],\ \phi(\psi^{k+1}) = 0, \ldots, \phi(\psi^r) = 0.$$

Now, since $(n-1)-\lambda \geq 2$, it is easy to show that this elementary operation on the group level can be realized by operations with our handles (we need codimension ≥ 2 in order to realize $\alpha, \beta, \ldots \longrightarrow \alpha - \beta, \beta, \ldots$); hence, we shall manage to find a manifold

$$\chi(M; h^1, \ldots, h^r, \lambda + 1),$$

diffeomorphic to N, such that the homotopy class of $h^i(S_\lambda \times 0)$ is $\phi(\psi^i)$. Now, if we manage to isotop $h^i(S_\lambda \times 0)$ for $i = 1, \ldots, k$ into $\phi_i(S_\lambda)$, then the handle cancellation lemma will enable us to finish our proof.

But, in the range of dimensions we consider, and since $\pi_1(\text{Bd } M) = 0$, a theorem of Whitney (see [13], the argument can be very easily seen in [7]), tells us that $h^i(S_\lambda \times 0)$ and $\phi_i(S_\lambda)$ are isotopic. This finishes the proof of the handlebody theorem.

We go back now to our homotopy sphere M_n. We shall consider that $n \geq 5$.

We consider a Morse function f on M_n, which is nice and has exactly one minimum and one maximum. If we assume that f has no critical points of indexes $1, 2, \ldots, \lambda - 1$, for $n \geq 2\lambda + 2$, then we can find on M_n a new nice function with no critical points of index $1, 2, \ldots, \lambda$. This is done in the following way: $\{f \leq \lambda + \frac{1}{2}\}$ is obviously an (n, h, λ)-handlebody M'. $N = \{f \leq \lambda + \frac{3}{2}\} = \chi(M'; g', \ldots, g^r, \lambda + 1)$. Since $\pi_\lambda(M_n) = 0$ and since the handles of index $> \lambda + 1$ do not modify $\pi_\lambda(M')$, we have $\pi_\lambda(N) = 0$. Hence the handlebody theorem can be applied and is an $(n, r - h, \lambda + 1)$-handlebody. If we read this in terms of Morse functions, we have defined a new nice Morse function f', on M_n, with no critical points of index $1, 2, \ldots, \lambda$.

This, of course, does not tell us how to eliminate the critical points of index 1. For this we need an extra trick. We know anyway that $\{f \leq \frac{3}{2}\}$ is an $(n, h, 1)$-handlebody and that $\pi_1(\{f \leq 2 + \frac{1}{2}\}) = 0$. $N' = \{f \leq 2 + \frac{1}{2}\}$ is deduced from $N = \{f \leq \frac{3}{2}\}$ by adding r, 2-index handles. To N', let us add k trivial (i.e., attached by null-homotopic maps) 2-index handles. We find a new manifold P. Now, since $\pi_1(N') = 0$, the new 2-index handles can be changed, by sliding, so as to cancel the 1-index handles of N. This means that P is an $(n, r, 2)$-handlebody. On the other hand, since

$$\{f \leq 3 + \tfrac{1}{2}\} = \chi(N', p_1, \ldots, p_q, 3)$$

and the handles added from N' to P are trivial, one easily sees that

$$\{f \leq 3 + \tfrac{1}{2}\} = \chi(P, p_1', \ldots, p_{r+q}', 3).$$

Hence, by starting with P, we can eliminate the singular points of index 1.

There are two cases now: if n is even, $n = 2k + 2$, then we have eliminated the critical points of index $1, 2, \ldots, k$; and by considering the function $n - f$ and applying to it the same arguments, we can eliminate the critical points of index

$$(n-1), (n-2), \ldots, (n-k) = k + 2.$$

Hence we find on M_n a Morse function F which has one maximum, one minimum, and possible critical points of index $k + 1$. If these points would really exist, $\pi_{k+1}(M_n)$ would be different from O since these $(k + 1)$ added cells would not be killed (homotopically) by $(k + 2)$-cells. (The final n-cell does not kill them.) Hence F has only one minimum and one maximum.†

If $n = 2k + 1$, we consider $2M_n$, which (as we have observed) is h-cobordant to S_n. We can apply to the h-cobordism N_{n+1} ($\mathrm{Bd}\, N_{n+1} = 2M_n - S_n$) the same argument as before and construct hence a function f, *without singularities*, on N_{n+1} such that $f^{-1}(0) = 2M_n$, $f^{-1}(n) = S_n$. This proves that $N_{n+1} = S_n \times I$; therefore $2M_n$ is diffeomorphic to S_n, and M_n is homeomorphic to S_n.

BIBLIOGRAPHY

[1] Ehresmann, C., "Introduction à la théorie des structures infinitésimales et pseudo-groupes," *Coll. Top. Strasbourg*, 1953.

[2] Milnor, J., *Morse Theory*. Princeton, N.J.: Princeton University Press, 1963.

[3] ———, *Differentiable Manifolds* (Mimeographed) (1958).

† We can use, instead of this argument, the observation from the end of Sec. 7.

[4] Milnor, J., "On manifolds homeomorphic to the 7-sphere," *Ann. Math.*, **64** (1956), 399–405.

[5] Smale, S., "Generalized Poincaré Conjecture, in dimensions greater than four," *Ann. Math.*, **74** (1961), 391–406.

[6] ———, "On the structure of manifolds," *Amer. Jour. Math.*, **84** (1962), 387–99.

[7] Shapiro, A., "Obstructions to the imbedding of a complex in Euclidean space I," *Ann. Math.*, **66** (1957), 256–69.

[8] Steenrod, N., *The Topology of Fiber Bundles.* Princeton, N.J.: Princeton University Press, 1951.

[9] Sternberg, S., *Differential Geometry*, Prentice-Hall, Inc., Englewood Cliffs, N.J. (1964).

[10] Rham, G. de, Variétés différentiables, Paris, Hermann, 1955.

[11] Thom, R., "Quelques propriétés globales des variétés différentiables," *Comm. Math. Helv.*, **28** (1954), 17–86.

[12] ———, "Un lemme sur les applications différentiables," *Bol. Soc. Mat. Mexicana* (1956), 59–71.

[13] Whitney, H., "The self intersections of a smooth n-manifold in $2n$-space," *Ann. Math.*, **45** (1944), 220–46.

INDEX

† (f = footnote)

MY 13 '78			